THE HUMAN DEVELOPMENT HOAX:

TIME TO TELL THE TRUTH

BY

C. Ward Kischer, M.S., Ph.D.
Associate Professor Emeritus
College of Medicine
Department of Cell Biology
   and Anatomy
University of Arizona
Tucson, Arizona 85724

Dianne N. Irving, M.A., Ph.D.
Professor Philosophy/Bioethics
Dominican House of Studies and
The Catholic University of America
Washington, D.C.

Cover Photo: Human embryo six weeks post-fertilization in-utero. Amniotic membrane has been removed.

Library of Congress Catalog Card Number 97-92690

TABLE OF CONTENTS

Authors' Biographies

C. Ward Kischer received his Bachelor's degree in Secondary Education and Biology in 1953 from the University of Omaha. After working as a laboratory technician in cytopathology and as a high school teacher of biology and general science, he entered Iowa State University in 1958, receiving the Master of Science degree in 1960 and the Ph.D. degree in 1962, majoring in Embryology. After an NIH Fellowship in biochemistry at M.D. Anderson Hospital and Tumor Institute in Houston, Texas, he assumed a faculty position in the Department of Anatomy at the University of Texas Medical Branch in Galveston, then at the University of Arizona College of Medicine in Tucson. His career research has been in the field of deep injury, in particular the sequelae of burns and equivalent injuries. He has taught human embryology to medical students, upper division and graduate students since 1960.

Dianne N. Irving received her Bachelor's degree in Chemistry in 1964 from Dunbarton College of the Holy Cross, Washington, D.C. After working for the National Institutes of Health, National Cancer Institute, Bethesda, Maryland, as a career-appointed research biochemist, she pursued extensive graduate courses in biology at Georgetown University in Washington, D.C. In 1989 she received her Master of Arts degree in Metaphysics and Epistemology, and in 1991 she was awarded her Ph.D. degree in Philosophy from Georgetown University, with concentrations in the History of Philosophy and Bioethics. From 1989 to 1997 she taught the history of philosophy and bioethics at the De Sales School of Theology in Washington, D.C. She is presently teaching the same subjects at the Dominican House of Studies, and Ethics and Engineering at the Catholic University of America, Washington, D.C.

Preface to the First Edition

This is an anthology of recent articles which concern human pre-natal development (embryology), its true science, and its relation to philosophy and public policy. It was prepared in order to widen the dissemination of and to correct the misstatements about Human Embryology, and to encourage others to use the correct Human Embryology in their own fields of endeavor.

Although the occasional tedious and academic details of the science and the philosophy may tend to make the eyes of some persons "glaze over", we think it is critical for the public to understand that it is precisely these "academic" details which have been driving so many influential arguments and important public policy decisions. We will re-examine the details of these influential arguments and decisions which have already significantly touched all of us, and in the process we will separate out the true facts from the political fictions inherent in them. Our task is accomplished by dividing this book into three inter-relating sections: The Science, The Philosophy, and Public Policy.

Since <u>Roe</u> v. <u>Wade</u> was adjudicated in 1973, a rising crescendo of false information concerning human development has been placed before an unknowing public. This scientific misinformation has then been appropriated by scientists, philosophers, theologians, bioethicists, and public policy experts, and touted to be relevant to the issues of abortion, *in vitro* fertilization, fetal tissue research, and now, human embryo research. When significant, fundamental and definitive facts within those fields are falsified, manipulated and politicized, the objective truths about ourselves and our world are obfuscated, and the public is harmed by the application of these false theories. Where are the voices of the professional experts within these fields who know that such science is incorrect, and who have the professional responsibility to respond? We consider corrections to the massive misinformation abounding in the literature today a matter of not only personal responsibility but also of responsibility to the several professions and to the welfare of the public-at-large.

Trying to correct this dementia of "scientific" misinformation has proven to be an immense task, mainly because there are few readily available outlets among the lay publications or scientific journals which have been willing to publish corrections. Under ordinary circumstances there are built-in mechanisms within each field to identify, address and respond to such problems. Under ordinary circumstances those professionals who become aware of such problems appeal to their colleagues' sense of justice, proper concern for the integrity and survival of their fields, and their professional codes of ethics. Under ordinary circumstances the discussions concerning these problems are carried out in a thoroughly professional and collegial manner.

But such has proven not to be the case when the issue has involved the science, philosophy and public policy decisions concerning the early development of the human being.

For many years the degree of politicization within our respective fields has prompted us to professionally and patiently attempt to correct this outrageous fraud which constitutes a hoax of major proportions concerning the pre-natal human being. Years of attempts have failed to produce even the slightest interest in acknowledging and correcting these incorrect scientific facts.

These are not ordinary circumstances. Since we have tried every possible professional avenue to set the record straight, and since those in control of communications have chosen to close down discussion about the incorrect facts concerning our human development, or have condoned it by silence or self-imposed ignorance, this anthology is our attempt to by-pass the collegial processes which are usually operative in every profession, and to bring the correct facts to the public square. It is also our attempt to undo the pervasive damage already done to the public's perception of its own human biological development through the use of incorrect science.

Some of the articles included here are simply not "politically correct", and have thus been rejected by major publications, both lay and scientific (some, multiple times). But, although they are not "politically correct", they are scientifically correct, and contain from the point of view of the authors the correct philosophical and ethical relevance of these scientific facts and their proper infusion into public policy. It is our judgment that the very culture of our society is at stake.

The human being is the only creature able to direct its own evolution. Our "technological culture" especially demands that at least the correct scientific information is used in those complex and consequential technical, ethical and public policy decisions confronting our country today. We can choose to allow fake science to drive these politicized decisions and thus mis-shape our culture and evolution; or we can choose to insist on the objective truth. This will require the cooperative and intellectually honest interfacing of accurate science with sound ethics and morals, and with responsible public policy decisions. It will also require respect for the integrity of the science of embryology, as well as respect for human life at all of its stages. But just as we all have the choice to shape the kind of individuals we are and the kind of culture that is to be, we also bear the responsibility and accountability for the results - both individually and collectively.

We hope that, in the course of "telling the truth", we can stimulate a more correctly informed public discussion and debate on these critical issues, and help to fortify and encourage counter arguments to the destructive and one-sided public policy directives so negatively impacting our present society. We further encourage all students, educators, clergymen, scientists, physicians, lawyers, the media and various policy makers - such as federal officials, congressmen and judges - to use the complete and accurate scientific truth about pre-natal human development whenever they invoke it as a basis for ethical and public policy decisions.

If the following articles are fairly and justly studied, we are confident that one will find the truth in what the articles contain. Finding that truth is paramount to recovering our individual human identities. We hope to ignite a restoration of our societal evolutionary direction. To that end what we present here is our contribution. Somehow, we must extricate ourselves from our present educational and moral abyss and cultural vacuum.

C. Ward Kischer, M.S., Ph.D.
Tuscon, Arizona

Dianne N. Irving, M.A., Ph.D.
Washington, D.C.

Preface to the Second Edition

Since the first edition was published the abortion and related issues remain unresolved. Indeed, many state legislatures have considered, and are considering, ancillary legislation, such as parental notification of intended abortions by minor pregnant females. The partial birth abortion procedure has caused considerable heat, especially since Congress passed a ban on it, but President Clinton vetoed the ban. Fetal tissue research, via implants of "embryonic" tissue for supposed relief of Parkinson's Syndrome is still being touted as effective. The human embryo research issue remains unresolved. A panel commissioned by the Director of NIH, Harold Varmus, recommended eight experimental procedures using human embryos as experimental subjects. The Director has yet to decide upon those recommendations by the NIH Panel. In the meantime, President Clinton announced that no federal funds would be used to support research using "experimental" human embryos. Yet, he said nothing about the use of "spare" embryos, those left over from IVF procedures. Nor does his "ban" affect the use of early human embryos in private research. In essence, however, these procedures remain ethically the same. Also, in July, 1996, the House voted to prohibit federal funding of destructive experimentation on living human embryos created in the laboratory.

The controversy surrounding the action, and future use, of RU 486, and the FDA protocol for its testing, has become an additional issue. There are also questions as to whether or not birth control chemicals (e.g., morning-after pills, RU 486) prevent fertilization, implantation, or are, in actuality, abortifacients. In July, 1996 the FDA approved the use of morning-after pills having accepted the argument from members of the pharmaceutical industry that "there is no embryo there until after two weeks, post-fertilization."

Neither these issues, nor the fake science inherent in them, will go away. But unfortunately, neither will the false science! In all of the above issues, there continues to be false and misleading information issued and used concerning Human Embryology. Indeed, the false term *preembryo*, or the more subtle claim that the embryo does not begin until 2 weeks, are enjoying an undeserved popularity in lay and scientific literature and the media. The message has simply not gotten out.

Therefore, we feel it germane to address these issues with renewed vigor. In this edition there are additional articles which we feel are a necessity to the contemporary issues surrounding human development. Once more, we place before the public the truth about Human Embryology and how it is being distorted in the scientific and philosophical discourse, and the dangers this is causing in real and potential public policy.

C. Ward Kischer, M.S., Ph.D.
Tucson, Arizona

Dianne N. Irving, M.A., Ph.D.
Washington, D.C.

THE HUMAN DEVELOPMENT HOAX:
TIME TO TELL THE TRUTH

SECTION ONE: THE SCIENCE

We begin our anthology by focusing on the **science** of human development. One reason is that the constant stream of incorrect embryology (as well as incorrect genetics, biochemistry and developmental biology), which has pervaded the lay and professional presses and media for years, is objectively false, and has corrupted the science of human development per se. It also seriously erodes and further brings into question the already shaky trust which the public has placed in the integrity of scientific research, which it in great part funds. In fact, along with the increase lately in scientific fraud, it does not bode well for the future viability of the scientific enterprise itself.

The first article in this section speaks directly to the single most important element in the science of Human Embryology, the beginning of life. Even though the Supreme Court refused to define the beginning of life in Roe v. Wade, and, in fact, said it could not be defined in the Webster case, the article demonstrates that the consensus of human embryologists confirms that the new individual human being begins at fertilization of the oocyte. In the article, "In Defense of Human Development", the author cites four of the basic elements of human embryology which most often have been misused and falsely referenced in the socio-legal issues of abortion, fetal tissue research, in vitro fertilization (IVF) and (most recently) human embryo research.

The article, "Human Development and Reconsideration of Ensoulment", is a direct confrontation between what is the correct embryology and the incorrect "embryology" which was used in an article by the Rev. Richard McCormick, S.J., in the Kennedy Institute of Ethics Journal. It is also a correction to McCormick's assault on the "moral status" of the early human embryo, an assault based directly on that incorrect "embryology". McCormick (a member of the early 1979 HEW Ethics Advisory Board, as well as of the Ethics Committee of the American Fertility Society) argues that an "individual" human being (or "person") is not present until 14 days after fertilization. Therefore, he concludes, before that point there is only a "pre-embryo", or a "pre-person", with less than the full moral status of a human "person". On the contrary, using

1

the correct human embryology, the author thoroughly negates McCormick's contentions of "individuation" (and therefore of "moral status") at 14-days, as well as the fabricated term "pre-embryo" which has no scientific validity.

In the article, "'New Age' Embryology Text Books: 'Pre-Embryo', 'Pregnancy' and Abortion Counseling: Implications for Fetal Research", the author carefully (indeed, painfully) scrutinizes two recent editions of a popular and widely-used textbook on human embryology. Virtually every scientific definition basic and fundamental to the science of human embryology has been incorrectly redefined, most terms actually having multiple and contradictory definitions throughout the text. These scientifically incorrect "redefinitions", in turn, are then selectively used to assuage the "fear of women who might be pregnant" that the intentional destruction of their "pre-embryo" by the use of the morning-after pill (or RU486) would not be technically classified as "abortion". The author discusses the further implications of the "racheting of embryological definitions" for fetal research.

"The Big Lie In Human Embryology" provides the origin of the term "pre-embryo" and why Clifford Grobstein invented the term. It also describes the scientific and logical fallacies upon which this term was based.

Another reason for focusing first on the **science** is that this current scientific hoax has already successfully confused and obscured the truth about our own self-understanding as human beings. In "Post-Abortion Trauma: Bring on the Facts" the author responds to the arguments of a feminist psychiatrist who intends to reduce the phenomenon of post-abortion trauma to scientific misinformation and religious sentiment. The author counter claims that most women today (in the name of "feminism") have bought into the fake science and fake moral claims of the "experts", and thereby justify and rationalize abortion as the simple elimination of some of their own "tissues". Eventually, many of these women do find out the truth about the pre-natal development of the fetuses they have naively aborted, but with profound psychological consequences.

One must wonder if women - who are aborting, donating their children's fetal tissues or "surplus" IVF human embryos for experimental research - can really be said to have given legally valid

2

informed consent. How could they, if they have been so thoroughly mis-informed about the nature of that which they are aborting or donating? In the following sections of this anthology, the authors will address further deficient judgments and conclusions which have followed directly on the use of such incorrect science.

In "Human Embryology and the Media" it is clearly shown how deficient media pundits are in their knowledge of the subject. The responsibility for getting the scientific information correct falls to them. However, human embryologists bear some responsibility for not being alert enough to such scientific misrepresentations in the press and other media, and correcting them appropriately and timely.

Given that so much incorrect science has been used and mis-used, why isn't any one doing anything about it? Could it be that disclosing the factual truth about our pre-natal human development might be "politically incorrect" or "unpopular", and upset more than a few political (and financial) apple-carts and agendas? In the article "Quid sit veritas?", the author chronicles an almost comical (if it were not so devastating) voyage of trying to "set the record straight". Source after source refuses to allow the light of day to shine on this fraud. But if professionals and experts, especially those within the various fields of science, refuse to allow these corrections and clarifications to reach other scientific professionals as well as the lay public, then our professions and our culture are in very serious trouble. Considerable harm to the public is the result. Several examples of these disturbing themes will be the focus of the following sections of this anthology.

The Beginning Of Life And The Establishment Of The Continuum.

by C. Ward Kischer

The beginning of life and the establishment of the continuum of life are not difficult facts to comprehend for the biologist (embryologist). Unfortunately, these facts have been reinterpreted and redefined in order to satisfy a political point of view. Thus, Human Embryology is in danger of being rewritten as a socio-legal political statement.

Roe v. Wade, adjudicated in 1973, has proven to be the watershed between law and science. Justice Blackmun, writing for the majority, said: "We need not resolve the difficult question of when life begins. When those trained in the respective disciplines of medicine, philosophy, and theology are unable to arrive at any consensus, the judiciary, at this point in the development of man's knowledge, is not in a position to speculate as to the answer." [1]

By essentially eliminating the question of life as the time related *value* for defining rights of the conceived - as opposed to disposal of the conceived - the court was free to establish an arbitrary point, or condition, which turned out to be convenient for the mother, prior to which disposal would be the legal right of the mother. This point was decided to be *viability*, which was cited to be between 24 and 28 weeks post-fertilization.[2] Blackmun tied *viability* to *personhood*, and marked it as the time at which the fetus could survive "outside the mother's womb, albeit with artificial aid."[3]

• ## 167 DISTINGUISHED SCIENTISTS

Later, in the Webster decision, the majority opinion also written by Blackmun, the decision of Roe v. Wade was affirmed. However, in this decision, Justice Blackmun used an *Amici Curiae* Brief of 167 Distinguished Scientists and Physicians including 11 Nobel

4

Using a reliable source to list the credentials of the 167, the volumes of American Men and Women of Science were consulted.[5] True, the 1992-93 edition was used and this might account for 66 not found if they had died and their listing removed in the interim. But, with that caveat understood 101 were found in the listing. Of that number only 31 used 'development' or 'developmental' in their bios. Of those 31 scientists, 9 were index-described embryologists and one was self-described, but not one was *a human embryologist!*[6] Clearly there is a major problem in establishing credibility for what these scientists say about human development (or what they do not say) "in support of appellees." The human embryologist knows human development best; but, this source of science was not consulted even though the compelling reasons were obvious.

- ## THE BEGINNING OF A HUMAN LIFE

In the above-referred-to Brief, it is written: "there is no scientific consensus that a human life begins at conception, at a given stage of fetal development, or at birth."[7] Conception, fetal development and birth are wholly biological (more specifically, embryological) terms. There are no implications of philosophy or theology implied or intended in their statement. The error of this statement is manifest by simple deductive reasoning and through countless observations, experimentally, that the result of fertilization is *the beginning of a new life*.

- ## THE ESSENCE OF HUMAN LIFE

Later, in this Brief, it is further written: "The question of when a human life truly begins calls for a conclusion as to which characteristics define the *essence* of human life. While science can tell us when certain biological characteristics can be detected, science cannot tell us which biological (sic) attributes establish the existence of a human being."[8] Here it is absolutely clear that the *amici* refer to

5

"biological" characteristic(s) to the exclusion of philosophy and theology.

The answer to their statement has been known in human embryology for decades. The best response is to be found in the statement by Wendell M. Stanley, Nobel Prize winner and discoverer of the tobacco mosaic virus:

> "The *essence* of life is the *ability to reproduce*. This is accomplished by the utilization of energy to create order out of disorder, to bring together into a specific predetermined pattern from semiorder or even from chaos all the component parts of that pattern with the perpetuation of that pattern with time. This is life."[9]

• **THE FALLOUT FROM ROE v. WADE**

The Supreme Court has disdained to reconsider what they decided in Roe v. Wade that the beginning of life could not be determined.[10,11] Thus , in this artificial vacuum many nonsensical statements have been made, such as that by Eleanor Smeal (then President of the National Organization of Women, NOW) in 1989: "Everybody knows that life begins only after birth."[12] Such a vacuum also generates specious arguments as to when the *individual* becomes *human* or a *human being*. Thus one finds published such bizarre claims that the fertilized ovum, or *zygote* does not have the information for full development;[13] that genetic control of development is the equivalent of "molecular control" and that such control is retained by the pregnant mother;[14] that *sentience*, self-awareness, marks the onset of *individuation*, which is the equivalent of becoming *human*.[15] These are all interesting academic exercises but have no relevance or significance in defining the beginning of life.

By denying the knowledge of when life begins, the Supreme Court established as a priority that point at which the new individual becomes a human being or is invested with *personhood*. This has led to invoking such ancillary qualities as genetic, developmental,

6

functional, behavioral, social and psychic individualities.[16] Thus, this is in concert with Blackmun's applying the fields of medicine, philosophy and theology towards the "difficult question of when life begins."[1]

- ## LIFE AND FIRST CONTACT

Life as a phenomenon began in the evolutionary sense approximately 3.5 billion years ago when a replicative (reproductive) event became sustained. Many replicative events probably occurred and were not sustained. But, eventually, one of those events marked the beginning of the *continuum* of life, within which we exist, today. Now we can see the significance of recognizing reproduction as the *essence* of life. It sustains the *continuum* of life.

Thus, in sexual reproduction, which evolved later, and produced the advantage of variety, *fertilization* became the time at which the *new individual* began and sustained the *continuum*. This means that *first contact* between sperm and ovum, the initial event in fertilization, became (and is) the supreme moment for initiation of the *continuum*.

With the timed sequence of events after *first contact*, a process occurs which brings together the chromosomes of the spermatozoan with the chromosomes of the ovum. This is called *syngamy*. This so-called stage has been suggested as the onset of *individuation*. In the technical sense this might be correct; however, *syngamy* occurs as a consequence of *first contact*, so it will occur anyway.

The failure to recognize *first contact* as the initiation of the new individual has permitted other arbitrary moments for *individuation*. Thus, the condition of monozygotic twinning (2 individuals split from one fertilized egg) was introduced as a defining moment of individuation because it was assumed that the early embryo had the potential to divide up to, but not after, 14 days post-fertilization. Therefore, individuation was delayed until the 14 day time.[15] It was, however, ignored that the known embryological facts state that 35% of monozygotic twins occur from splitting of the embryonic cells

7

(blastomeres) *early* in development from the first one or two division stages.[17] Retrospectively, this speaks for early determination of the so called individual.

• CONCEPTION, FERTILIZATION AND PREGNANCY

Another attempt to delay the identification of the new individual (thus, that of new life) may be found in the conversion of the definition of *conception*. Taber's Cyclopedic Medical Dictionary defines conception as: "The union of the male sperm and the ovum of the female; fertilization."[18] Mosby's Medical Dictionary also declares conception is equivalent with fertilization.[19] Stedman's 22nd edition medical dictionary defines it as: "*implantation* of the blastocyst in the uterine lining." It says nothing about fertilization.[20] However, Stedman's 26th edition defines conception as: "the act of conceiving or becoming pregnant; fertilization...."[21] This same edition defines pregnancy as "conception until birth of the baby".[21] Dorland's Medical Dictionary uses two definitions of conception: 1. "the onset of pregnancy, marked by implantation of the blastocyst"; and 2. "the formation of a viable zygote."[22] Dorland's dictionary is somewhat contradictory in that pregnancy is defined as: "having a developing embryo or fetus in the body."[22] Taber's dictionary defines pregnancy as: "carrying a developing embryo in the uterus."[18] Mosby's Dictionary defines pregnancy as: "the gestational process, comprising the growth and development within a woman of a new individual from conception through the embryonic and fetal periods to birth."[19] From where might such contradictions arise? The following might provide a clue: In Albert Rosenfeld's book Second Genesis, [23] in a discussion of chemical contraceptives, a footnote states as follows:

> "Because these substances do not prevent the sperm from penetrating and fertilizing the ovum - the classic definition of conception - they are not strictly contraceptives. What they do is prevent the newly-fertilized egg from implanting itself in the uterus. Since the interference occurs after conception, some hold that

8

such practice constitutes abortion. A way around this impasse has been suggested by Dr. A.S. Parkes of Cambridge: Equate conception with the time of implantation rather than the time of fertilization - a difference of only a few days."

Political correctness weaves its way in and out of the science of human embryology!

• WHAT HUMAN EMBRYOLOGISTS SAY

Embryology is the study of development of the new individual from *beginning* to end. We should, therefore, be alerted as to what contemporary and renowned human embryologists have to say about the beginning of a new life and the beginning of the human being:

• Moore, Keith L. "This fertilized ovum, known as a zygote, is a large diploid cell that is *the beginning, or primordium, of a human being.*"[24]

• Larsen, William J. ". . . gametes, which will unite at fertilization to initiate the embryonic development of *a new individual.*"[25]

• Carlson, Bruce M. "Human *pregnancy* begins with the *fusion* of an egg and a sperm . . . ."[26]

• Patten, Bradley M. p. 13 "Fertilized ovum gives rise to *new individual*". P. 43: ". . . the process of *fertilization* . . . marks the initiation of the *life of a new individual.*"[27] Quoting F.R. Lillie: P. 41: ". . . in the act of fertilization . . . two lives are gathered in one knot . . . and are rewoven in *a new individual* life-history."[28]

• Sadler, T.W. "The development of *a human being* begins with *fertilization.*"[29]

• Moore, Keith L. and T.V.N. Persaud. "*Human development* is

9

a *continuous* process that begins when an oocyte (ovum) from a female is *fertilized* by a sperm (spermatozoan) from a male."[30]

- O'Rahilly, Ronan and Fabiola Müller. *"Fertilization* is an important landmark because, under ordinary circumstances, a *new* genetically *distinct human organism* is thereby formed."[31]

Conversely, it is worthwhile to note that this author has never seen a statement denying the truth of the above. Only when the biological facts have become politicized has there appeared any equivocation.

The Supreme Court of the United States must ultimately come vis-a-vis with the known biological facts of human embryology and admit to the disingenuous interpretation of the beginning of life embodied in Roe v. Wade and affirmed in the Webster case.

- **SUMMARY**

In summary: The fertilized egg is a living entity, a *human being,* a human *individual,* and, a *person,* all one and inseparable. The reason why this is true is the following:

from the moment when the sperm makes contact with the ovum, under conditions we have come to understand and describe as *normal,* all subsequent development to birth of a living newborn is a *fait accompli.* That is to say, after that initial contact of sperm and egg there is no subsequent moment or stage which is held in arbitration or abeyance by the mother, or the embryo or fetus. Nor is a second contribution, a signal or trigger, needed from the male in order to continue and complete full development to birth. Human development is a *continuum* in which so-called stages overlap and blend one into another. Indeed, all of life is contained within a time *continuum*. Thus, the beginning of a new life is exacted by the beginning of fertilization, the reproductive event which is the *essence* of life.

REFERENCES

1. Syllabus: Roe et al. v. Wade, District Attorney of Dallas County. No. 70-18 Decided January 22, 1973. p. 44.

2. Ibid___. p. 45.

3. Ibid___. p. 45.

4. William L. Webster et al. v. Reproductive Health Services et al. Amici Curiae Brief of 167 Distinguished Scientists and Physicians, Including 11 Nobel Laureates In Support of Appellees. October, 1988.

5. American Men and Women in Science. 1992-93. R.R. Bowker, New Providence, New Jersey.

6. Solomon, Susan A. 1996. Laws In Embryology, But Embryology In The Law? In preparation.

7. William L. Webster et al. v. Reproductive Health Services et al. Amici Curiae Brief of 167 Distinguished Scientists and Physicians, Including 11 Nobel Laureates In Support of Appellees. October, 1988. p. 2.

8. Ibid___. p. 6.

9. Stanley, Wendell M. 1957. The nature of viruses, cancer, genes and life - a declaration of dependence. Proc. Amer. Philosoph. Soc., 101:357-370.

10. J.M. Individually v. V.C. et. al. On Petition for Writ of Certiorari to the Supreme Court of New Jersey. Supreme Court of The United States. October Term, 1993. No. 93-1149.

11. Alexander Loce v. The State of New Jersey. On Petition for Writ of Certiorari to the Supreme Court of New Jersey. Supreme Court of The United States. October Term, 1993. No. 92-1934.

12. Smeal, Eleanor. 1989. Speech before convention of NOW.

13. Gardner, Charles A. 1989. Is an Embryo a Person? The Nation, November 13th issue, pp. 557-559.

14. Bedate, Carlos and Robert Cefalo. 1989. The Zygote: to be or not be a person. J. Med. Phil. 14:641-645.

15. Grobstein, Clifford. 1988. Science and The Unborn. p. 33. Basic Books, New York.

16. Ibid___. pp. 21-39.

17. Moore, Keith L. and T.V.N. Persaud. 1993. The Developing Human, 5th ed. p. 135. W.B. Saunders co., Philadelphia.

18. Taber's Cyclopedic Medical Dictionary 1989. 16th edition. F.A. Davis Co., Philadelphia.

19. Mosby's Medical, Nursing, and Allied Health Dictionary. 1994. Fourth edition. Mosby, St. Louis.

20. Stedman's Medical Dictionary. 1972. 22nd edition. Williams and Wilkins Co., Baltimore.

21. Ibid___. 1995. 26th edition.

22. Dorland's Medical Dictionary. 1988. 27th edition. W.B. Saunders co., Philadelphia.

23. Rosenfeld, Albert. 1969. Second Genesis. The Coming Control of Life. p. 108. Prentice-Hall, Englewood Cliffs, N.J.

24. Moore, Keith L. 1988. Essentials of Human Embryology. p. 2. B.C. Decker Co., Toronto.

25. Larsen, William J. 1993. Human Embryology. p. 1. Churchill-Livingston, New York.

26. Carlson, Bruce M. 1994. Human Embryology and Developmental Biology. p. 3. Mosby, St. Louis.

27. Patten, Bradley M. 1968. Human Embryology, 3rd Ed. p. 13. McGraw-Hill, New York.

28. Lillie, F.R. 1919. Problems of Fertilization. The University of Chicago Press, Chicago.

29. Sadler, T.W. 1990. Langman's Medical Embryology, 6th Ed. p 3. Williams and Wilkins, Baltimore.

30. Moore, Keith L. and T.V.N. Persaud. 1993. The Developing Human, 5th Ed. p. 1. W.B. Saunders Co., Philadelphia.

31. O'Rahilly, Ronan and Fabiola Müller. 1992. Human Embryology and Teratology. p. 5. Wiley-Liss, New York.

In Defense of Human Development

by

C.Ward Kischer, Ph.D.

Efforts to influence policy decisions relative to abortion, whether on the federal or state level, have inevitably included statements about human development invoked especially to support a particular political point of view.

The cumulative effect of the many statements has given rise to an ugly spectre of human development, which is being reinvented as a derivative of the socio-legal aspect of the abortion issue.

Since Roe v. Wade, in 1973, more public statements have been made concerning human development than perhaps in all of our previous recorded history. Many of those statements have been misguided, if not outright inaccurate. The abortion issue has crystallized the public's need to know the truth about our own development. Yet, the significance of this truth goes far beyond the abortion issue.

Elective abortion is intervention. But, in a similar sense, so are *in-vitro* fertilization, *in-utero* fetal surgery, fetal tissue research, drug addicted newborns, smoking pregnant women (and proximal consorters) and pregnant women who drink and produce fetal alcohol syndrome babies.

Because of the consequences to human development by the above-mentioned procedures and conditions, and with the advent of such technology as gene synthesis, selection, modification and repair, it is high time we take a closer look at our developmental history.

Four major concepts have fallen prey to contemporary socio-legal issues: The Beginning of Life, The Quality of Being Human, Viability, and Sentience.

14

The Concept of the Beginning of Life

Ernest Van Den Haag writing in *The National Review*[1] states that prochoice advocates argue "the infant is unquestionably alive, unquestionably human and viable outside the mother, whereas the fetus may not be." We know fetuses can be dead, and anything dead had to have been, at some previous time, alive. But the possibility of the existence of a *dead* fetus is not mentioned by Van Den Haag.

The fetus *is* unquestionably alive and is evidence of the continuum of the phenomenon called "life." Fetal cells and components within those cells are metabolizing, but more importantly, reproducing, which is the essence of life.[2] The progressive increase in size of the embryo and fetus is due to an increase in the number of cells, which are reproducing faster than others which are dying, and an increase in cell proteins.

Van Den Haag repeats the prolife claim that "life begins at conception." He states: "this makes sense." It makes even more sense that life does not really *begin* at conception because it was already present in the sperm and the egg prior to their union. Life as a phenomenon was, in fact, a singular event, which occurred approximately 4.5 billion years ago when an instant of replication became sustained and eventually gave rise to all further consequences of that one fortuitous moment through reproduction. *That* was life. What happens at the union of a sperm and an egg is a new expression of the continuum of that life process. Bradley Patten, an embryologist now deceased, wrote in his textbook: "Although in a sense, an embryo preexists in the gametes from which it arises, its life *as a new individual* must be regarded as commencing at the moment of fertilization."[3]

Among the many errors in the Roe vs. Wade decision was the Court's view as to when life began. Indeed, the Court stated "We need not resolve the difficult question of when life begins." They then stated that those trained in medicine, philosophy and religion could not arrive at a consensus.[4] *Indeed!* Although medical practice often relies on empirical procedures, it should be, and mostly is, based on scientific fact, and science has never relied on philosophy or religion for a definition of biological life, nor should it.

By accepting the concept that life begins at conception, the previous biological history of life is abrogated and is rendered relatively insignificant. Therefore, the greater biological significance is that from the instantaneous moment of life (which can never recur) a system of reproduction has been designed, engineered, evolved and entrusted within the female of our species for the care and perpetuation of humankind.

The Quality of Being Human

Another supposed vagary produced by the abortion issue is the question as to when the embryo or fetus becomes *human*. Rivers Singleton, Jr. states in his article in *Perspectives in Biology and Medicine*, that, for some, conception defines the point of being human, whereas, for others, various periods of development suffice to "distinguish human from non-humans."[5] Such statements promote the legal dilemma as expressed during the arguments of the Webster case before the Supreme Court. Justice Scalia described the fetus to Attorney Sussman as, "This thing that we don't know what it is."[6]

Singleton and Van Den Haag call into question whether the fetus is human or prehuman. Carl Sagan and his wife, Ann Druyan[7] wrote a layman's article in the nationally distributed *Sunday Parade* magazine and questioned when human qualities emerge. The fetus, and all preceding stages, can only be human for the reason that cross-specie fertilization is not known to occur in the human. That is, only a human can mate with a human and produce offspring. Special exceptions, however, are known among mammals in which cross specie fertilization may occur. For example, a Jackass can mate with a Mare (different species) and produce a Mule, which, however, is always sterile. The biological quality of being human arose somewhere back in time when, most probably, the first hominids were developed on earth. However, an equal case could be made for the quality of being human being embodied within the chromosomes derived from certain genomic mutative events which locked in the human quality and locked out all other species. Hominids were the evidence for that. Therefore, we could reasonably say that our chromosomes embody our *human* quality. The apparent basis for questioning being human is that early developmental stages do not *look like* the newborn.

Van Den Haag claims the embryo is "prehuman." In support of

16

this he relates the embryo to a human baby as a larva relates to a butterfly.[1] This comparison may satisfy contemporary social engineers but it is biologically absurd. Even an entomologist would be grievously offended by such a notion.

Van Den Haag further states that as development proceeds, the embryo acquires "human characteristics." He actually means the change from an embryo to a fetus, occurring at about 9 weeks post-fertilization age, which is the time when *facial* characteristics accelerate their development. Sagan and Druyan refer to different developmental stages as resembling a worm, reptile and a pig. In 1866 the axiom was promoted in zoology that *Ontogeny Recapitulates Phylogeny* (The Basic Biogenetic Law).[8] This meant that during development, as it would relate in the case of the human, stages of lesser vertebrate organisms were reflected, morphologically. It was believed that developmental archives contained a telescoped evolutionary history. From this statement a frivolous notion was generated that in actuality a fish, lizard or perhaps a rabbit (or as Sagan and Druyan would have it, a worm, reptile and pig) was somehow enjoined in the early developmental stages of what later became human. This is an example of the reinvention of human development, for, 30 years earlier (1828) the published laws of von Baer precluded the Basic Biogenetic Law.[9]

Van Den Haag states the embryo lacks distinctly human characteristics that might entitle it to a social protection and follows by asking: "when does intrauterine life become human life?"[1] To the embryologist (who knows the subject best) no such quandary exists. The dilemma is wrought by his confusing "human" characteristics with "facial" characteristics. The period of transition between an embryo and a fetus is approximately 9 weeks post-fertilization. This is a time at which facial characteristics become "human" in terms of their positions or proportionate size so that the structures of the face begin to resemble those with which we are born. Prior to this, development of the face has been rather slow because the presumptive face is impacted against the primitive heart bulge due to a flexure in the neck area. Upon relief of that flexure, due to differential growth rates, development of the face may proceed more rapidly.

When the eye fields migrate from the lateral to more medial positions the interposition of a head structure called the *frontonasal prominence*, which includes the presumptive nasal structure, impedes

17

their further movements. However, in rare instances this does not happen. The eye fields merge, become one, and give rise to a condition known as *cyclopia*. A few of these individuals are born alive. By the reasoning of Van Den Haag, a cyclops individual would certainly lack "human" characteristics and would not be entitled to "social protection." It is interesting to note that in true cyclopia the nose structure (not a true nose) would always appear above the eye. In contrast, the typical Hollywood cyclops shows the nose below the eye. Singleton describes an embryo as a "poorly differentiated aggregation of cells" and that "early human fetuses [sic] with their primitive gill slits and tails more often than not resemble some primeval sea creature than a cuddly human baby."[5] (It is worthwhile to note that the only opportunity for a gill to form in human development would be during the stage of the *embryo*, not that of the fetus.) Sagan and Druyan describe the four week embryo with "something like the gill arches of a fish or an amphibian" and also say it has a "pronounced tail." No gills *ever* occur in development of the human.[10] Embryologists and embryology texts continue to this day to use the term "tail process" or "tail bud". This is most unfortunate and begs an inaccurate use of the term "tail". The real truth is that a tail *never* occurs in normal development. What occasionally occurs in the case of the human is a caudal appendage, which is an anomaly and cannot reasonably be called a "tail." It has no intrinsic movement and most are composed solely of subcutaneous tissue.

Sagan and Druyan compound their errors by stating that "300 million also-rans of sperm have not yet arrived" at the site of fertilization of the egg.[7] The fact is they never do. Only about 100 or less sperm out of about 200 million in a given ejaculate every arrive at the usual site of fertilization. They also state a "hollow sphere" as an embryo (meaning the blastocyst) "sucks blood" from maternal capillaries![7] Wrong, again. A sucking process never occurs, and the "sphere" has considerable more structure to it than simply being hollow.

Today we recognize that the Biogenetic Law, at least, was an overstatement. Thus, with advancing knowledge we have been able to satisfactorily dismiss the false conclusions generated from Ontogeny Recapitulates Phylogeny and, instead, come to the correct conclusion that developmental processes among vertebrates (including man) are simply similar in the embryo stage and exhibit aspects of the same kind of developmental plan. This makes much more sense. As such, each organism retains its own special identity from fertilization to death.

Charles A. Gardner, while a graduate student in anatomy at the University of Michigan, wrote an article for *The Nation* entitled, "Is an Embryo a Person?"[11] He stated the embryo is not a person and not a "human being." His reasoning: "the fertilized egg knows nothing about how to make a finger, a nose or eyes." He then contradicts himself by admitting that the fertilized egg contains all the DNA necessary for development of all the body parts; but, then he states that the egg does not contain all of the information to put those parts together.

Of course it does not, not at any given moment in time. But, if this disqualifies the embryo as being human, how come in every case the end result is human? The sequencing of events is predetermined and takes place over time according to cues given to the genome.

Wrongfully, embryonic and fetal characteristics have been evaluated against adult characteristics.

Keith Moore, in his textbook *Before We Are Born* responds to the question "*When does the embryo become human*," as follows:[12]

> This is a difficult question to answer because one's views are affected by one's religion and the views of one's peers. The *scientific* answer is that the embryo *always* had human potential, and no other, from the time of fertilization because of its human chromosome constitution. Two things are definite: (1) human development begins at fertilization and (2) the zygote and early embryo are living organisms. My personal view is that the embryo becomes a human being during the eighth week when it acquires distinctive human characteristics, but you will have to decide for yourself after wide consultation.

Moore has provided two answers: the biological one and the socio-legal one. It is little wonder humankind has difficulty living compatibly with the laws of nature when we keep redefining those laws to justify socio-legal proclivities.

Viability

In Roe v. Wade, the court defined a "person" (ergo-the fetus)

19

as one being "capable of an independent existence," and independent existence as the point of viability.[13]

The question of a fetus being viable outside the mother, of course, has biological and medical significance, but its relevancy to the abortion issue is highly questionable. Van Den Haag states: "Infanticide kills a human being that is independently alive." But, this seems to beg the question as to whether or not a fetus which cannot live" independently" may be disposed of with impunity. True, newborns and infants are "independently alive," but only temporarily so. Although physically independent from the mother, in that they are no longer connected via umbilical cords, they cannot feed, bathe, or adequately protect themselves from the hostilities of their environment or other equivalent threats. Even though they breathe "on their own" (actually independent respiratory actions occur in the fetus) this continues only as long as other needs are met. They require as much total care as they were receiving *in-utero*, in fact, more so.

Insofar as the abortion issue is concerned, of what particular significance is it that a 24 week old fetus (or a fetus of any age) could survive outside of the womb? It is important to prolife advocates because it drives back the time of "independent existence." Thus, they may claim abortion would be illegal after the time of "independent existence' (personhood). Improved technology may sustain prematurely delivered fetuses, but would include those who may not overcome a severely reduced quality of life. Thus, the socio-legal term of "personhood" has reduced the *biological* quality of a newborn in terms of its ability to use its lungs to aerate blood with the aid of an incubator, respirator, chemical additives and round-the-clock nursing attendants. "Personhood" has thus become a captive issue and is entirely socio-legal in content. From the biological point of view, it is irrelevant.

Sentience

Singleton differs from Roe v. Wade and cites the beginning of personhood as when the fetus is capable of having an interest in its own existence and, further, when awareness of the existence occurs. Van Den Haag concurs and uses the term *sentience*. He states the embryo has neither a brain nor the neural system which makes *sentience* possible.

In terms of survival value for subsequent developmental stages of the human embryo and fetus, no better mechanism (in a teleological sense one could say "interest") can be demonstrated than the very aggressive special tissue surrounding the embryo proper differentiated within the first 12 days post-fertilization called *syncytiotrophoblast.* It is a premier invasive tissue and may assist in preventing rejection of this "foreign tissue" by the mother.[14,15] No neural pathway is necessary for this activity to occur.

Clifford Grobstein, a Ph.D. and developmental biologist, interviewed in *Psychology Today*, maintains there are six essential aspects of individuality.[16] He related them to specific stages or times of development. Psychic individuality, he states, occurs at 26 weeks, but admits this is arbitrary. He couples this with sentience, or thought.

But, thought is a concept and needs an historical component. Those interpreting EEGs on premature infants, or fetuses from elective abortions are normally *very* cautious concerning their interpretation. Grobstein's stages are arbitrary and are not scientifically founded.

Sentience is not a topic which is taught in basic embryology courses by embryologists. The concept of sentience has undoubtedly arisen from psychologists who have tried to relate muscular movements to *willful* and *protective* behavior in the fetus. The newborn does not respond to vocal commands. thus, its movements are the result of virtually the same kind of stimuli that prompt movements at 5 to 6 weeks of embryonic age, such as chemical (change in oxygen supply) or mechanical (stretch of a muscle cell).[17] The surgeon's probe, or an environmental change, can essentially provoke the same kind of movement in the embryo as well as in the newborn. In this sense there is no difference between the two stages. At about 17 weeks of development, enough of a communication system has developed so that as more muscle cells have been produced more will respond to the same magnitude of stimulus and, thus, be felt by the mother as "quickening." If movements are manifestations of "awareness of one's self" and thus valuable in defining "personhood," then the embryo at 5 to 6 weeks of age qualifies.[17]

Van Den Haag's premise implies that there is some point in development at which a brain or a neural system, and/or sentience,

21

suddenly appears and dispenses "awareness." Sagan and Druyan suggest that "thinking" - "human thought" and all of its advantages - is the most dramatic "human characteristic" and occurs at 30 weeks of fetal age. They state this should be related to the end point of permissible abortions, (coincidentally implying they should be allowed up to 30 weeks). Of course, thinking is not unique to humans. We simply do more of it than other living creatures. However, they suggest that fetuses after 30 weeks can "think" and, by inference, that prior to this they cannot.

Development of the nervous system is a progressive phenomenon. Our best evidence from the standpoint of functional embryology unequivocally states that as soon as the first synapse forms, it functions. This occurs during embryonic age, *before* nine weeks post-fertilization. What would occur at any given later stage, perhaps at 30 weeks, would be enough electrical potential to evoke a tracing on an electroencephalogram. Thus, it would seem the value of a human fetus is reduced to its ability to move a stylus on a graph paper. By this reckoning the previous 29 weeks and 6 days of synchronized and orchestrated preparation has all gone for nought and could be dismissed as irrelevant.

Human Embryology and The Socio-Legal Issue

The failure by contemporary writers to acknowledge what is current and true about human development sustains and nurtures the continuing controversy surrounding abortion. Two different types of consequences which significantly mold public opinion may be illustrated:

1) The joint Lost Angeles Times-Washington Post Service recently issued the following statement (Tucson citizen, January 1, 1991):

> Should parental choice be limited to eliminating serous genetic defects? or does the procedure involve such early embryos-*they are still microscopic specks*-that few people would object to discarding them for such reasons as having an unwanted hair color or being the wrong sex? (Italics-my emphasis.)

Our existence as a "microscopic speck" is certainly not trivial, because our "specks" represent the history of more than 4.5 billion years of trials, failures, and successes. Yet, the sense of such a characterization actually diminishes our early embryology and its survival.

2) The Rev. Richard McCormick, writing in the Kennedy Institute of Ethics Journal, now questions the judgment of the Catholic Church relative to the time of ensoulment from conception to sometime later in development.[18] He uses the term *preembryo* which is not an established embryological term.

He relies specifically on Grobstein's definition of "developmental individuality" which he claims occurs when the inner cell mass no longer will divide to produce monozygotic twins or multiple copies. World-wide this would account for less than 4% of the total population. Based on this statistic, 96% would be denied 'ensoulment' until 4% have been *determined*. In fact, 30% of that 4% are determined in the first 3 division stages after fertilization.[12] Grobstein's concept of "developmental individuality" is frought with errors and is not scientifically founded.

Conclusion

Development is an integrated biological progression of events, involving each cell, tissue, organ and organ system, all dependent on their preceding events for any particular biological significance. If these events are of proper significance to policy formulation and law making in deciding whether the embryo or fetus may be disposed of with impunity, they must be considered *in toto* and in context of a *continuum*. No point, time or stage of our development stands alone to the exclusion of all others to be judged relevant or irrelevant to any socio-legal consideration.

References

1. Van Den Haag, E: Is there a middle ground? *National Review* 22 December, 51:29-31, 1989.

2. Stanley, WM: The nature of viruses, cancer, genes and life-a declaration of dependence. *Proc Amer Philosoph Soc* 101:357-370, 1957.

3. Patten, B: *Human Embryology*. 3rd Ed. New York, McGraw-Hill, 1968.

4. Roe v. Wade. *Syllabus of Opinion*. p. 48, 1973.

5. Singleton Jr. R: Paradigms of science/society interaction: The abortion controversy. *Persp Biol Med* 32:174-194, 1989.

6. Scalia, A: *in* arguments of Webster vs. Reproductive Health Service, cited by *USA Today*, 27 April, 1989.

7. Sagan, C and Druyan, A: Is it possible to be pro-life and pro-choice? *Parade, The Sunday Paper Magazine* April 22, pp. 4-8, New York, 1990.

8. Haeckel, E: *Generelle Morphologie der Organismen.* Berlin, 1866

9. Baer, K.E. von: 'Uber Entwicklungsgeschicte der Thiere', *Beobachtung und Reflexion*. Konigsberg, 1828.

10. Blechschmidt, E: *The Beginnings of Human Life* p. 63. New York: Springer-Verlag, 1977.

11. Gardner, C: Is an Embryo a Person? *The Nation*, November 13th issue, pp. 557-559, 1989.

12. Moore, K: *Before We are Born*, 3rd Ed. Philadelphia, W.B. Saunders, Co. 1989.

13. Roe v. Wade. *Syllabus of Opinion*. p. 159, 173.

14. Berkowitz, R: Cross-reactivity of monoclonal antibodies directed against lymphocyte markers and trophoblastic cells of normal placenta, hydatidiform mole and gestational choriocarcinoma. *Gynec Oncol* 29:94-100, 1988.

15. Wegmann, TG: Maternal T-cells promote placental growth and prevent spontaneous abortion. *Immunol Lett* 18:19-25, 1988.

24

16.   Grobstein, C: When does life begin: *Psychology Today* September Issue, pp. 43-46, 1989.

17.   Humphrey, T: Some correlations between the appearance of human fetal reflexes and the development of the nervous system, *in*, Growth and Maturation of the Brain. *Prog. Brain. Res.* 4:93-135, 1964.

18.   McCormick, RA: *Who or what is the pre-embryo?* J. Kennedy Instit Ethics 1:1-15, 1991.

Human Development and Reconsideration of Ensoulment

Clayton Ward Kischer, Ph.D.
Department of Cell Biology and Anatomy
The University of Arizona
College of Medicine
Tucson, Arizona 85724

Will and Ariel Durant state in the preface to their book, entitled *The Lessons of History,* that their aim in preparing the essay was not originality but inclusiveness.[1] We expect that from historians. But, we also expect it form scientists and, more specifically of late, those writing about human development. Within the past few years, many statements have been published concerning human development which have been misleading, out of context, or outright false.

Human embryology is now in danger of being rewritten as a stratagem statement of current socio-legal, but also of late, even theological, issues. Unless the errors are corrected now, we will be in danger of entering a protracted period of false concepts concerning our own development. History records previous difficult periods; for example, when the theory of recapitulation, conceived by Haeckel in 1866, preoccupied biologists for decades.[2] This became the Biogenetic Law which stated that our embryonic stages telescoped the morphology of lesser vertebrates. The laws of von Baer had been published 38 years earlier, and had precluded such a theory. Correctly stated, embryonic stages of the vertebrates are simply similar in form.[3]

The So-Called Pre-embryo

The Reverend Richard A. McCormick has recently written an essay proposing a "new moral status," for a stage of development of the human embryo, called the "pre-embryo."[4] The pre-embryo theoretically extends from fertilization to a stage about 5 to 6 days post-fertilization and, he states, might be for that period of time not entitled to moral status.[5] His new "moral status" is actually a reconsideration of the time granted for ensoulment by the Catholic Church.[6]

The authenticity for the term pre-embryo is derived from a justification given by Grobstein: "greater accuracy in characterizing the initial phase of mammalian and human development."[7] McCormick states: "the term pre-embryo was adopted because the earliest stages of mammalian [sic] development primarily involve establishment of the non-embryonic trophoblast, rather than the formation of the embryo."[8] This is an involuted statement and, in the case of the human, is not true. In the human the trophoblast does not appear until the 4th day. In the human the trophoblast and *some*, not all, of its derivatives are involved in establishing the placenta. While this is going on development of the embryo is certainly not arrested but proceeds apace. If in the early stages certain cells not directly involved in development of the embryo justify establishment of a pre-embryo state and possible reconsideration of ensoulment, what status might be established for the embryo, or the fetus, in which multitudes of cells, including massive numbers of brain cells, and others which are organized into whole structures, never become part of the fetus or the infant? Specifically, as nerve cells (neuroblasts) are rapidly dividing, forming the nervous system including the brain, many are dying.[9,10] Additionally, many cells, not just nerve cells, are programmed for cell death in the embryo, many others in the fetus, and still others at all stages of life, post-birth.[11]

It is important to examine what has been, and is, common usage among those who are most familiar with the subject of human development, the embryologists. The most recent edition of Stedman's Medical Dictionary (1990) defines *embryo* as "an organism from conception until approximately the end of the second month," after which it is termed a fetus.[12] None of the established human embryology texts use the term pre-embryo, and it is not to be found in the scientific literature of human development. Bradley Patten, now deceased, but one of the renowned deans of human embryology, regarded the fertilized ovum and subsequent cleavage stages as *the embryo* and stated; "stages of development are purely arbitrary. Development is a *continuous process* and one phase merges into another without any real point of demarcation."[14]

It is not a question as to whether science can or cannot decide the question of personhood. Science is not *interested* in deciding personhood. However, if the socio-legal status of personhood cannot be decided without invoking what is known scientifically, then the *whole* of scientific data should be used and not arbitrarily selected bits and pieces of data.

Developmental Individuality

McCormick's reliance on *developmental individuality* is derived from Grobstein's recently published "stages".[15,16] Grobstein[17,18] claims the stage of *developmental individuality* is reached when division of the inner cell mass no longer can divide to produce twins or multiple identical individuals. Ancillary support for this contention comes from a report by the American Fertility Society, which states that at least up to the eight-cell stage the developmental singleness of one person has not yet been established.[22] This, quite simply, is not true. Seventy percent of all identical twins (monozygotic origin, that is, derived from one fertilized egg) are accounted for by division of the inner cell mass. The other 30% are accounted for by division at the two-cell to eight-cell stage of cleavage.[20,21] Multiplicity of birth from dizygotic origin (two different ova) appears to be familial. However, the factors determining the origin of monozygotic multiplicity are not known, but, statistical data does not support a familial origin. The fact that 30% of all monozygotic twinning is determined in early cleavage stages strongly suggests that the singleness of all cases other than monozygotic twinning is determined at fertilization, or, perhaps at the first cleavage division. Compounding the problem explaining the onset of individuation is the fact that multiplicity beyond twinning may include a combination of dizygotic *and* monozygotic-derived embryos.[21]

The fact is, not a shred of evidence exists which would explain the origin of monozygotic multiplicity. The kind of evidence which McCormick needs to support singleness occurring at the inner cell mass stage, and which would justify his "new moral status", is simply not in existence.

28

The overwhelming majority of individuals on this earth now and since the beginning of hominid development have been, and are, derived from one fertilized egg without further separation of the blastomeres. If exceptions to this fact prompt a new definition for the right of ensoulment, it would be done for a very *small* fraction of the total human population now and in the future. Further, there would be no certain way ethically to withhold ensoulment from stages prior to formation of the blastocyst, because the factors or stimuli which produce monozygotic twins are not known and therefore not predictable.

By designating developmental commitment to a single individual (singleness) as a determining factor for ensoulment, then in cases in which totipotentiality is lost early in development (called determinant cleavage), for example, in the annelids (worms), would there be an entitlement to ensoulment? Certainly there has never been a suggestion that the Catholic Church, nor any traditional religion, should recognize ensoulment for other than humans. Therefore, it would seem that the *human quality* would have to exist. This quality is established at fertilization. But, by qualifying this entitlement and restricting it to a later stage, such as the inner cell mass, the human quality is thereby equivocated. Indeed, a stronger case can be made for developmental individuality occurring at the time of fertilization of the ovum rather than at the inner cell mass stage.

McCormick states that the potential for a fertilized egg to become an adult is a theoretical and statistical potential because only a small minority actually achieve this in the natural process.[22] But, so what? What does that have to do with those zygotes which *do* successfully develop? A significant number of zygotes, embryos, fetuses and born individuals encounter biological faults, many of which precipitate early death before and after the inner cell mass stage.

There are other significant facts about human development that are commonly misstated. For example, in the case of human development, we have traditionally believed in the totipotentiality of the cleaving blastomeres (cells) until the inner cell mass stage (the blastocyst). but, not each blastomere has the same potential as the zygote, not even in cases where subsequently there might be a division of the inner cell mass into multiple copies of the embryo. Some of the blastomeres are destined to assume a peripheral position of the cleaving mass. During the formation of the blastocyst, these peripheral blastomeres will assume the identity of the trophoblast. The innermost blastomeres correspondingly, become distinguished from the peripheral-most cells by forming the inner cell mass. Positional differences are not to be exempted from consideration of totipotentiality.

McCormick states the organization of the inner cell mass into two layers (referred to as the bilaminar embryo) is reflected by the formation of the primitive streak.[23] That is incorrect. The appearance of the streak marks the beginning of the formation of the *trilaminar* embryo.

It has also been reported by Short that it is untrue that identical twins may have progressed through two distinct inner cell masses at the fifth day.[24] They certainly could have and could have been derived from separate earlier stages, which would have been derived from early monozygotic twinning.[20] Short also states if "cleavage of the embryo is delayed until eight or more days after fertilization, the two resulting embryos have come from a single inner cell mass, and share one common set of all placental membranes." If twinning is delayed until eight or more days after fertilization, the two resulting twins *will* share a common placenta, but also a common amnion. They represent an anomalous condition and are rarely born alive.[20]

Functional Individuality

The arbitrary nature of Grobstein's "stage of developmental individuality" may be seen in his other examples: He defines the onset of *functional individuality* "by the beating of a simple two-chambered heart."[18] In the human, the first beats are irregular and occur prior to the presence of any blood to be moved. This occurs by the 22nd day post-fertilization,[25] some texts may indicate it occurs a bit later. The first *contraction* may be considerably earlier, perhaps 4 to 5 days earlier.[26] As development proceeds more blood corpuscles are formed, accumulate in the fusing blood channels, and the beats (contractions) become progressively more regular and stronger due to the formation and arrangement of more cardiac muscle cells. By this time, the beat of the heart becomes detectable. At what point would it be most appropriate to assign functional individuality? Can a case be made for functional individuality occurring when the first contractile unit in the first myoblast cell is formed. Or when the paired endocardial tubes are formed? Or when the cardiogenic cords are differentiated? Or when the first potential cardiac cell migrates to the presumptive heart area?

Are these important questions? Not to the embryologist. The simple reason is that we recognize that all of development is a *continuum*, and any point in development derives its significance from the most previous point in development.

Psychic Individuality

McCormick ties his argument for a reassessment of the time of ensoulment to the "light of scientific data."[27] But the "scientific data" he cites has been highly selected and leaves out the overwhelming amount of "data." Another example of Grobstein's stages is that of *psychic individuality* (1989, p.44) which, he states, occurs at 26 weeks, but admits that point in time is "arbitrary."[18] He claims that time may change with more knowledge. He identifies this stage as *sentience* and relates it to the onset of thought. Those claiming sentience in the human fetus usually cite as evidence the recordings of brain waves. What studies have been made demonstrating brain wave recordings at 26 weeks of fetal age? A search of the literature within the last 11 years indicates that *no* studies have been conducted on 26 week old fetuses. Those *studies* using electroencephalogram (EEG) recordings have been done during labor on full-term fetuses. Actually, these are not *studies*. They are either case reports or highly selected data. Some recordings have apparently been made at approximately 20 weeks presumably on premature births, but possibly on elective abortions.[28] The waves are anarchic and asymmetric. They are different from the newborns which, in turn, are very different from a juvenile or an adult.

Sentience, awareness of one's self, is a concept born of psychology. Thought must have an historical component, such as a record or interview. The newborn does not respond to vocal commands. On that basis, a newborn does not reveal thought. If one is testing alertness by an EEG, then *psychic individuality* is reduced to the ability of enough neurons developing enough electrical potential to move a stylus on a graph. Further, one would be recording "alertness" of neurons, not necessarily of the individual, one of the reasons being

31

that many interneurons are added post-birth up to two years of age. Those who regularly perform EEGs on newborns will admit it is not an easy task and interpretation is not a simple matter. Brain wave recordings might be refined later with microstructuring of the detection apparatus and perhaps could be eventually the result of the very first synapse formed, which would then place the time in the embryo stage at 8 to 9 weeks post fertilization, or before. But, what about the preparative events prior to production of detectable electrical potential, the growth of axons, dendritic connection and synthesis of appropriate enzymes? Have they no significance?

Conclusion

In sum, for the human embryo, a new stage of human development, which would be excluded from a moral status (ensoulment) should have full scientific support. Such is not the case. Church documents used in recognizing the rights of the conceptus have not had their scientific bases, as yet, abrogated. If moral reconsiderations of ensoulment are based on scientific data, as McCormick states they should be, *all* available scientific data should be used and not be selective or arbitrary.

The scientist, in this case the human embryologist, should have no political or theological agenda. There is no dilemma such as accounting for doctrinal or moral error when defining scientific data. Yet, we recognize from time to time the importance of what we observe, not just with respect to the next scientific question but with respect to our place in all of creation and within the order of all things in the universe.

To that end, present Catholic doctrine appears to recognize the supreme significance of fertilization, that of the "new individual" being an extension of the unbroken continuum of life which began some 4.5 billion years ago. More than that, each fertilized egg represents the consequence of a biological history of all of the successes of that continuum and its survival against unceasing environmental assaults. Minor exceptions notwithstanding, our biological redemption lies within our biological history which is unified at the moment of fertilization.

Epilogue

There is no stage in human development as the *pre-embryo*. No such stage (or any stage) exists which could be the basis for equivocating the presence of a *living* entity, its quality of being *human*, its status as a human *individual*, or, in the case of religious consideration, time of ensoulment. The reason why this is true is the following: from the moment when the sperm makes contact with the ovum, under conditions we have come to understand and describe as *normal*, all subsequent development to birth of a living newborn is a *fait accompli*. That is to say, after that initial contact of sperm and egg there is no subsequent moment or stage which is held in arbitration or abeyance by the mother, or the embryo or fetus. Nor is a second contribution, a signal or trigger, needed from the male in order to continue and complete full development to birth. Human development is a *continuum* in which so-called stages overlap and blend one into another, even after birth and unto death.

References

1. Durant, Will and Ariel. 1968. *The Lessons of History.* New York: Simon and Schuster.

2. Haeckel, E. 1866. *Generelle Morphologie der Organismen.* Berlin.

3. Baer, K.E. von. 1828. *Uber Entwicklungsgeschicte der Thiere, Beobachtung und Reflexion.* Konigsberg.

4. McCormick, Richard A. 1991. Who or What is the Pre-embryo? *Kennedy Instit. Ethics J.*, 1:1-15.

5. This stage is called the blastocyst. It is composed of cells of the embryo proper and cells destined to become part of the placenta and fetal membranes.

6. McCormick, pages 5 & 8. These references to edicts from Pope Pius IX (1869) and Pope John Paul II (1982) leave no doubt.

7.   Grobstein, Clifford, 1988. *Science and the Unborn.* p. 61. New York: Basic Books.

8.   McCormick, Page 1.

9.   Cowan, W.M., J.W. Fawcett, D.D.M. O'Leary and B.B. Stanfield. 1984. Regressive events in neuro-genesis. Science, 225:1258-1265.

10.   Williams, R.W. and K.Herrup. 1988. The control of neuron number. Ann. Rev. Neurosci., 4:17-42.

11.   This is a process called apoptosis by which certain cells are programmed genomically to die. This is a method invoked during development which, in significant manner, accounts for sculpturing and modeling of different tissues and organs in the embryo and fetus.

12.   Stedman's *Medical Dictionary.* 1990. Baltimore: Williams and Wilkens.

13.   Patten, Bradley, 3rd Ed. 1968. *Human Embryology.* p. 49. New York: McGraw-Hill.

14.   McCormick, p. 2.

15.   Grobstein, 1988, p. 61.

16.   Grobstein, Clifford. 1989. When does life begin? *Psychology Today, September, pp. 43-46.*

17.   Grobstein, 1988, p. 25.

18.   Grobstein, 1989, p. 44.

19.   American Fertility Society, Ethics Committee of the. 1986. Ethical Considerations of the New Reproductive Technologies. Fert. & Ster. 46(Suppl.l):265.

20.   Thompson, James S. and Margaret, W. 4th ed. (Rev., M. Thompson) 1986. *Genetics in Medicine.* p. 274. Philadelphia: W.B. Saunders.

21.   Moore, Keith, 4th Ed. 1988. *The Developing Human.* pp. 122-126. Philadelphia: W.B. Saunders.

22.   This is called atresia. It is a degenerative process for ova, fertilized ova (zygotes), and further stages alike. The exact reasons why this occurs are not known; however, development relies on a synchrony of events, prior to and after fertilization. Therein, most probably lie the answers.

23.   McCormick, p. 4.

24.   Short, R.V. 1990. Letters: Ethics, Science and Embryos. *The Tablet* (Feb. 3):141.

25.   Moore, p. 294.

26.   Patten, p. 100.

27.   McCormick, p. 12.

28.   Tuchmann-Duplessis, H., M. Auroux and P. Haegel. 1975. *Illustrated Human Embryology* Vol. III Nervous System and Endocrine Glands. New York: Springer-Verlag.

"NEW AGE" HUMAN EMBRYOLOGY TEXT BOOKS:
"Pre-embryo", "Pregnancy" and Abortion Counseling; Implications for Human Embryo and Fetal Research

Dianne N. Irving, M.A., Ph.D.

I. Introduction

As curious as it is that so much incorrect science has been and still is being used in the scientific, medical and bioethics literature to argue that fetal "personhood" does not arrive until some arbitrary biological marker event during human embryological development, we are now beginning to experience the "new wave" consequences of passively allowing such incorrect "new age" science to be published and eventually accepted by professionals and non-professionals alike. Once these scientifically erroneous claims, and the erroneous philosophical and theological concepts they engender, are successfully imbedded in these bodies of literature and in our collective consciousnesses, the next logical step is to imbed them in our text books, reference materials and federal regulations.

Such is the case with the latest fifth edition of a human embryology text book by Keith Moore - *The Developing Human.*[1] This text is used in most medical schools and graduate biology departments here, and in many institutions abroad. It will be demonstrated that the contradictory definitions and redefinitions of many of the most basic scientific terms it uses lend scientific credence to the "new age" political agenda of abortion, human embryo and fetal research. In fact this human embryology text book for students actually explicitly engages in abortion counseling - a quite inappropriate use of a basic scientific text book - and uses these incorrectly defined scientific terms to ground and justify its own conclusions about the "scientific correctness" of abortion. What is often not appreciated is that these redefinitions would justify human embryo and fetal research as well.

Of particular concern is Moore's sudden use of the scientifically erroneous term "**pre-embryo**" in his most recent fifth edition - a fact recently pointed out by Dr. C. Ward Kischer[2], a professor of *human* embryology for over 30 years, who along with others have rejected the scientific validity of this term.[3] There has never been any such thing as a "pre-embryo" in human embryology text books until now. Scientifically, fertilization is the beginning of a human being as well as the beginning of a human embryo. The term "pre-embryo" implies that this entity comes *before* the embryo. This in turn implies that a "pre-embryo" is a "pre-human being". This is scientifically ridiculous.

What is true in the bioethics fetal personhood arguments is true in medical and scientific educational text books. The term "pre-embryo" is based on incorrect science and should not be used. Unfortunately, as Dr. Kischer has also pointed out, the erroneous term "pre-embryo" has also been incorporated in the latest edition of *Nomina Embryologica*[4] - the international nomenclature reference text which certainly will urge medical and human embryology text books world-wide to comply with the inclusion of this erroneous terminology - and presumably with abortion counseling, human embryo and fetal research as well.

There are simply no valid or sound scientific, philosophical or theological bases for the use of the erroneous term "pre-embryo", for its use in arguments on fetal "personhood", or for its inclusion as a legitimate stage of human development in any article, book or text - especially a human embryological text book or official international reference for embryological nomenclature. Nor should this scientifically erroneous term be allowed to be used as a scientific rationale to justify the abortion of a pre-born child, or for his or her use in fetal research. Scientific and ethical reasons would certainly preclude these texts from being used or sanctioned in any Catholic educational or health care institutions or facilities.

It is a given that any scientific text must be updated and changed to keep up with the rapid scientific advancements in basic knowledge. But there is a point past which updating ends, and politicizing begins. I leave it up to the readers to determine if that point has been passed with this text.

An examination and comparison of Moore's third and fifth editions will indicate considerable contradictions and confusion in very basic human embryology terminology. Concomitantly this confusion lends itself to a definite progression in the definitions and uses of several of the most basic scientific terms, terms which will ground the eventual use of the erroneous term "pre-embryo" in his fifth edition. In turn, the use of the term "pre-embryo" in the fifth edition will ground and scientifically justify the abortion counseling which is also inappropriately incorporated in this student text book.

And it will be demonstrated that if Moore's texts were to be referred to by public policy makers in their considerations for the use of "human" subjects in experimental medical research, the present OPRR regulations could be "corrected" to allow for unfettered research on preborn human beings up to the ninth week of embryological development.

Furthermore, the erroneous conceptual precedents being established now in the arguments on "personhood" in the abortion, human embryo and fetal research issues could surely be transferable to certain "classes" of adult human beings, rendering them "non-persons" as well, and therefore arguably prime candidates for their use in basic and medical research as well.

In order to demonstrate these concerns I will first turn to a comparison of these two editions, and trace in particular the confusing etiology of the terms "pre-embryo", "embryo", and "pregnancy".

II. Evolution of the definition of the scientifically erroneous term "pre-embryo"

The term "pre-embryo" has an interesting recent history. It was originally used in bioethics debates on the use of "early human embryos" in experimental medical research. The term was actually implied as far back as 1979 by the Ethics Advisory Board to the United States Department of Health, Education and Welfare: "... the [early] human embryo is entitled to profound respect, but this respect does not necessarily encompass the full legal and moral rights attributed to persons".[5] In the 1984 Warnock Committee Report in Great Britain, a similar sentiment was expressed: "The human embryo... is not under the present law of the United Kingdom accorded the same status as a living child or adult, nor do we necessarily wish it to be accorded the same status. Nevertheless, we were agreed that the [early] embryo of the human species ought to have a special status."[6] The debate was then taken up in Australia and the term "pre-embryo" was finally rejected by the 1986 Harradine "Human Experimentation Bill".[7] It was similarly rejected by several other international commissions, e.g., the 1986 and 1989 reports of the Parliamentary Assembly of the Council of Europe.[8]

In the United States, the Ethics Committee of the American Fertility Society claimed in its 1986 special report that early events in mammalian development concern, above all, the formation of extraembryonic - rather than embryonic - structures. "This means that the zygote, cleavage and early blastocyst stages should be regarded as preembryonic rather than embryonic."[9] This theme, that there is a significant developmental structural (and therefore moral) difference between the "extraembryonic" and the "embryonic" membranes of the early human embryo, was echoed by many members of the Ethics Committee of the American Fertility Society.

For example, Howard Jones, a pioneer in infertility "therapy" and *in vitro* fertilization (IVF) clinics, argued: "While the embryoblast segregates and is recognizable toward the end of [preimplantation], it consists of only a few cells, which are the rudiment of the subsequent embryo."[10] Another member, John Robertson[11], uses the same rationale in the legal arena to argue for "brain-birth". He often quotes full pages from the work of yet another member of the Ethics Committee of the American Fertility Society, Clifford Grobstein,[12] who is also involved in IVF studies, but whose specialty is amphibian embryology (not human embryology).

Yet another member of the Ethics Committee of the American Fertility Society, Richard McCormick, S.J., in his own arguments about the "moral" status of the human "pre-embryo", quotes from Grobstein's "embryology", as well as from "an unpublished study of a research group of the Catholic Health Association entitled 'The Status and Use of the Human Preembryo'".[13] According to Grobstein and McCormick,[14] "pre-embryos" are merely "genetic individuals" and not "developmental individuals" yet, and therefore they are not "persons". Since they are not legitimate full-blown "persons" yet, they do not have the moral or legal rights and protections that actual human persons possess (and therefore these "pre-embryos" could be aborted, experimented with, disposed of, etc.).

As noted, the new fifth edition of Keith Moore's *The Developing Human* incorporates the scientifically erroneous embryological term "pre-embryo" for the first time as a formal legitimate period of human development. For example, in Chapter

Two, Moore begins his summary of the first week of human development by stating: "The **pre-embryonic** period of human development begins at fertilization..." (p. 37). In Chapter Eight Moore states: "*in vitro* studies of cleaving human zygotes (**pre-embryos**) less than 5 days old have revealed a high incidence of abnormalities." And in the same chapter he states: "Inactivation of genes on one X chromosome in somatic cells of female **pre-embryos** occurs at about the time of implantation..."(p. 144).

Perhaps it is worth noting the source on which Moore bases his nomenclature in his fifth edition: "The terminology in this book is based on the third edition of *Nomina Embryologica* which was published as part of the sixth edition of *Nomina Anatomica* (Warwick, 1989)".[15] Yet a number of writers have argued cogently and vigorously that the science used to ground the term "pre-embryo" is erroneous, and therefore the ethical and legal conclusions about the "personhood" of the early developing human being (based on that erroneous science) are also erroneous. Why would Moore or *Nomina Embryologica* suddenly use such a controversial term as "pre-embryo" now?

The term simply has no basis in fact, and has been flatly rejected by many other human embryologists who refuse to use the scientifically erroneous term in their own human embryology text books. As Kischer so succinctly noted, human embryologists do not use or acknowledge the term "pre-embryo". For example, O'Rahilly and Muller state quite emphatically in their human embryology text book: "The **ill-defined** and **inaccurate** term "pre-embryo" which includes the embryonic disk is said either to end with the appearance of the primitive streak (or in the *Nomina Embryologica*) to include neurulation. **The term is not used in this book**"[16] (emphasis mine). Kischer also points out that the term is not indexed or used in the most recent edition of *Stedman's Medical Dictionary*,[17] in any of the established human embryology texts - e.g., in Larsen's[18] or in Patten's[19] texts - nor in the scientific literature on human development. As he notes, there is no such stage in human development as the "pre-embryo", and he cautions that: "Human embryology is now in danger of being rewritten as a stratagem statement of current socio-legal, but also of late, even theological, issues. Unless the errors are corrected now, we will be in danger of entering a protracted period of false concepts concerning our own development".[20]

A. Ambiguity in Moore's texts

In their arguments, Grobstein and McCormick claim that the "pre-embryo" is not a "developmentally single individual" (and therefore not yet a "person") because, for example, in the 5-6 day old blastocyst, <u>all</u> of the cells of the outer trophoblast layer are discarded after birth. <u>Only</u> the cells from the inner embryoblast layer become the later fetus and adult human being.[21]

Strangely, in both the third and the fifth editions of Moore's texts, such scientific statements about the blastocyst are made by Moore in the early chapters of the texts. But in other later chapters of both texts, Moore bluntly contradicts those scientific statements, and thus in effect contradicts any supposed claims that could be made about "pre-embryo's" and "personhood". These scientific contradictions are confusing. For example, in the early chapters of both texts he states:

Third Edition	**Fifth Edition**
During stage 3 of development (about four days), cavities appear inside the compact mass of cells forming the morula, and fluid soon passes into these cavities from the uterine cavity. As the fluid increases, it **separates** the cells into two parts: (1) an outer cell layer, the **trophoblast**... which **gives rise to part of the placenta**, and (2) a group of centrally located cells, known as the inner cell mass (or **embryoblast**), which **gives rise to the embryo**. (p. 33; also in summary, p. 37)	Shortly after the morula enters the uterus (about four days after fertilization), spaces appear between the central blastomeres of the morula. Fluid soon passes through the zona pellucida into these spaces from the uterine cavity. As the fluid increases, it **separates** the blastomeres into two parts; (1) a thin outer cell layer (or "mass") called the **trophoblast**... which **gives rise to part of the placenta**, and (2) a group of centrally located blastomeres, known as the inner cell mass (or **embryoblast**), which **gives rise to the embryo**. (p. 35; also in summary, p. 38)

[In Figure depicting the cleavage of the zygote and the formation of the blastocyst](p. 34) NOT MENTIONED	[In Figure depicting cleavage of the zygote and formation of the blastocyst]: The inner cell mass, or **embryoblast, gives rise to the tissues and organs of the embryo**. (p. 34)
NOT MENTIONED	[formulation of the morula] Compaction permits greater cell-to-cell interaction and is a prerequisite for **segregation** of the internal cells that **form the embryoblast** or inner cell mass of the blastocyst. (p. 33)

The strong implication here is that there is a clear separation between the inner and outer cell layers. The cells from the outer trophoblast layer are essentially non-embryonic, and in fact are all discarded after birth as placental membranes, etc. Only those cells from the inner layer, i.e., the embryoblast, actually really ever become or make up the cells, tissues and organs of the later embryo, fetus and adult human being. The philosophical (and theological) implication that Grobstein and McCormick want to draw is that because of this early strict separation and eventual separate and different "ontological" destinations and fates, there is as yet no "developmental" individual present (and therefore no "person"). The "pre-embryo", then, is to be considered as a "pre-person".

However, in Chapter 7 (in both editions), i.e., "The Fetal Membranes and Placenta", Moore contradicts his own earlier scientific statements about the relation between the inner and outer cell layers, and whether or not, in fact, both cell layers intermingle from the beginning, and both in fact are represented later in the embryo, fetus and the adult human being:

Third Edition	**Fifth Edition**
During stage 5 of development (7-12 days), as the **blastocyst** is implanting, early	At about 7 days, a flattened layer of cells called the **hypoblast** (primitive

differentiation of the **inner** cell mass occurs. A flattened layer of cells, the **hypoblast** (primitive endoderm), appears on the surface of the inner cell mass facing the blastocyst cavity at about seven days... Recent evidence indicates that the **hypoblast is probably displaced to extraembryonic regions.** (p. 33)

The chorion, the amnion, the yolk sac and the allantois constitute the embryonic or fetal membranes. These membranes develop from the zygote, but do not form parts of the embryo, **with the exception of portions of the yolk sac and allantois.** The dorsal part of the yolk sac is incorporated into the **embryo** as the primordium of the primitive gut... The allantois is represented in the **adult** as a fibrous cord, the median

endoderm) appears on the surface of the inner cell mass facing the blastocyst cavity... [THERE IS NO DISCUSSION OF ITS DISPLACEMENT] (p. 36)

Cells, probably from the hypoblast, give rise to a layer of loosely arranged tissue, called the extraembryonic mesoderm, around the amnion and primary yolk sac... [footnotes 1,2] The origin of the exocoelomic membrane in the human embryo is thought to be derived from the hypoblast... From studies in the rhesus monkey, there is evidence for the formation of extraembryonic mesoderm from the hypoblast. (p. 42)

The chorion, the amnion, the yolk sac and the allantois constitute the embryonic or fetal membranes. These membranes develop from the zygote but do not form parts of the embryo, **with the exception of portions of the yolk sac and allantois.** The dorsal part of the yolk sac is incorporated into the **embryo** as the primordium gut... The umbilical ligament, which extends from the apex of the urinary bladder to the umbilicus. (p. 111)

allantois is represented in the **adult** as a fibrous cord, the median umbilical ligament, which extends from the apex of the urinary bladder to the umbilicus. (p. 113)

These statements from the later chapters are a clear and direct contradiction of his own statements in the earlier chapters. Moore can't have it both ways. Scientifically and factually, either all of the cells of the trophoblast layer are discarded after birth, or they aren't. Again, some parts of his text imply a black and white separation of the two cell layers; other parts of his text indicate an intrinsic intermingling between the two layers. Scientifically and factually, either there is absolutely no intermingling of the cells of the two layers, or there is. Aside from the confusion these contradictions cause on the purely scientific level, different possible philosophical anthropological conclusions about "personhood" follow from these different and contradictory scientific claims. And different conclusions about ethical and legal rights and protections follow from these contradictory philosophical anthropological definitions of "personhood".

The stakes surrounding these "personhood" arguments are, after all, rather high for preborn human beings. If there is no such thing as an absolute separation; if there is always an intermingling of and communication between the two cell layers; if throughout all of human embryological development the two cell layers and the cells, tissues and organs which are produced from them intermingle; then individuality - both genetic and developmental - is present from fertilization on, and therefore so is "personhood".

On the other hand, if Moore, Grobstein and McCormick are scientifically correct, if there is no continuum of development, and therefore no human "person" yet present in this 5-6 day old human blastocyst (even assuming that the argument is a valid one), what is wrong, then, with using them in destructive experimental basic and medical research? Couldn't one also scientifically and ethically rationalize any type of abortion, including the use of the "morning after" pill, or the French RU486 abortion pill - since what is being aborted is really a "non-person", i.e., a "pre-embryo", or a "pre-human being"?

What is rarely perceived is that the stakes in these "personhood" arguments are just as high for adult human beings as well. Consider that many of the other positions for abortion, human embryo and fetal research argue that these early developing human beings are not persons because they do not exercise "rational attributes"[22] (e.g., self-awareness, self-consciousness, awareness of the world around one, etc.) or have advanced levels of "sentience"[23] (the ability to feel pain and pleasure). Since empirically we know that the actual exercising of "rational attributes" and the actual capacity for full "sentience" are not present until well after birth[24], these same writers have argued for years that infanticide of normal healthy infants and young children is ethically permissible.

But it needs to be appreciated that such "conceptual tools" (i.e. redefinitions of "personhood") would also allow one to conclude logically that certain classes of adult human beings who also do not exercise "rational attributes" or "sentience" would also not be "persons", e.g.: patients with Alzheimer's and Parkinson's diseases, the mentally ill, the mentally retarded, the comatose, drug addicts, alcoholics, stroke victims and paraplegics, etc. If they are not "persons", then they will also not be entitled to ethical or legal protections. Couldn't one also logically argue that these human adults can be terminated or used in experimental medical research - if the "proportionate" need were to arise? (In fact this has actually already taken place in the bioethics literature, where Frey,[25] an animal rights activist) argues that human beings with mental illness or mental retardation should be substituted for the higher animal primates in destructive experimental research because those human beings with mental illness or mental retardation are not persons and the higher primate animals are).

These redefinitions of "personhood" are simply politically correct or "new age" criteria used for "quality of life" arguments and decisions. When used within the context of adult medical issues this same concept of "personhood" plays a major role in the debates about cortical brain-death, organ transplantation, the withholding and withdrawal of medical treatments, allocation of scarce medical resources, euthanasia, and any informed consent issues (e.g., living will, informed consent for medical treatment or to take part in experimental or therapeutic medical research, etc.). Whether or not one is politically correct about abortion, human embryo and fetal research, it would seem at least prudent to be aware that these redefinitions of "personhood" could be applied to most of us as well.

B. Shifting definitions of related scientific terms

A comparison of several of the basic definitions related to the terms "pre-embryo" and "abortion" that Moore uses in the third and fifth editions will demonstrate considerable contradiction and confusion. These shifting definitions would subtly support his inclusion of the erroneous term "pre-embryo" in that later edition. Once the early human embryo is relegated to a non-person, i.e., a "pre-embryo", then it is logical to give the sort of abortion counseling which is also found in the text.

In comparing the two editions, an attempt will be made to determine during which time period this supposed "pre-embryo" might exist, as well as when the "embryo" begins to exist. In analyzing these texts, there seems to be an effort to dissociate and eliminate from the fifth edition any terminology which would indicate an integral relationship between the developing human before the embryonic period as well as after the embryonic period. Additionally, it is practically impossible to determine from these texts exactly when the embryo itself actually begins. Even a comparison of the differences in the titles of the various chapters in the Table of Contents is instructive:

Third Edition	Fifth Edition
Table of Contents (pp. ix-x)	Table of Contents (pp. vii-viii)
Chapter One: Introduction	Chapter One: Introduction
Chapter Two: Beginning of Human Development (first week)	Chapter Two: The Beginning of Human Development (first week)
Chapter Three: Formation of the Bilaminar Embryo (second week)	Chapter Three: Formation of the Bilaminar Embryonic Disk (second week)
Chapter Four: Formation of the Trilaminar Embryo (third week)	Chapter Four: Formation of the Human Embryo (third week)

Chapter Five: The Embryonic Period (four to eight weeks)	Chapter Five: Development of Tissues, Organs and Body Form (four to eight weeks)
Chapter Six: The Fetal Period (from the ninth week to birth)	Chapter Six: The Fetal Period (from the ninth week to birth)

Note that in the third edition, the clear unambiguous term "embryo" is used in both the second and third weeks. That is, in chapter three the subject is the bilaminar embryo; in chapter four the subject is the trilaminar embryo. However, in the fifth edition, the clear unambiguous term "embryo" is not used until chapter four which concerns the third week only, where the subject is the formation of the "human embryo". Note also that the "embryonic period" is from 4-8 weeks in the third edition; the fifth edition does not mention the "embryonic period" at all.

In reference to the fifth edition, does this mean that before three weeks (21 days) there is no embryo - i.e., a "pre-embryo"? And in reference to the third edition, how can the embryonic period be from 4-8 weeks, when it has already begun at 2 (or 3) weeks? Why doesn't the embryonic period start when the embryo starts - at 2 (or 3) weeks? Would the "pre-embryo" be from fertilization to 2 weeks, 3 weeks or up to the beginning of the 4th week (28 days)? So far the candidates for the "pre-embryo" period are 2 weeks (14 days), 3 weeks (21 days), or 4 weeks (28 days). If what is before the 4th week is not an embryo, but is a "pre-embryo", then would abortion and human embryo research be permissible up to the 4th week? This would also make the "pre-embryo" period much later than the implantation stage (5-6 days) or the 14-day stage which several writers claim is the biological marker event of "personhood". So when precisely is the "embryonic period"? It is certainly not clear.

Third Edition	**Fifth Edition**
Introduction (p.1) Prenatal Period...Note that the most striking advances in development occur during the	Introduction (p.1) Prenatal Period...Study of these timetables reveals that the most striking advances in

first eight weeks, in which the embryonic period is included.

development occur during the third to eighth weeks, which is known as the embryonic period.

Thus the third edition implies that the embryonic period is included in the first 8 weeks, but not necessarily from fertilization on. The fifth edition states that the embryonic period extends from the 3rd to the 8th week - which contradicts the third edition's claim of 4-8 weeks. This, again, would allow for a "pre-embryo" either from fertilization to the 3rd week (21 days) in the fifth edition - or to the 4th week (28 days) in the third edition. Which is it? And when does an embryo begin? Either sometime during the first 8 weeks; or at the third week (21 days)? And this is a scientific text book?

Even the definition of the term "embryology" - the very subject matter of these human embryo text books - is confusing. In Moore's own words:

Third Edition

Scope of Embryology (p.7)

The term embryology can be misleading; literally, it means the study of an embryo (second to eighth weeks, inclusive). However, embryology refers to the study of both the embryo and the fetus, that is, the study of prenatal development.

Fifth Edition

Scope of Embryology (p.7)

Embryology literally means the study of embryos (third to eighth weeks, inclusive); however, the term generally refers to prenatal development, i.e., the study of both embryos and fetuses ...

Here we have the third edition clearly stating that an embryo exists from 2-8 weeks (14-56 days); and the fifth edition stating that an embryo exists from 3-8 weeks (21-56 days). And in both editions, "embryology" is defined as a science which only studies embryos and fetuses - which then would not include the "developing human" from fertilization to 2, 3 or 4 weeks (depending on the page or edition) - i.e., a "pre-embryo". Aside from this contradictory and confusing scientific account of "the developing human", what science, then, would have as its subject matter "the developing human" from fertilization to the formation of the "embryo"? Is there a "new science" which would have as its subject matter the study of the "pre-embryo" only? This sounds like a new classification of the sciences.

Thus there seems to be a distancing between the time of fertilization and the embryonic period (i.e., a "pre-embryonic" period) in the fifth edition. There is also the surprising claim that the embryo itself does not begin until the third, or fourth, week - i.e. 21-28 days - a period well after even the 14-day stage of "personhood" argued for by Grobstein and McCormick (Grobstein also argues contradictorily for "personhood" at several other human embryological periods as well). That is, now the "pre-embryonic" period could literally extend up to the third or fourth week, and not just up to the time of implantation (5-7 days) or the formation of the primitive streak (14-days).

There is also a gradual shift in terminology to isolate the "embryonic period" from the later "fetal period", as well as subtle changes in references to "abortion". For brevity, let me simply set out some of the different definitions which are ultimately related to the later use of the term "pre-embryo" and of the term "abortion" in this text book.

Third Edition	Fifth Edition
1. "Abortion"	1. "Abortion"
This term refers to the birth of an embryo or a fetus before it is viable (mature enough to survive outside the uterus) ...	This term refers to the birth of an embryo or a fetus before it is viable (capable of living outside the uterus). Threatened abortion is a common complication in about 25% of clinically apparent pregnancies. Despite every effort to prevent abortion, about 1/2 of these pregnancies ultimately abort.
All terminations of pregnancy that occur before 20 weeks are called abortions. About 15% of all recognized pregnancies	All terminations of pregnancy that occur naturally or are induced before 20 weeks are

end in spontaneous abortions (ones that naturally occur), usually during the first 12 weeks. Legal induced abortions are brought on purposefully usually by suction curettage (evacuation of the embryo and its membranes from the uterus).

abortions. A complete abortion is one in which all the products of conception have been expelled from the uterus. About 15% of all recognized pregnancies end in spontaneous abortions (i.e., they occur naturally), usually during the first 12 weeks. Legally induced abortions, often called elective abortions, are usually produced by suction curettage (evacuation of the embryo and its membranes from the uterus). Some abortions are induced because of the mother's poor health or to prevent the birth of a severely malformed child (e.g., one without most of its brain).

If the term "abortion" applies only to the terminations of pregnancies up to 20 weeks, does that mean that the terminations of pregnancies after 20 weeks are not to be classified as "abortions"? That's odd. What are they to be classified as? And if the term "abortion" applies only to the birth of an embryo (or a fetus), does that mean that it would not be applied to the termination of a "whatever" that comes before the "embryo" stage? In the third edition, the first part of the reference applies the term "abortion" to all terminations of pregnancy that occur before 20 weeks, which would imply that the termination of a fetus would also be considered an abortion. In the latter part of the reference, the term applies only to the embryo, and not to the fetus as well. The same is true for the fifth edition. Thus the latter parts of the definitions of the term "abortion" would not refer to either the so-called "pre-embryo" or to the fetus. Also, note the fifth edition adding reasons for induced abortions, e.g., the birth of a severely malformed child [such as an anencephalic child].

Third Edition	Fifth Edition
2. "Abortus"	2. "Abortus"
This term describes any product or all products of an abortion. An embryo or a nonviable fetus and its membranes weighing less than 500 grams is called an abortus.	This term refers to the products of an abortion (i.e., the embryo/fetus and its associated membranes, such as the amnion and chorionic sac). An embryo or nonviable fetus and its membranes weighing less than 500 grams is called an abortus, but often one refers to them as aborted embryos or fetuses.

The term "abortus", like the term "abortion", does not refer to a so-called "pre-embryo" either. It does still refer to both embryos and fetuses in both editions. But when the above term "abortion" refers only to an embryo (and not also to a fetus), then the term "abortus" could not refer to the fetus as well. Thus, if one were going by the latter part of the definition of "abortion", if a fetus were to be terminated the fetus would not be referred to as an "abortus". Thus, again, the so-called "pre-embryo" is left out of the definition of the term "abortus"; and the fetus could be left out of the term "abortus" if one wanted to use the latter terminology of "abortion".

Note also that the fifth edition now includes a reference to the "associated membranes" as inclusive of the amnion and the chorionic sac. As noted earlier, Moore was contradictory between his earlier and later chapters about the intermingling of the two cell layers of the blastocyst. In his earlier chapters he stated that all of the cells of the trophoblast layer are discarded after birth as the placental membranes, etc. In his later chapters he stated that this was true with the *exception* of cells from the yolk sac and allantois - cells derived from the trophoblast, both of which he later traces to the developing embryo, fetus and adult human being. In this present statement here he adds a reference to "membranes" which are part of the abortus - but neglects to mention these include the two cell types of the trophoblast which are later incorporated into the embryo, fetus and adult. The attention in this fifth edition to these membranes which were of such interest and importance to Grobstein and McCormick is interesting enough. His failure to mention the eventual destination of cells from the yolk sac and the allantois in the later fetus and adult human being, along with no mentioning at all of the amnion and the chorionic sac, is disingenuous at best.

Third Edition	**Fifth Edition**
3. "Zygote" This cell results from fertilization of an oocyte, or ovum, by a sperm, or spermatozoon, and is the beginning of a human being.	3. "Zygote" This cell results from fertilization of an oocyte by a sperm. A zygote is the beginning of a new human being.

At least Moore still acknowledges here that the zygote is the beginning of a "developing human being" (although given the above references it is an odd human being, i.e., one that is not an embryo yet). But even though he admits that fertilization marks the beginning of an individual human being, the questions for some (e.g., Grobstein and McCormick) is whether or not it is also a human "person", i.e., a "developmental individual".

It could also be very confusing for Moore to use the simplistic term "oocyte". There are primary and secondary "oocytes", and ova - all very different terms depicting different stages during oogenesis and fertilization. Since a primary oocyte has not proceeded through the first meiotic division (which won't happen until after puberty) and still contains 46 chromosomes (instead of 23 chromosomes), it cannot yet be fertilized by a sperm, and so they would not be usable yet in IVF "therapy" or in human embryo research. Given the studies proposed in Scotland to use the "eggs" from aborted female fetuses in IVF "therapies" for post-menopausal women, such a distinction would be very critical. Those "aborted eggs" cannot be fertilized or used in human embryo research or implanted, because each of them still contains 46 chromosomes and thus can not be fertilized.

Third Edition	Fifth Edition
4. "Blastocyst" After the morula enters the uterus, a cavity develops inside it and fills with fluid; This converts the morula into a blastocyst.	4. "Blastocyst" After the morula enters the uterus from the uterine tube, a fluid-filled cavity develops inside it; this converts the morula into a blastocyst. Its centrally located cells called the embryoblast or inner cell mass, will form the embryo.

Without repeating, the fifth edition again seems to be focusing on the issue argued by Grobstein and McCormick - i.e., that only the cells from the embryoblast (inner layer) of the blastocyst - not any of the cells from the trophoblast (outer layer) - will form the later embryo, fetus and adult human being. Yet, as already indicated, Moore contradicts those claims in his later developing chapters.

Third Edition	Fifth Edition
5. "Embryo" This term refers to the developing human during the early stages of development. The term is usually not used until the second week, after the embryonic disc forms ... The embryonic period extends until the end of the eighth week, by which time all major structures are present.	5. "Embryo" This term refers to the developing human during its early stages of development. The term is not usually used until the middle of the second week. The embryonic period extends to the end of the eighth week, at which time the beginnings of all major structures are present.

Here we have the embryo beginning both the "second" week, and the "middle of the second" week. And recall that the third edition contradicts its own Table of Contents in which the "embryonic period" is defined as from four to eight weeks. The fifth edition contradicts its own previous claim of 3 weeks. Both editions contradict each other.

Third Edition	Fifth Edition

6. "Fetus"
[in the Table of Contents, this stage extends from the ninth week to birth]

6. "Fetus"
[In the Table of Contents, this stage extends from the ninth week to birth]

7. "Conceptus"
This term refers to the EMBRYO (OR FETUS) and its membranes, the products of conception. It includes all structures that develop from the zygote, both embryonic and extraembryonic. Hence it includes not only the EMBRYO OR FETUS, but also the embryonic or fetal membranes.

7. "Conceptus"
This term refers to the EMBRYO and its membranes, i.e., the products of conception or fertilization. It includes all structures that develop from the zygote, both embryonic and extraembryonic. Hence it includes the EMBRYO as well as the fetal part of the placenta and its associated membranes, e.g., the amnion and chorionic sac ...

Note now that while in the third edition the term "conceptus" refers to the embryo and fetus, in the fifth edition it refers only to the embryo, and not also to the fetus. Note also in the fifth edition the same elaboration of the placenta and its associated membranes (the amnion and chorionic sac) - again with no mention of the eventual destination of the cells of the yolk sac and the allantois in the later fetus and adult human being. The shift in the ordering of the terms "fetus" and "conceptus" will be addressed momentarily.

If we are not totally confused yet as to what a "pre-embryo", an "embryo", a "conceptus" or an "abortus" is - or when each of these begins to form, or what an "abortion" is (and exactly what it is that is being aborted), consider the end of Chapter One (p. 12), where (as in every chapter) there is a set of "clinically oriented problems" or "questions" prepared for the bright inquiring medical or graduate biology students.

Third Edition	Fifth Edition
Question 3: Differentiate between the terms conceptus and abortus.	Question 3: How does a conceptus differ from an "abortus"?
Answer (p. 446): The term "conceptus" is used when referring to an embryo or a fetus and its membranes, i.e., the products of conception. The term "abortus" refers to any product or all products of an abortion, e.g., the embryo (or part of it) and/or its fetal membranes and placenta (or parts of them).	Answer (p. 458): The term "conceptus" is used when referring to an embryo and its membranes, i.e., the products of conception. The term "abortus" refers to any products or all products of an abortion, e.g., the embryo (or part of it) and/or its membranes and placenta (or parts of them). An abortion, therefore is an aborted conceptus.

Now, this is really confusing. One has to wonder how these bright inquiring medical or graduate biology students ever study for their exams. First of all, neither the third edition nor the fifth edition refer to a so-called "pre-embryo", or whatever comes before the embryo (whenever that is). Thus a "pre-embryo" is not aborted, nor is it called an abortus or a conceptus. Second, in the fifth edition, now an "abortus" is an aborted "conceptus", and an aborted "conceptus" is only an embryo. That is, since a fetus is not included in the definition of a "conceptus", the term "abortus" does not apply to an abortion of a fetus either. This is why, in the listing of these terms, the third edition lists the term "fetus" before the term "conceptus", while in the fifth edition, the term "fetus" is listed after the term "conceptus". For some reason the latter part of the definition of the term "abortion", and the definitions of the terms "conceptus" and "abortus" in the fifth edition do not refer to the fetus.

Now one cannot refer to a fetus as having been aborted, or referred to as an abortus or a conceptus. If it is aborted, then what is it to be referred to as? And how could it not be considered a conceptus (i.e., the product of conception)? If it is not the product of conception, then what is it the product of? I suppose that if IVF is ever really perfected, neither the act of intercourse nor the mother's womb would be necessary, and the fetus would truly be considered the "product of IVF". Perhaps that could be the "subject matter" of the "new science" that the present science of embryology (by definition) does not study - along with the study of the "pre-embryo". "Embryology", then would really only study "embryos" - period. Eventually I suppose we could do away with all of the above related terms, since there would technically be nothing to which the terms "abortion", "abortus" or "conceptus" could refer - since no women would have to be "pregnant". Indeed, I am sure that the work on the "artificial placenta" will ensure that. What a brave new world!

Second, in the main text of the third edition, there is no difference between a "conceptus" and an "abortus"; and both terms refer to both an embryo or a fetus. Yet in this "clinically oriented question", a "conceptus" still refers to both an embryo and a fetus; but an "abortus" now refers only to an embryo. Thus the third edition is contradicting its own definitions. In the main text of the fifth edition, the term "conceptus" refers only to the embryo, and the term "abortus" refers to both the embryo and the fetus. Yet in its "clinically oriented question", both terms refer only to the embryo and not to the fetus.

Part of our confusion may be resolved, however, when we get to the "study" questions at the end of chapter two. The following question and answer do not appear in the third edition; only in the fifth edition:

> Question 5 (p.38): A young woman who feared that she might be pregnant asked about the so-called "morning-after pills" ... What would you tell her? Would termination of such an early pregnancy be considered an abortion?

> Answer 5(p. 458): Postcoital birth control pills ... will usually prevent implantation of the blastocyst ... Pregnancy occurs, but the blastocyst does not implant. The term abortion would <u>not</u> be applied to such an early termination of pregnancy.

"The term abortion would not be applied to such an early termination of pregnancy". And so, presumably, one can terminate "it" and still not have had an abortion. How is this explainable? Is it that, unless the embryo (or "pre-embryo") has implanted, then the woman is not yet "pregnant"? It would seem not, since the answer states "such an early termination of pregnancy". Thus, presumably Moore acknowledges, at least, that the woman is pregnant.

No, it would seem that it is because the woman's stage of pregnancy is "early". But what does "early" have to do with it? I would argue that just as Grobstein and McCormick use the term "pre-embryo" in order to justify experimentation on the early human blastocyst (and actually until the 14-day stage), here Moore has set up the terms with such confusion, and incorporated in this edition the erroneous term "pre-embryo", in order to justify the termination of the "early developing human being" without calling it "abortion".

Now it is scientifically justifiable to use the "morning after pills" - which Moore admits does not prevent fertilization, but only implantation - to eliminate what is basically, after all, only a "pre-embryo" - i.e., a non-person - if one is "fearful" that one is experiencing an "early" pregnancy. The term "pre-embryo", then, would also justify the use of the French abortion pill RU486. The term would also justify the use of these early developing human beings in experimental medical research.

So, amid this confusion of contradictory and inconsistent definitions and terms, the concrete result is that what most of us refer to as "abortion" is scientifically justified. "Abortion" during "early pregnancy" simply disappears. I suppose such an "early pregnancy" might be termed a "pre-pregnancy". And with these "redefinitions" goes the guilt, regrets, and moral rebukes that women may fear from the termination of these "early" pregnancies.

Note that "abortion" of a fetus also disappears. The term "abortion" no longer can be referred to the termination of a fetus; it will be restricted to the embryo only. Perhaps the termination of a fetus will be called a "post-pregnancy". Perhaps we also need to clarify exactly what is meant by the term "pregnancy". What is a "pregnancy"? Does it only have reference to the woman, and not also to what she is pregnant with? How is the critical term "pregnancy" defined?

III. "Pregnancy": the case of the missing definition

It would seem at this point that a relevant "clinically orientated question" to be addressed to those bright inquiring medical and graduate biology students is: "How would you define 'pregnancy'"? If before implantation (5-6 days) - (or 2, 3 or 4 weeks) - there is only a "pre-embryo", and therefore a "pre-pregnancy", how then does one define a "pregnancy"? After all, abortion is commonly understood as the termination of a pregnancy - right? Well, then, scientifically speaking, just when does a woman become "pregnant"?

Again Moore is extremely confusing and contradictory. In fact, a thorough search of both the third and the fifth editions of Moore's text books reveal no formal definition of the term "pregnancy". Imagine a human embryology text book, replete with virtually thousands of formal definitions about the developing human and the female uterus ... Imagine a counsel to students that the term "abortion" would not apply to such an "early termination of pregnancy" - or to the termination of a fetus either, for that matter - and no definition of the term "pregnancy". Even an attempt to decipher one amid the various contexts in which the term is used is, once again, contradictory and confusing. Indeed, both fertilization and implantation (or later) are implied:

Third Edition	Fifth Edition
NOT MENTIONED	Within 24-48 hours after fertilization an immuno-suppressant protein, known as the early pregnancy factor (EPF), appears in the maternal serum. EPF forms the basis of pregnancy tests during the first week of development (p.32)
About 15% of all zygotes result in detectable spontaneous abortion, but this estimate is undoubtedly low because the loss of zygotes during the first week is thought	At least 15% of zygotes die and blastocysts abort ... another 30% of women abort very early, unaware that they were pregnant (p.36)

to be high. The actual rate is unknown because the women do not know they are pregnant at this early stage. (p.36)

It would seem here that "pregnancy" begins at fertilization. The pregnancy tests imply the detection of pregnancy during the first week. The terms "zygote" and "blastocyst" are used which also indicate 1-7 days. Note also the reference that zygotes and blastocysts "abort" during this earliest of early stages. Yet recall the abortion counseling, i.e., the term 'abortion" would not apply to such an "early" stage of pregnancy. Confusing?

Third Edition	Fifth Edition
NOT MENTIONED	Enough hCG is produced by the syncytiotrophoblast at the end of the second week to give a positive pregnancy test even though the woman is probably unaware she is pregnant.(p. 40)
IBID (p. 46-48)	Implantation of the blastocyst usually occurs in the endometrium of the uterus. If implantation occurs elsewhere, a misplaced or ectopic pregnancy results (p. 43)
IBID (p. 48)	Intrauterine pregnancy can be detected by highly sensitive radioimmune assays of hCG as early as the end of the second week ... The blastocyst may implant outside the uterus. These implantations are referred to as ectopic pregnancies (p. 46)

Here pregnancy is detectable by the end of the second week. And the woman is pregnant at least by the time of implantation (5-7 days).

Third Edition	**Fifth Edition**
The administration of relatively large doses of estrogen (morning-after pills) for several days after sexual intercourse will prevent pregnancy by inhibiting implantation of the blastocyst that may develop. (p. 49)	The administration of relatively large doses of estrogen ("morning-after pills") for 5 days, beginning 72 hours after sexual intercourse, will usually prevent pregnancy by inhibiting implantation of the blastocyst (pp. 49-50)
Relatively simple and rapid tests are now available for detecting pregnancy as early as the third week. These tests depend on the presence of human chorionic gonadotropin (hCG), a hormone produced by the trophoblast and excreted in the mother's urine ... There is no absolute sign of pregnancy during the early weeks because a gravid (pregnant) uterus may be mimicked by several other conditions. (p. 53)	Relatively simple and rapid tests are now available for detecting pregnancy. Most tests depend on the presence of an early pregnancy factor (EPF) in the maternal serum ... and human chorionic gonadotropin (hCG) ... (p. 53)

Does "will prevent pregnancy by inhibiting implantation" mean that unless implantation has taken place a woman is not pregnant and that if implantation does take place then she is pregnant? The reference to a "gravid (pregnant) uterus" would seem to imply this also. This would contradict the first of these references, which clearly imply strongly that a woman is pregnant from fertilization on.

Third Edition	**Fifth Edition**
Almost all abortions during the first three weeks occur spontaneously; that is, they are not induced. The frequency of early abortions is difficult to establish because they often occur before the woman is aware she is pregnant. (p. 49)	Most abortions of embryos during the first three weeks occur spontaneously; i.e., they are not induced ... The frequency of early abortions is difficult to establish because they often occur before women are aware that they are pregnant. (p. 49)

The third edition acknowledges that "early" abortions may occur during the first three weeks, a contradiction of the fifth edition's abortion counseling about "early pregnancies". The fifth edition only refers now to abortions of embryos during the first three weeks, implying that the terms "zygote" and "blastocyst" would not be referred to the term "abortion". Yet simultaneously it uses the term "early abortions" during this 3 week period "before women are aware they are pregnant". One is still hopelessly confused as to exactly when "pregnancy" begins, how it is defined, and what it is a woman is pregnant with.

Third Edition	**Fifth Edition**
Question 2: A 25-year old woman with a history of regular menstrual cycles was five days overdue on menses. Owing to her mental condition and the undesirability of a possible pregnancy, the doctor decided to do a "menstrual extraction", or uterine evacuation. The tissue removed was examined for evidence of a pregnancy. What findings would indicate an early pregnancy? How old would	IBID (p. 68)

the products of conception be?
(p. 68)

Answer 2: The presence of embryonic and/or chorionic tissue in the endometrial remnants would be an absolute sign of pregnancy, but this tissue would be very difficult to find at such an early stage of pregnancy. By five days after the expected menses, i.e., about five weeks after the last menstrual period, the embryo would be in the third week of its development. (p. 448)

IBID, with the addition of: the blastocyst would be about 2 mm in diameter.(p.459)

Here, in the third edition an absolute sign of pregnancy corresponds with a 3-week embryo which has implanted. Also, in the fifth edition, the term "blastocyst" is added. However, a blastocyst (5-7 days) predates an embryo (2, 3, or 4 weeks) and has not necessarily implanted as yet. Thus there could be no "embryonic and/or chorionic tissue" present. Besides, I thought a blastocyst was really a "pre-embryo", and therefore there would be no abortion, no abortus, no conceptus, and no pregnancy. Really confusing. But to continue:

Third Edition

Fifth Edition

Question 2: A woman who had been raped during her fertile period was given large doses of estrogen ... (DES twice daily for five days) to interrupt a possible pregnancy. If she happened to be pregnant, what do you think would be the mechanism of action of the DES? What do laypeople call this type of

Question 2: A woman who was sexually assaulted during her fertile period was given large doses of estrogen twice daily for five days to interrupt a possible pregnancy. If fertilization had occurred, what do you think would be the mechanism of action of this hormone? What do laypeople call this type of medical treatment? (p. 51)

treatment? Is this what the media refer to as the "abortion pill"? If not explain the method of action of this pill. How early can a pregnancy be detected?(p. 50)

Answer 2: DES appears to affect the endometrium by rendering it unsuitable for implantation, a process regulated by a delicate balance between estrogen and progesterone. The large dose of estrogen given to the patient upset this balance. Progesterone makes the endometrium grow thick and succulent so that the blastocyst may become embedded and be nourished adequately ... DES pills are referred to as "morning after pills" by laypeople. (p. 447)

Answer 2: ... (DES) appears to affect the endometrium by rendering it unsuitable for implantation, a process that is regulated by a delicate balance between estrogen and progesterone. The large doses of estrogen given to the patient upset this balance. Progesterone makes the endometrium grow thick and succulent so that the blastocyst may become embedded and be nourished adequately. DES pills are referred to as "morning after pills" by laypeople. When the media refer to the "abortion pill" they are usually referring to RU486. This drug, developed in France, also interferes with implantation of the blastocyst. It blocks the production of · progesterone. Its use has not been authorized in North America (at the time of this writing). A pregnancy can be detected at the end of the second week after fertilization using highly sensitive pregnancy tests. Most tests depend on the presence of an early pregnancy

factor (EPF) in the maternal
serum. (p. 459)

In the third edition does "interrupt a possible pregnancy" imply that
unless the blastocyst implants the woman is not pregnant? Yet in the
fifth edition a distinction is made between fertilization having occurred
and a possible pregnancy. This edition also adds the latest information
on drug use. Interestingly, the "morning after pills" are not to be
properly referred to as an abortion pill (as we have already seen) - and
therefore women might take them, being assured that they are not
causing an abortion. Why the "morning after pills" would not be
referred to as abortion pills has been made clear - i.e., abortion does not
refer to an "early pregnancy" - i.e., when there is only a "pre-embryo"
there. But why, then, would only RU486 be referred to as an abortion
pill? The "entity" terminated is still a "pre-embryo" and the pills also
act by preventing implantation. At least Moore should be consistent.
And we still have no clue as to when "pregnancy" begins.

Such mind-boggling contradictions and multiple definitions of
the most basic of human embryology terms in these human embryology
text books by Moore render students, nurses, physicians, psychiatrists,
psychologists, social workers, ministers, government officials,
bioethicists, philosophers, theologians - even women seeking abortion
counseling - completely and thoroughly confused.

IV. Connection between abortion and fetal research

If one is not a scientist, and if one wants to know what these
most basic of human embryology terms mean and how they are
defined, one would logically turn to a current human embryology text
book for guidance. Consider a "blue-ribbon" governmental or private
ethics panel or committee, or even the new non-government
independent NABER[26] (started with seed money from the American
Fertility Society, whose board members include many of the scientists,
physicians, bioethicists, lawyers and other professionals who are great
proponents of abortion, IVF, fetal research, etc.) brought together to
weigh and judge the appropriate "ethical" issues and responses to the
various burgeoning issues in experimental research and "reproductive
health" (NAROL's new focus and new name). Where would they turn
to obtain the most reliable scientific definitions of the "entities" which
are about to be experimented on for the advancement of medical

knowledge, "reproductive health" concerns, the obtaining of purely scientific knowledge not possible by any other means, and the greater good of society?

One very reasonable possible scientific reference source would be Moore's text book on human embryology, especially the most recent fifth edition. And what would they find there now? They would find that until the fourth week, i.e., 28 days, there is really only a "pre-embryo" there - a "non-person" with no ethical or legal protections. Consequently, not only would "early" abortions be acceptable up to 28 days, but also unfettered experimental research would be acceptable up to 28 days. Thus, both human "pre-embryos" and human "embryos" would be ethically acceptable materials on which to experiment, with no ethical squabbles or regulatory oversights. That should give us pause enough.

But what about the possible use of human fetuses in experimental research? Moore has defined the fetal period from nine weeks to birth. Most human embryology text books do. So certainly the early developing human being would be protected from abortion and experimental research at least up to the ninth week - right? Well, Moore has not included the fetus in his definitions of abortion, abortus, or conceptus. No - Moore's text would not protect a fetus from abortion. But luckily at least the present OPRR governmental regulations do protect the fetus - right? A look at the present governmental OPRR regulations, and how they define the terms "pregnancy" and "fetus" should clarify the situation and relieve this tension.

It is interesting to note that the definition of "pregnancy" in the O.P.R.R. regulations on the use of human subjects in experimental research is: "the period of time from confirmation of implantation [5-7 days] ... until expulsion or extraction of the fetus."[27] Thus, theoretically, a woman is not even "pregnant" from the time of fertilization until implantation. I suppose she would be considered "pre-pregnant" with a "pre-embryo". At the present moment, then, developing human beings up to the time of implantation are not protected from destructive experimental research, as that definition stands in the OPRR regulations. If the regulations were to incorporate Moore's new term of "pre-embryo", then it would be acceptable to use developing human beings even up to the 28-day stage. Thus it is not only acceptable to "terminate" the "early pregnancy" of a "pre-embryo". It would also be acceptable to use these "terminations" in destructive experimental research. This would also apply, of course, to the products of IVF. Clearly, this sets the stage for unregulated experimentation on IVF human embryos - with or without implantation. That is, even when it is planned to implant IVF human "embryos" (if that is what they are), if a scientist wants to experiment on them before implantation, then there are no regulations covering such experiments (although we will now have the expert ethical advise from NABER at our disposal).

But how do the OPRR regulations define "fetus"? A fetus is defined as: "the product of conception from the time of implantation... until a determination is made, following expulsion or extraction of the fetus, that it is viable."[28] Does this mean that the fetal stage begins at implantation? How could such a blue-ribbon governmental panel of such experts have defined for so many years the critical term "fetus" as beginning at implantation? Were they just being "cautious"?

Suppose that one of these "blue-ribbon" government or private ethics panels or committees were to consult Moore's third or fifth editions, a "fetus" would not exist until the ninth week, i.e., 63 days. Would this mean that if an "ethics panel" were to square its definitions with Moore's text book, that before nine weeks the developing human being (the "pre-fetus") could be aborted, experimented on, or harvested for tissues and organs with no regulations? Consider that in his fifth edition, Moore does not use the term "abortion", "abortus" or "conceptus" to refer to the fetus - only to the "embryo". So presumably, to terminate a "fetus" would no more be properly defined as "abortion" than was the termination of an "early pregnancy". Would "correcting" the present "outmoded" definition of "fetus" in the present federal regulations provide for an even longer period during the life of the "developing human" that it could be experimented on - i.e., up to nine weeks - without regulations?

Coincidentally, the optimum time to harvest fetal brain tissue is between eight and nine weeks - just before Moore's cut-off point of nine weeks in his definition of a "fetus". Given the new grants to several research institutions to use fetal brain tissue in research on Parkinson's disease, Alzheimer's disease, and several other neurological and brain disorders, the future looks grim for "developing human beings". What further "developing definitions" are in store for us in the future? Who else will be scientifically defined away as "pre-persons" or

66

"non-persons" for the sake of basic and medical researchers? Might it be those very desperate adult human subjects who have Parkinson's disease, Alzheimer's disease, who are comatose, mentally ill, paraplegic, drug addicts, etc. - i.e., those human beings who do not exercise "rational attributes" or sufficient "sentience", and who are therefore not human "persons"? What an incredible scenario! Basic and medical researchers experimenting on two classes of vulnerable human beings, neither of which are human "persons" - with no regulations or ethical dilemmas! Their "personhood" has been defined away!

And nobody did anything about it.

V. Conclusion

Whether such contradictory and confusing scientific definitions of important basic terms used in human embryology occur because of ignorance, sloppiness, or design is debatable. Certainly the massive amounts of contradictory definitions presented in these texts would warrant a similar analysis of many other basic scientific and medical texts being used by professionals and students alike. It would appear to this writer that these various key definitions are being "ratcheted" in order to scientifically justify abortion, human embryo and fetal research. This is the ultimate in the on-going politization of science. And unless the errors and inconsistencies are corrected immediately, we are not only entering a protracted period of "false concepts concerning our own development"; we are entering a protracted period of abysmal abuse of human beings in medical research - pre-born and adult. The stage has already been set.

References

1. Moore, Keith, L. and T.V.N. Persaud (eds.), The Developing Human (5th ed.), (Philadelphia: W. B. Saunders Company, 1993): will be compared with Moore, Keith L. (ed.), The Developing Human (3rd ed.), (Philadelphia: W. B. Saunders Company, 1982).

2. Kischer, C. Ward, "A New Wave Dialectic. The reinvention of human embryology." 1994 The Linacre Quarterly, 61: 66-81.

3. For discussions on the scientific invalidity of the term "pre-embryo" see: Kischer, C. Ward, "Human development and reconsideration of ensoulment", Linacre Quarterly 60:1 (Feb. 1993), 57-63; Irving, Dianne N., Philosophical and Scientific Analysis of the Nature of the Early Human Embryo (doctoral dissertation, Washington, D.C.: Georgetown University, 1991), 134-149; Irving, "Philosophical and scientific expertise: An evaluation of the arguments on 'personhood'", Linacre Quarterly 60:1 (Feb. 1993), 18-46; Irving, "The impact of scientific 'misinformation' on other fields: Philosophy, theology, biomedical ethics, public policy", Accountability in Research 2:4 (April 1993), 243-272; LeJeune, Jerome (testimony) Davis vs Davis, Circuit Court for Blount County, State of Tennessee at Maryville, Tennessee (1989); Carberry, James J. and Douglas W. Kmiec, "How law denies science", Human Life Review 18:4 (1992), 105; Fisher, Anthony, "Individuogenesis and a recent book by Fr. Norman Ford", Anthropotes 2 (1991), 199ff. For discussions on the philosophical and theological invalidity of the term "pre-embryo" see: Irving, Fisher (above), and Ashley, Benedict, "Delayed hominization: Catholic theological perspectives", The Interaction of Catholic Bioethics and Secular Society, R.F. Smith (ed.) (Braintree, MA: The Pope John Center, 1992), 163-180; Benedict Ashley, "A critique of the theory of delayed hominization" in D.G. McCarthy and A.D. Moraczewski (eds.), An Ethical Evaluation of Fetal Experimentation: An Interdisciplinary Study (St. Louis, MO: The Pope John Center, 1976), 113-133; Grisez, Germain, "When do people begin?", Proceedings of the American Catholic Philosophical Association 63 (1990), 27-47; Howespian, A.A., "Who or what are we"?, Review of Metaphysics 45 (March 1992), 483-502; May, William E., "Zygotes, embryos, and persons", Ethics and Medics, Part I 16:10 (Oct. 1991); Regan, A., "The human conceptus and personhood", Studia Moralis 30 (1992), 97-127.

4. Warwick, R., Nomina Anatomica (6th ed.), includes Nomina Embryologica (3rd ed.), (Edinburgh: Churchill Livingstone, 1989).

5. Ethics Advisory Board, 1979, Report and Conclusions: HEW Support of Research Involving Human In Vitro Fertilization and Embryo Transfer, Washington, D.C.: United States Department of Health, Education and Welfare, p. 101.

6. Warnock, Dame Mary, Report of the Committee of Inquiry into Human Fertilization and Embryology, (London: Her Majesty's Stationary Office, 1984), 27, 63.

7. Commonwealth of Australia, Select Senate Committee on the Human Embryo Experimentation Bill, (Canberra, Australia: Official Hansard Report, Commonwealth Government Printer, 1986).

8. Parliamentary Assembly of the Council of Europe, On the Use of Human Embryos and Foetuses for Diagnostic, Therapeutic, Scientific, Industrial and Commercial Purposes, Recommendation 1046, 1986; and On the use of Human Embryos and Foetuses in Scientific Research, Recommendation 1000, 1989.

9. Ethics Committee of the American Fertility Society, "Ethical Considerations of the New Reproductive Technologies", Fertility and Sterility (Supplement 1, 1986) 46:27S.

10. Jones, Howard W., "And just what is a preembryo?", Fertility and Sterility 52:189-91; Also Jones and C. Schroder, "The process of human fertilization: Implications for moral status", Fertility and Sterility 48:2 (August 1987), 192.

11. Robertson, John A., "Extracorporeal embryos and the abortion debate", Journal of Contemporary Health Law and Policy 2:53 (1986), 53-70.

12. Grobstein, Clifford, "The early development of human embryos", Journal of Medicine and Philosophy (1985) 10:213-236; also, Science and the Unborn (New York: Basic Books, 1988), 61.

13. McCormick, Richard, S.J., "Who or what is the preembryo?", Kennedy Institute of Ethics Journal 1:1 (1991), 14.

14. McCormick, Richard, S.J., "Who or what is the pre-embryo?", Kennedy Institute of Ethics Journal (1991) 1:1.

15. Moore (1993), 5th edition, 11-12.

16. O'Rahilly, Ronan and Fabiola Muller, Human Embryology and Teratology (New York: Wiley-Liss, 1992), 55.

17. Stedman's Medical Dictionary (Baltimore: Williams and Wilkens, 1990).

18. Larsen, William J., Human Embryology (New York: Churchill Livingstone, 1993).

19. Patten, Bradley, Human Embryology (3rd ed.) (New York: McGraw-Hill, 1968), 49.

20. Kischer, C. Ward (1993), 57-63.

21. McCormick (1991), 3; Grobstein (1985), 213-236.

22. Englehardt, H.T., The Foundations of Bioethics (New York: Oxford University Press, 1985), 111; Tooley, Michael, "Abortion and Infanticide", in The Rights and Wrongs of Abortion, M. Cohen et al (ed.) (New Jersey: Princeton University Press, 1974), 59, 64.

23. Singer, Peter and Helga Kuhse, "The ethics of embryo research", Law, Medicine and Health Care 14:13-14 (1987); Kuhse and Singer, "For sometimes letting - and helping - die", Law, Medicine and Health Care 3:40 (1986), 149-153; Kuhse and Singer, Should The Baby Live? The Problem of Handicapped Infants (Oxford University Press, 1985), 138; Singer, Peter, "Taking life: abortion", in Practical Ethics (London: Cambridge University Press, 1981), 122-123.

24. Moore, Keith L., The Developing Human (Philadelphia: W.B. Saunders Company, 1982), 1; Jones, D. Gareth, "Brain birth and personal identity," Journal of Medical Ethics 15:4 (1989).

25. Richard G. Frey, The ethics of the search for benefits: Animal experimentation in medicine", in Raanan Gillon (ed.), Principles of Health Care Ethics (New York: John Wiley & Sons, 1994), pp. 1067-1075.

26. National Advisory Board on Ethics in Reproduction, 409 12th Street, S.W., Washington, D.C. 20024-2188.

27. Code of Federal Regulations 45CFR46, OPRR Reports "Protection of Human Subjects", Department of Health and Human Services, National Institutes of Health, Office for Protection From Research Risks, 1983 (revised 1989, 1991), 12.

28. Ibid., 12.

The Big Lie In Human Embryology: The Case of the Preembryo

by   C. Ward Kischer, Ph.D.
        Department of Cell Biology and Anatomy
        University of Arizona
        College of Medicine
        Tucson, AZ 85724

Since Roe v. Wade, adjudicated in 1973, the public interest in human embryology has markedly increased. Unfortunately, those supplying the "information" about Human Embryology have been political analysts, newswriters, bioethicists and theologians, few of whom have bothered to consult human embryologists for accurate information. As a consequence more misinformation, misrepresentations and outright lies about Human Embryology have found their way into the public discourse than ever before in our history.

In addition, an amphibian embryologist introduced a new term, *preembryo,* for the early human embryo, and applied a *reduced status* for this so-called period. It has subsequently been seized upon and used for the justification for discarding human embryos in abortion procedures, their use in fetal tissue research[1] and human embryo research. This *reduced status* has come to mean a *reduced moral status*[2]. This arbitrary period of human development, *preembryo,* was conceived and has been promoted without the sanction or sponsorship of a single human embryologist.

- ## Grobstein Introduces The Term Preembryo

Clifford Grobstein authored an article entitled: "External Human Fertilization", published in Scientific American in 1979.[3] He introduced the equivalent terms *preembryonic* and *preembryo* in this article. The theme of this article was designed to answer public policy questions raised by then Secretary of Health, Education and Welfare, Joseph A. Califano, Jr. Policy questions had been raised because of the external fertilization techniques performed in 1969 by R.G. Edwards, B.D.

Bavister and P.C. Steptoe, and which resulted in the birth of Louise Joy Brown in England.

In addition to his introducing the above terms in this article he also used a third equivalent term: the *preimplantation embryo*. This is significant because during the hearings in 1994 by The Human Embryo Research Panel, assembled by the NIH Director, Harold Varmus, the Panel chose not to use the term *preembryo* because of the strong objections to its use (not by the Panel members, but by witnesses and correspondents). Instead, they used the equivalent term *preimplantation embryo.*[4] It is doubtful that anyone objecting to the term *preembryo* knew that Grobstein had used the equivalent term *preimplantation embryo.*

Grobstein claims in his article that external fertilization "as reported by Steptoe and Edwards, is based on a confluence of *new understandings*". He then equates the "*new understandings*" with "*new knowledge*"! It is important to keep in mind this *new knowledge* is brought about by deliberate technical manipulations of the early embryo, but which revealed no new or different principles of development, which would alter the character or destiny of the *continuum* of development. In other words Louise Brown developed as one would normally predict. She was human, an individual and a person in every respect.

Grobstein then invokes the philosophical concept of "person" and asks at what stage in human development this occurs "in the ethical and legal sense". He admits the fertilized oocyte is *human* and an *individual,* which years later he rejects. But, then, he makes an extraordinary claim:

"A particular stage such as the entry of the sperm head or the fusion of pronuclei might be thought of as the critical moment of emergent individuality, *but neither of them is a step that is essential to subequent development:* in various animal eggs other kinds of activation of the egg cortex are sufficient to initiate development without a paternal contribution (parthenogenesis), and even when paternal chromosomes are present, they have been shown to

72

have no effect until well beyond fertilization".

Grobstein has cited two abnormal circumstances, which do not lead to a normal, sustained *continuum*. What he has ignored is that under *normal* circumstances, *all* the known events of *normal* fertilization are essential and *needed* for subsequent development. He claims that parthenogenesis and formation of a hydatidiform mole (only paternal chromosomes present in the fertilized egg) prove *scientifically* that a "person" does not exist at fertilization. This is disingenuous and misleading because he cites the *faults* in embryology and not the *normal* sequence of events.

Grobstein then questions when the "individual" or "person" occurs and cites the examples of monozygotic twinning (MZ) and anencephaly. Years later, he decides the two terms are the same and substitutes *individual* for *person*[5]. In the case of monozygotic twinning, he says "it is possible for two individuals to be produced from one fertilized egg", and in the case of anencephaly for "no true person to be produced at all".

What Grobstein meant, and affirmed in later writings, was that the early developing embryo was not an *individual* until at least 14 days post-fertilization, because he declared the embryo could split and form multiple individuals up to that time. He also claimed that after 14 days post-fertilization the embryo could not duplicate, that twinning was not possible.

Again, he is disingenuous and misleading because, retrospectively, we know from observations of the placentae, that 35% of all monozygotic twins result from separation of blastomeres (embryonic cells) at the first or second cleavage (multiplication) stage.[6] Therefore, a case could be made that the *individual* is determined early. It could be equally postulated that all of those embryos which do *not* divide at all could also be determined early. Experiments on lesser species indicate that the blastomeres of the cleavage stages are totipotent and if separated, can give rise to a complete individual. We assume this is the case in humans without the experimental evidence. Even if it may be true, we do not know what triggers the separation. In the case of MZ splitting occurs in only about one in every 270 births. That leaves 269 of every 270 births which do not split. What is it that governs the splitting? We simply do not know.

It does not seem to follow the statistical pathways which account for dizygotic twinning (twins from two different fertilized eggs). Most articles claiming a statistical basis have been dependent on interviews *after* the fact.[7,8] Actually, one can postulate some kind of activator for blastomere separation, or an inhibitor to an activator, which later is removed (by what mechanism?), or simply an inhibitor alone, which for some reason(s) does not appear in every embryo, nor would appear at the same time in every embryo. The truth is we do not know the mechanism. Therefore, we cannot say when the potential for separation actually occurs or actually is ended.

Also, monozygotic twinning *does* occur after 14 days, but the process will be complete only to the extent of degree of fate of the embryonic cells (differentiation). This is the time when conjoined twins (Siamese twins) and *fetus-in-fetu* (parasitic) twins occur.

In the case of anencephaly (failure of brain development), here, again, Grobstein invokes an abnormal circumstance and wants to apply it to normal circumstances.

Grobstein relies on "external signs" for distinguishing embryos from *preembryos*. He admits to "continuously intergrading phases" (the *continuum*), but, nevertheless, wants to separate them, so he can claim a "true person" is not present at any given time. He claims that the "external signs", are those recognized *as human* by "other persons". Since one of the main characteristics of the transition from the 8 week embryo to the 9th week fetus is more rapid development of the face (so that it *looks* human) his change from *"preembryos"*, which he also calls "prepersons", to the fetus would take place at approximately 9 weeks post-fertilization.

Grobstein also invokes *sentience*, "internal conscious awareness", which he claims does not occur "at least until 8 weeks." This is so arbitrary as to defy imagination. Sentience is not a biological, nor an embryological, term or concept. It is born out of psychology. From this unscientific claim has come multitudes of statements wholly unfounded. These include claims of electroencephalograms performed on 8 week embryos! In a later publication Grobstein claims there is

74

willful (sentient) movement of the human embryo at 7 weeks[9]. Such a claim has never been substantiated, and, most probably, could never be proved!

Grobstein then states that "since the criteria for *personhood* have not yet appeared (prior to 8 weeks) existing persons have not been manipulated and the rights of persons are not being violated". This is a neat technique, to erect a phantom stage, that of a *person,* then to draw conclusions about it.

Thus, it has been necessary to critique this landmark article by Grobstein because since 1979, lay literature and some scientific Journals have continuously used the term *preembryo,* and its equivalent terms, and have applied a *reduced moral status* to the *preembryo* in order to justify socio-legal procedures on the early human embryo. Grobstein claims that his definition of *preembryo* is scientifically based. He is wrong. He has also applied a philosophical term, *personhood,* to apparent embryological terms and attempted to make it seem credible.

• **The Warnock Commission And The American Fertility Society**

The term *preembryo* was later supported by the Warnock Commission of England in 1984, and in its committee report stated: "The human embryo. . .is not under the present law of The United Kingdom accorded *the same status* as a living child or adult, nor do we necessarily wish it to be accorded the same status. . .The embryo of the human species ought to have *a special status*".[10] That turned out to be a *reduced moral status* in order to allow manipulation and experimentation.

As would be expected, the Ethics Committee of The American Fertility Society (AFS) (Grobstein was a member of the committee) amplified the "existence" of the *preembryo* and on the basis of that "existence" justified experimentation on it. What they wrote in their supplement[11] was right out of Grobstein's handbook on public policy and experimentation of the early human embryo[5].

75

• The Several Individualities

Grobstein decided the fertilized human oocyte was not an individual because he later conceived of six (6) different individualities: Genetic, Developmental, Functional, Behavioral, Psychic and Social, in that order[5]. The overall purpose for these assignments was political. Here are the words of the AFS Ethics Committee: "How should these *facts* (citing the individualities), based on studies of species with similar, but not identical, developmental history to that of the human species, be related to the *status* (sic) of the human embryo?" Thus, in order to assign a *reduced moral status* to the early embryo the committee relied on psuedoscience in the form of "individualities."

Grobstein is in shallow waters. For example, he defines Functional Individuality as involving development of the heart. He makes a point of describing its beat "during the fourth week post-fertilization" and marks it as the defining time for Functional Individuality. But, lost in his assignment of the onset of Functional Individuality is the concept of the *continuum*.

What about the embryo just prior to a *detectable* heart beat? What about the first contraction of heart muscle cells (or of the first cell)? What about the establishment of the early organ field? Or of events which lead to its formation? Are they of no consequence? In other words, Grobstein has been completely arbitrary. A similar rationale can be applied to each of his other "individualities."

• Contemporary Human Embryologists

It is significant to ask if contemporary human embryologists use the term *preembryo or preembryonic* in their textbooks. Such authors as: Carlson[12], Sadler[13], Patten[14], and Larsen[15], do not use the term *preembryo*. O'Rahilly[16] not only does not use the term but includes a footnote on page 55 of the first edition of his text in which he states the following:

"The ill-defined and inaccurate term *preembryo*, which

includes the embryonic disc, is said either to end with the appearance of the primitive streak or (in the Nomina Embryologica) to include neurulation. The term is not used in this book."

Neither does he use it in his second edition, and lists 4 reasons why:[17] 1) it is ill-defined; 2) it is inaccurate; 3) it is unjustified, and 4) it is equivocal.

The equivalent term, *preembryonic, is* used in the current Nomina Embryologica. In discussions with several nomenclature committee members this author has been unable to learn how the term came to be included in the Nomina.

Do we have a clue as to why? On page ix of the 6th edition of Nomina Anatomica (3rd edition of Nomina Embryologica) it is stated for the 1985 Twelfth International Congress of Anatomists in London:

"Discussions at this *and thereafter* (my emphasis) led to the present. . . Third Editions of Nomina Histologica and Nomina Embryologica".[18]

In addition, Keith Moore had never referred to the term *preembryo* in any of his texts, until he introduced it in his 5th edition of The Developing Human[6]. He is the first, and only human embryologist to do so, so far. In this edition, he uses the term in a contradictory way. I wrote to Dr. Moore in 1993 and protested his use of this term. In his reply to me he stated that he would remove the term in the next printing.[19] In his third printing of the 5th edition, he has, indeed, removed from the index and text the term *preembryo*. However, he has not removed the equivalent term *"preembryonic"*.

• **Conclusion**

In summary, the equivalent terms *preembryo, preembryonic* and *preimplantation embryo* have come into the lexicon of human embryology with increasing frequency since first introduced by an amphibian embryologist, Clifford Grobstein, in 1979. All of these terms mean a *reduced moral status* and have no credible scientific justification. They are wholly arbitrary.

This "different status" has been used and has been proposed, to allow manipulation and experimentation up to 14 days post-fertilization, as recommended by the NIH Human Embryo Research Panel, or as late as 7 weeks post-fertilization (Grobstein's recommendation and new assignment for the onset of the fetal stage[9]).

In order to apply the concepts of "individualities" and a *reduced moral status* a nullification of the concept of the *continuum* of human development must occur.

Where have we seen this Aryan mentality before? A "different status" was arbitrarily assigned to the "Untermenschen" in Nazi Germany in the 1930s. Thus, experimentation, including medical, was deemed allowable, and justified, on the disabled, genetically and mentally impaired, Poles, Russians, Gypsies, Slavs, Jews, Priests, Pastors and even German Citizens.

It is my belief that human embryologists do not wish to be a part of this "reduced status" policy. It is my further belief that human embryologists, have an obligation to keep the science of Human Embryology straight and consistent. It is time to speak out.

The so-called *preembryo* is a false stage (period) of human development invented by an amphibian embryologist for political reasons, only. It has no credible scientific justification. Thus, the inclusion of this term into the language of Human Embryology has become a hoax of gigantic proportion. Adolph Hitler said: "The great masses of people . . . . will more easily fall victims to a big lie than to a small one."[20]

REFERENCES

1.   It is said that fetal tissue is used in fetal tissue research, e.g. implants for Parkinson's Syndrome. In actuality, 8 week *embryonic* tissue is considered optimum for that procedure.

2. National Institutes of Health, Transcripts of The Human Embryo Research Panel. 1994. September 27th session, page 2.

3. Grobstein, Clifford. 1979. External Human Fertilization. Scientific American, 240:57-67.

4. National Institutes of Health, Transcripts of The Human Embryo Research Panel. 1994. September 27th session, pages 2-7.

5. Grobstein, Clifford. 1988. Science And The Unborn: Choosing human futures. Basic Books, Inc., New York.

6. Moore, Keith L. and T.V.N. Persaud. 1993. The Developing Human, p. 135. W. B. Saunders Co., Philadelphia.

7. Parisi, P., M. Gatti, G. Prinzi and G. Caperna. 1983. Familial Incidence of Twinning. Nature, 304:626-628.

8. Philippe, P. 1985. Genetic Epidemiology of Twinning. Amer. J. Med. Gen.,20:97-105.

9. Grobstein, Clifford. 1993. The Status and Uses of Early Human Developmental Stages. in Ethical Issues In Research, ed. Darwin Cheney. The University Publishing Group, Inc., Frederick, Maryland.

10. Warnock, Dame Mary. 1984. Report of the Committee of Inquiry into Human Fertilization and Embryology. Her Majesty's Stationary Office: London, 27, 63.

11. The Ethics Committee of The American Fertility Society. 1986. The biologic characteristics of the preembryo. Fertility and Sterility, Supplement 1, 46:27s.

12. Carlson, B.M. 1994. Human Embryology and Developmental Biology. Mosby, St. Louis.

13. Sadler, T.W. 1996. Langman's Medical Embryology. 7th ed. Williams and Wilkins, Baltimore.

14. Patten, Bradley M. 1968. Human Embryology. 3rd ed. McGraw-Hill, New York.

15. Larsen, William J. 1993. Human Embryology. Churchill-Livingston, New York.

16. O'Rahilly, Ronan and Fabiola Müller. 1992. Human Embryology and Teratology. Wiley-Liss, New York.

17.   Ibid___. 1996. 2nd ed., p. 81.

18.   Nomina Embryologica. 1989. 3rd edition. in Nomina Anatomica, 6th edition. Churchill-Livingston, Edinburgh.

19.   Moore, Keith L. 1993. Personal communication.

20.   Hitler, Adolph. 1933. Mein Kampf, vol. 1, ch. 10.

Post -Abortion Trauma:
Bring On The Facts

by   Dianne N. Irving, M.A., Ph.D.

In her recent article (*JAMA*, Oct. 21, 1992) Dr. Stotland attempts to argue that post-abortion trauma is a "myth" and factually "non-existent". Clearly, she comments, more unbiased and expanded empirical studies need to be conducted in this area before the issue can be satisfactorily resolved.

I am not a trained psychiatrist. However, as a former biomedical researcher and present philosopher and bioethicist, I would like to suggest one possible source of Dr. Stotland's denial of such a trauma - i.e., the denial (by many of us) of the actual status of what it is that is aborted. It would seem that this is critical to any factual understanding of adverse reactions (however psychiatry would categorize them) several years after the abortion event. I applaud Dr. Stotland's desire to "bring the discussion into the scientific medical literature", yet there must be an unbiased effort to be truthful and consistent in acknowledging in that literature what are "facts" and what are "myths".

Many of us have been thoroughly convinced by the scientific (and the bioethics) literature itself (before the fact of abortion) that the human embryo or human fetus is either not a human being, or if it is, that it is not a human person.[1] If either is factually the case, the decision of a woman to abort or not to abort her unborn child is *a priori* made considerably more justifiable and "rational".

Elaborate scientific arguments have been flooding the biomedical literature for some years now, positing such scientific claims as: the human embryo or human fetus is just a "blob" or piece of the mother's tissues; that all of the genetic information specific for a human being is not present at fertilization; that human embryos can give rise to teratomas or hydatidiform moles and therefore are not "human"[2]; that all of the cells from the 5-6 day embryo trophoblast layer are discarded after birth and therefore it is really a "pre-embryo", that totipotent cells can each develop into later individual human beings, and that twinning can not take place after 14 days - and therefore the early human embryo is not a true "individual", and therefore not a true human being yet[3]; that full differentiation is completed by 14 days[4]; and that true "personhood" is not present until "brain-birth", i.e., the formation of the nerve-net, neocortex or whole brain integrating system[5].

If such "medical facts" (and others like them) were actually true, it is small wonder that not only young teen-age girls and younger women, but also boy friends, husbands, parents, grandparents, priests, ministers and councilors, physicians, nurses, researchers, public policy makers, Supreme Court Justices - and yes, even psychiatrists - have bought into such "scientific" claims which are really, themselves, in fact, "myths" and "non-existent". Surely such scientific misinformation has bolstered at least temporarily their firm convictions that the early human embryo or human fetus is not really a human being or a human person, and therefore disposable or insignificant in contrast to the autonomous rights of "women who become pregnant under problematic circumstances". Unfortunately, these "scientific facts" in the biomedical literature are virtually all incorrect; yet I do not hear Dr. Stotland calling for an objective purging of these "myths" from the biomedical and bioethics literature in the name of scientific accuracy and the physician-patient relationship. Why?

The real scientific facts are the following. To determine if the human embryo is a human being, all one has to do is count the number of chromosomes in any cell of that human embryo or human fetus under a microscope, and observe the functions and activities which are present immediately after fertilization. It is immediately observed empirically that the early human embryo and human fetus is not a "blob" or piece of tissue of the mother. When the 23 chromosomes of the sperm and the 23 chromosomes of the ovum are combined, a new, unique living individual with 46 chromosomes (the number and quality specific for the human species)[6] is formed. Although this means that the human embryo is a human being, the chromosomal make-up of the human embryo and fetus is qualitatively different from that of either the mother or the father. That is, the genetic identity of the human embryo is different from the genetic identity of the tissues of the mother or the father. Thus the human embryo or fetus is not only a human being, it is clearly not, scientifically, just a "blob" of the mother's tissues.

Furthermore, at fertilization the human embryo is already a male or a female; immediately specifically human enzymes and proteins are formed; specifically human tissues and organs will be formed (not cabbages or giraffes).[7]   Virtually all of the genetic information the human being will ever have or need is present immediately at fertilization.   No genetic information is gained or lost throughout development - only the use of some information is lost through mechanisms such as methylation.[8]

This original genetic information then "cascades" throughout the course of human development, continuing to determine specifically human molecular information, tissues and organs.[9]   All of the genetic information is there that will ever be needed during growth and development, including the genetic information needed for differentiation,[10] totipotency (which is quite normal) and all of the processes of embryogenesis - sometimes even twinning.   Entities such as teratomas and hydatidiform moles do not arise from genetically normal human embryos, but from abnormal embryos to begin with (e.g., dispermy).[11]   All of the cells from the trophoblast layer are not all discarded after birth, but many from the yolk sac and allantois are incorporated into the embryo-proper as the early blood cells and the primordium of the primitive gut, and in the human adult as the median umbilical ligament and blood cells.[12]   Twinning is possible after 14 days, e.g., with fetus-in-fetu and Siamese twins.[13]   And there is no scientific physiological basis for a valid parallel between "brain death" and "brain birth", sentience or self-consciousness.[14]   Interestingly, full human development is not complete until after 20 years of age,[15] and full brain integration and the actual exercising of "rational attributes" are not present until several years after birth.[16]

Thus any arguments about physiological "preconditions" for either sentience or rational attributes are themselves arguments from potentiality, and actually depend physiologically on the precondition of the single-cell human zygote itself.   It should be carefully noted that if either actual sentience or rational attributes are indeed the rationale for human "personhood", then newborns, young children, Alzheimer's and Parkinson's patients, alcoholics, drug addicts, the mentally ill and retarded, the depressed, comatose patients, and paraplegics (to name but a few) are not "persons" either, and thus, by the very same logic, could be "disposed of".

The position that the early human embryo and human fetus is not a human being or a human person, then, is itself scientifically and medically a "myth".   Such incorrect medical information should be brought out into the "light" of professional scientific scrutiny as well as any information concerning the "myth" of post-abortion trauma. Yet how many physicians, or psychiatrists, are willing to "provide [this] sound scientific information [to their patients] to help them make informed decisions about health issues"? Not many. Why not?

Yes, Dr. Stotland is correct to note the increase in the conflict concerning abortion, especially since the Roe vs Wade decision. But she implies that religious and personal opinions which reject abortion are factually misplaced and are being imposed on women who have the absolute autonomous right to choose whatever they want in regard to their unborn child. She also implies that these irrational (because personal and/or religious) claims about post-abortion trauma are hampering the physician's and the psychiatrist's role to "counsel, advocate for, and treat individual patients on the basis of medical knowledge and in the patient's best interest".

Yet Dr. Stotland refuses to consider that she is dealing here with two patients - the pregnant woman and the unborn child. She does not see any need to consider the best interests of the unborn child, and she counsels her pregnant mother on the incorrect embryological facts, so that the mother in turn could never make a truly informed decision about aborting her child - thus precluding any meaningful autonomy or informed consent at all. Why?

Consider the possible consequences of such a physician-patient relationship. Dr. Stotland conveniently refuses to consider that perhaps some personal opinions and some religious convictions are actually rooted in non-relative, objective facts. (For example, the human embryo and the human fetus are human beings.) And perhaps the aborting woman does not know them or want to know them at that moment. Yet later she does learn these correct embryological facts, even years after the abortion. Or perhaps the woman eventually puts two + two together in some other indirect way. That correct embryological information, coupled with a religious commitment to respect all innocent human beings (regardless of their race, sex, disabilities, nationality - or size), could conceivably trigger such a "traumatic" event as post-abortion syndrome in the mother who has previously naively autonomously aborted what she thought at the time was just a "blob" of her own tissue.

If she has also donated her aborted unborn child for fetal tissue transplant research or for human embryo research, perhaps she could also come to the realization of another medical "fact" - that her fetus

84

was not dead or anesthetized when his or her brain cells were removed for tissue transplant "therapy" or when her embryo was sacrificed in destructive human embryo research for "the greater good". These medical "facts" should also be constitutive of any realistic physician-patient counseling or relationship - and yet they are not. Why?

An aborted woman could also come to the gradual realization that a woman's - or any other human being's - "pure absolute autonomy" is also a "myth". Certainly the field of bioethics is finally beginning to come to grips with that dialogue. No one - male or female - has an absolute right to choose absolutely anything just because conditions are difficult or a mistake was made. Our choices are always qualified; and our choices always have consequences - with which we must all live.

Finally, I respect Dr. Stotland's concern about what has come to be identified as a "woman's issue". I myself am a professional woman, and I know perfectly well that women have been the subject of serious and unjustified abuse and discrimination. However, this does not condone the current "rationalization" and legalization of everything and anything, simply because many women "want" it. Abortion is, in fact, ultimately an aggression against women. The sooner women acknowledge that fact the sooner more realistic and objectively based counseling of women in "problematic" situations can be provided by physicians and psychiatrists alike.

In sum, Dr. Stotland should not be so selective about which "facts" to explore in the biomedical literature. Nor should she be so quick to selectively accept as "facts" things which are in fact "myths".

References

1. But see Irving DN. *Philosophical and Scientific Analysis of the Nature of the Early Human Embryo*. Doctoral dissertation, Department of Philosophy, Georgetown University, Washington, D.C.:1991; Irving DN. Scientific and philosophical expertise: an evaluation of the arguments on fetal personhood. *Linacre Quarterly*. Feb. 1993 (forthcoming); Irving DN. The impact of scientific misi1. But see Irving DN. *Philosophical and Scientific Analysis of the Nature of the Early Human Embryo*. Doctoral dissertation, Department of Philosophy, Georgetown nformation: philosophy, theology, biomedical ethics, public policy. *Accountability in Research*. Feb. 1993 (forthcoming); Carberry J, Kmiec DW. Abortion: how law denies science. *Chicago Tribune*. July 14;

Fisher A. Individuogenesis and a recent book by Fr. Norman Ford. *Anthropotes.* 1991:2:199; McCullagh P. *The Foetus as Transplant Donor: Scientific, Social and Ethical Perspectives.* New York, John Wiley and Sons:1987.

2. Bedate C, Cefalo R. The zygote: to be or not be a person. *Journal of Medicine and Philosophy.* 1989:14:6:641. Also Bole J.T. Metaphysical accounts of the zygote as a person and the veto power of facts. *Journal of Medicine and Philosophy.* 1989:14:647-653, and Zygotes, souls, substances and persons. *Journal of Medicine and Philosophy.* 1990:15:637-652.

3. Grobstein C. The early development of human embryos. *Journal of Medicine and Philosophy* 1985:10:213-236. Also McCormick R. Who or what is the preembryo? *Kennedy Institute of Ethics Journal.* 1991:1:1-15.

4. Ford N. *When Did I Begin?.* New York: Cambridge University Press: 1988:137, 156.

5. Jones DG. Brain birth and personal identity. *Journal of Medical Ethics* 1989:15:4:173-178; MacKay D. in Jones 1989; Rahner, Ruff and Haring, in Jones 1989; Sass H. Brain death and brain life: a proposal for normative agreement. *Journal of Medicine and Philosophy* 1989:14:45-59; Singer and Wells, in Jones 1989; Tauer C. Personhood and human embryos and fetuses. *Journal of Medicine and Philosophy.* 1985:10:253-266; Lockwood M. Warnock versus Powell (and Harradine): when does potentiality count? *Bioethics* 1988:3:3:187-213; Goldenring J. Development of the fetal brain. *New England Journal of Medicine.* 1982:307:564, and The brain-life theory: towards a consistent biological definition of humanness. *Journal of Medical Ethics* 1985:11:198-120; Kushner T. Having a life versus being alive. *Journal of Medical Ethics.* 1984:10:5-8; Gertler, in Singer P. *Practical Ethics.* London, Cambridge University Press: 1981; Bennett MV. Personhood from a neuroscientific perspective. in Doerr et al. *Abortion Rights and Fetal "Personhood".* Long Beach, Cresline Press:1989.

6. Moore KL. *the Developing Human.* Philadelphia:W.B. Saunders Co.:1982:14; Lewin B ed. *Genes III.* New York: John Wiley and Sons:1983:9-13, 386-394, 401; Emery AEH. *Elements of Medical Genetics.* New York: Churchill Livingstone:1983:19, 93; also obvious from the following research: Gordon K et al. Production of human tissue plasminogen activator in transgenic mouse milk. *Bio Technology.* 1987:5:1183: Weishous T et al. Secretion of enzymatically active human renin from mammalian cells using an avian retroviral vector. *Genes.* 1986:45:2:121-129; Tanaka A, Fujita D. Expression of a molecularly cloned human C-SRC oncogene by using a replication-competent retroviral vector. *Molecular and Cellular Biology.*

1986:6:11:3900-3909; Schnieke A et al. Introduction of the human pro alpha 1 (I) collagen gene into pro alpha 1 (I) - deficient Mov-13 mouse cells leads to formation of functional mouse-human hybrid type I collagen. *Proceedings of the National Academy of Science - USA*. Feb. 1987:84:3:764-768; Hart C, Awgulewitch A et al. Homeobox gene complex on mouse chromosome II:molecular cloning, expression in embryogenesis, and homology to a human homeobox locus. *Cell*. 1985:43:1:9-18; Kollias G et al. The human beta-globulin gene contains a downstream developmental specific enhancer. *Nucleic Acids Research*. July 1987:15:14:5739-47; Olofsson, B, Pizon V et al. Structure and expression of the chicken epidermal growth factor receptor gene locus. *European Journal of Biochemistry*. 1986:160:2:261-266; Saez L, Leinwand S. Characterization of diverse forms of myosin light chain gene: unexpected interspecies homology with repetitive DNA. *Archives of Biochemistry and Biophysics*. 1984:233:2:565-572; Olle R et al. Structural relation among mouse and human immunoglobulin VH genes in the subgroup III. *Nucleic Acids Research*. 1983:11:22:7887-97; Proudfoot N et al. The structure of the human zeta-globin gene and a closely linked, nearly identical pseudogene. *Cell*. 1982:31:32:553-563.

7. Kollias 1987; Covarrubias L et al. Cellular DNA rearrangements and early developmental arrest caused by DNA insertion in transgenic mouse embryos. *Molecular and Cellular Biology*. 1987:7:6:2243-2247; Humphries RK et al. Transfer of human and murine globin-gene sequences into transgenic mice. *American Journal of Human Genetics* 1985:37:2:295-310; Khillan J et al. Tissue-specific, inducible and functional expression of the Ead MHC class II gene in transgenic mice. *EMBO Journal*. 1985:4:9:2225-30; Palmiter R et al. Cell lineage ablation in transgenic mice by cell-specific expression of a toxin gene. *Cell*. 1985:43:1:9-18.

8. Moore 1982:14; Lewin 1983:9-13, 202-203, 681; Emery 1983:93; Lejeune J in Martin Palmer ed. *A Symphony of the Preborn Child: Part Two*. Hagerstown, MD: NAAPC: 1989:9-10, 16-19, 30.

9. Lewin 1983:11-13, 202-203, 681; Emery 1983:93.

10. That differentiation is *not* caused by the mother and is determined by the embryo: Holtzer H et al. Induction-dependent and lineage-dependent models for cell-diversification are mutually exclusive. *Progress in Clinical Biological Research*. 1985:175:3-11; Mavilio F, Sineone A et al. Differential and stage-related expression in embryonic tissues of a new human homeobox gene. *Nature*. 1986:324:6098:664-668; Hart C et al 1985.

11. Szulmann AE, Surti U. The syndromes of hydatidiform mole. I. Cytogenic and morphologic correlations. *American Journal of Obstetrics and*

Gynecology. 1978:131:665-671; Moore 1982:30; Lejeune 1989:19-19; Wimmers MSE et al. Chromosome studies on early human embryos fertilized *in vitro. Human Reproduction.* 1988:7:894-900; Lawler SD, Fisher RA. Genetic studies in hydatidiform mole with clinical correlations. *Placenta.* 1987:8:77-88; Martin GR. Teratocarcinomas and mammalian embryogenesis. *Science.* 1980:209:768-776; Alberts et al. *Molecular Biology of the Cell.* New York:Garland Publishing: 1983.

12. Moore 1982:33,62-63,111,127; Chauda K et al. An embryonic pattern of expression of a human fetal globin gene in transgenic mice. *Nature.* 1986:319:6055:685-689; Migliaccio G et al. Human embryonic hemopoiesis. Kinetics of progenitors and precursor underlying the yolk sac-liver transition. *Journal of Clinical Investigation.* 1986:78:1:51-60.

13. Moore 1982:133; Dawson K, in Peter Singer et al. *Embryo Experimentation.* New York: Cambridge University Press;1990:43-52.

14. Jones 1989:15;4;173-178.

15. Moore 1982:1.

16. Jones 1989:173-178; Engelhardt T. *The Foundations of Bioethics.* New York: Oxford University Press. 1985:111.

The Media and Human Embryology

C. Ward Kischer, Ph.D.
Department of Cell Biology and Anatomy
University of Arizona
College of Medicine

A very informative book was published in 1990 entitled: "And That's The Way It Isn't. A reference guide to media bias."[1] The authors were Brent Bozell and Brent Baker. It is essentially a political expose and details the liberal bias by the media (which really means the reporters, writers and correspondents) relative to political issues. Beyond a shadow of a doubt the authors prove their point.

However, there is another related issue involved in this bias. In reading about the obvious *bias* on political issues, one wonders if some of it is generated by sheer *ignorance*. It is pretty obvious that some, if not many, of the reporters and TV news anchors express their emotional opinions, but that they also would (or should) never say them if they had checked facts or history for the truth.

Roe v. Wade was adjudicated by the Supreme Court in 1973. Prior to this decision there was little or no public interest in Human Embryology, the science of development. But, because the questions of *life* and *viability* were raised by the court, these subjects, and ancillary topics, increasingly were written about in newspapers, magazines, books and in scientific journals. They were (and are) also discussed on radio and television talk shows.

Incredibly, those most often talking about human development have been political analysts, lawyers, theologians and sociologists but very few physicians and virtually *no* human embryologists. Those doing most of the writing and talking have not checked the facts and certainly have not consulted human embryologists. Why this has been the case is something of a mystery, although it can be reasonably guessed at considering the investment in the political fallout from *Roe v. Wade*.

It is reasonable to say that more false information,

misrepresentations, half-truths and outright lies concerning Human Embryology have been stated since *Roe v. Wade* than at any previous time in history, including ancient times. Before Hippocrates (ca. 400 B.C.) the errors may seem to have been more outrageous, but there were not that many of them. The ancients, for the most part, knew when to keep their mouths shut contrary to contemporary times, in which virtually everyone has an opinion expressed as "fact."

Bias and ignorance, relating to Human Embryology, are often indistinguishable. However, one fact is provable: those writing about contemporary Human Embryology are not consulting proper, and available, references.

- The *Preembryo*

The most damning lie written about Human Embryology is the case of the *preembryo*.[2,3] This is a term invented in 1979 by an amphibian embryologist, Clifford Grobstein for one purpose only: to establish a *reduced moral status* for the human embryo up to at least 14 days post-fertilization.[4]

This reduced status was deemed necessary because *in-vitro* fertilization techniques were becoming a viable industry and some sort of justification had to be made for manipulating early human life. The rationale put forth by Grobstein later became the basis for guidelines set forth by the Ethics Committee of the American Fertility Society (of which Grobstein was a member)[5] and of The Ethics Committee of the American College of Gynecologists.[6] Grobstein's reasoning also became the basis for justifying human embryo research, as proposed by the National Institutes of Health Advisory Committee in 1994.[7]

The term *preembryo* has not been, and should not be, accepted by any reputable human embryologist. The one exception has been Keith Moore, who uses the term in his 5th edition of a Human Embryology textbook.[8] But, in a personal letter to this author, Moore said he would remove it in his next printing. Indeed, in the 3rd printing

90

of his text the term *preembryo* has been removed. But, its equivalent, *preembryonic,* is retained.

The failure to check facts relative to Human Embryology is not restricted to the pro-choice advocacy. In no less a publication than Donum Vitae, a Vatican publication on Bioethics, we find the use of the inaccurate and invalid term *preembryo.*[9] It is a virtual certainty that those who put this publication together did not know of the lack of credibility of the term, or, assuredly, that it means a *reduced moral status.* A nursing text also uses the term as a *bona fide* stage.[10]

This has been the unfortunate fall-out from a constant and unrelenting use of false information without proper correction from physicians and, especially, human embryologists. It is truly inexplicable as to why those who know the facts have failed to confront this term, which is the worst case of abuse of embryological facts concerning the human.

• *Monitoring the Media*

As a professor of Human Embryology for more than 30 years, I finally took an interest in what the media was saying about this subject. It was also my aim to make my students aware of the errors and false statements commonly made. Thus, for several years they were instructed to cull through the more commonly and popularly read newspapers, magazines and scientific journals for articles relating to Human Embryology. They were to cite the errors found and analyze them. The following citations illustrate just a sample of the types of errors found over the most recent years. Each citation is followed by the proper correction.

•*"[The forming embryo] looks a little like a segmented worm".* *. . " something like the gill arches of a fish or an amphibian have become conspicuous, and there is a pronounced tail." "The face is mammalian but somewhat piglike." "By the end of the eighth week, the face resembles a primate's, but is still not quite human."* - Carl Sagan and Ann Druyan. 1990. Is It

Possible To Be Pro-Life and Pro-Choice? Parade Magazine, April 22nd.

This is perhaps the most shameful display of both bias *and* ignorance. Sagan's ignorance is not restricted to the above quotes. The article is replete with outright lies.

The overall effect of the article is to diminish the *human* aspect of the human embryo. The truth is that our evolution as an embryo passes through changes which are *similar* to the changes in other vertebrate embryos. Such similarities speak eloquently for the basic biological plan of all living things subject to the same physical and chemical laws. The human embryo *never* develops gill arches, or gills, or a tail. Neither is the human embryo ever a worm, a pig or a primate. Carl Sagan is not a human embryologist, but an astrophysicist. He has done a great disservice to the general public, as has Parade Magazine.

> • *"You must remember, we're talking about Post Mortem tissue."* - Bernadine Healy, former Director of NIH, interviewed by Diane Sawyer on Prime Time Live, January 28th, 1993.

Sawyer had interviewed Healy about the use of live fetuses for transplant tissues for cases, such as Parkinson's Disease. The truth is that *dead* tissue would do nothing. The transplant *must* contain living cells, and the only way to ensure that is to obtain them from *living* fetuses.

> • *"In the emergency room we pronounce a person dead when the heart stops beating. I would like to propose we just reverse that, that life begins when the heart starts beating.* - a 3rd year medical student call-in to an afternoon talk show heard over KNST, Tucson, Arizona, April 17th, 1993.

Our medical students are not being taught very well in Human Embryology. Obviously, this student received little or no instruction in the subject. This is not surprising since about half of our nations' medical schools have no credit bearing course in Human Embryology. Virtually every human embryologist agrees that life begins at first contact of sperm and ovum, which is the only statement which makes sense.

•*"Can you imagine a world in which we jail women for drinking while pregnant?"* - Dr. Dean Edell, populist radio medical diagnostician, scoffing at the prosecution and jailing of pregnant women who drink alcohol and produce Fetal Alcohol Syndrome babies. Circa 1994.

He also ridiculed the idea that fetuses should have human rights prior to birth. He read a statement that would prohibit legal rights for fetuses to which he said: "Amen." Of course this violates the medical concept of regarding the fetus as a "second patient." His advocacy also conflicts with 31 states which allow lawsuits for the negligent death of a viable fetus and criminal prosecutions in at least 25 states.

Dr. Edell has also publicly declared that he "hated every second of medical school." Little wonder that he has no respect for Human Embryology.

•*"The placenta, which protects the fetus from toxic substances in the mother's bloodstream, also filters out most drugs."* - Joanne Silberner. U.S. News & World Report. "Fighting Disease Before Birth. 21 Nov. 105:62, 1988.

Unfortunately, the *opposite* is true. Virtually every human embryologist says: ". . . most drugs and drug metabolites pass the placenta without difficulty . . . . fetal drug addiction can occur after maternal use of drugs such as heroin and cocaine."[11]

•*"With the advance of medical technology during the last two decades, the age at which a human fetus can survive outside its mother's womb, the so-called age of viability, has steadily declined, . . . some premature infants of 20 weeks, and most of 24 weeks, can survive ex-utero."* - Meyer S. and D.K. De Wolf. 1995. "Fetal Position." National Review, 20 March, pp. 62-64.

Surviving outside the mother's womb is a misleading concept. It is rubbish! The newborn, whether term or premature may survive outside the mother's womb only *as long as its needs are met*! It needs more care after birth than before.

What is not said is that the younger the age of birth prior to term the greater reduction in the quality of life. Many problems of premature births are never resolved. It is irresponsible to speak of viability of early delivery without correspondingly revealing the many problems these infants have.

• *"Now many women live 'til they're 80 or 90; so, maybe its not so outrageous for them to have kids at 50."* - Elias, Marilyn. 1994. "Who Controls Reproductive Technology." USA Today, January 5th, A1:4.

On the contrary, it is! And it is outrageous to make a statement like that. It is well known there are increased birth defects when the pregnant mother is older, particularly with the case of Trisomy 21 (Down's Syndrome).

> • *"The AMA says use of live anencephalic infants - those born without brains - as organ donors is acceptable if the diagnosis of their condition is certain and the parents agree to donation."* - Amanda Husted. Atlanta Journal Constitution. 1995. Doctors Can Say No To Patients. Reported by the Washington Times. May 4th.

Shame on the AMA! What is not said and should be said is what would be said by any human embryologist. Anencephaly is a major developmental defect. Watch out for other defects before thinking about organ donation. Moore says: "Ninety percent of infants with three or more minor anomalies also have one or more major defects."[12] Although the reverse may not necessarily be true, most major defects are multiple and not singular in nature.

> • *"I will not sign this bill because . . . it does not provide for the exceptions of life of the mother or health of the mother".* -

President Clinton vetoing the Partial Birth Abortion Act on April 10th, 1996.

•*"Are there doctors in this country who would perform this procedure on a healthy baby in the third trimester?"* - Ed Bradley, 60 Minutes, interviewing Dr. Warren Hern on a program entitled: "Partial-Birth Abortion," June 2nd, 1996.
"I don't know of any. I don't know of any." - Response of Dr. Hern to the above question.

If the "life" or "health" of the mother is threatened by the head of the fetus remaining in the birth canal, the simplest procedure would be to *deliver the head* rather than poke a hole in it and suck out its brains. Therefore, the objective is not to preserve "life" or "health" of the mother, but to kill the fetus.

Serious defects of the fetus excepted, in a purely elective procedure, the "health" of the mother would be relieved because she would not be troubled with the expected care of the infant, nor to make a decision for adoption.

Both of the women featured in testimony by "60 Minutes" and all five of the women who appeared with President Clinton on the April 10th veto celebration received abortions from the late Dr. James McMahon. Along with Dr. Martin Haskell, they performed thousands of these partial-birth abortions, the vast majority of them being purely elective, 80% of them on perfectly healthy fetuses. Ed Bradley and 60 Minutes knew this before posing the above question to Dr. Hern.

•*". . . the embryo does not have the same moral status as infants or children and that research on such embryos hold the potential for great benefit. . . . . Others, like me, will find it hard to consider the tiny clumps of primitive cells as anything approaching a "person." . . . . I would find it easier to eliminate a handful of unfeeling, unaware cells than to destroy say, a living breathing animal."* - Cantwell, Mary. 1994. "Should We Make Research Embryos?" The New York Times, November 25th.

Perfect arrogance.   This was said of the proposed research
recommended by The NIH Human Embryo Research Panel. Obviously
Cantwell has no appreciation for Human Embryology and the reality of
the *continuum* of life. By her reasoning those individuals who, for one
reason or another, are unfeeling and unaware, may not escape medical
experimentation or outright extermination.   This is exactly what
happened in Nazi Germany in the 1930's and 40s.

> • *"Surely you don't believe a fertilized egg is a human being, do
> you?"* - said by Geraldine Ferraro on a Crossfire (CNN)
> program, August 7th, 1996.

This question was put to Gary Bauer, President of the Family Research
Council. He sat mute, did not respond but simply shrugged. Not even
Robert Novak, co-host of Crossfire, responded.

This kind of silence (Bauer made the claim to this author that
he did not hear the question) only exacerbates the problems of the Pro-
Life advocacy. Any high school biology student would have said: "Of
course," and asked Ms. Ferraro if she thought the fertilized human
oocyte would be a frog, pig or chimpanzee!

•   *Conclusion*

This is only scratching the surface.   No major media
publication, newspaper or magazine, and those scientific journals
reporting about Human Embryology, escaped our analysis.

True enough we did not use a scientific grading system for
accuracy. However, no publication got off clean with no errors or
misrepresentations.

What is reported here are examples and not necessarily all of
the type of errors found. Some publications exercise no quality control
at all, as is true of some writers.

Clearly, there is a major problem.   The public knows little

96

about Human Embryology, although some ignorant writers think they know more than they actually show. If these writers would make even a little effort and seek basic information, much of the problem would be relieved. It is not going to be solved by seeking out political analysts, politicians and ethicists.

Human embryologists are also at fault for not speaking out at the plethora of nonsense, gibberish and false information replete in the mainstream media. They have a responsibility, if only from the aspect of being a good citizen, to correct the misinformation. Why they are not doing this is a mystery. It should be explored.

REFERENCES

1. Bozell, L. Brent, III and Brent H. Baker. 1990. And That's The Way It Isn't. A Reference Guide to Media Bias. Media Research Center, Alexandria, Virginia.

2. Kischer, C.W. The Big Lie in Human Embryology. The Case of the *Preembryo*. The Linacre Quarterly (In Press).

3. Kischer, C.W. and D.N. Irving. 1995. The Human Development Hoax. Time to tell the truth. Gold Leaf Press, Clinton Township, Michigan.

4. Grobstein, Clifford. 1979. External Human Fertilization. Sci. Amer., 240:57-67.

5. Ethics Committee of the American Fertility Society. 1986. Fertility and Sterility, Suppl. 1, 46:275.

6. Ethics Committee of the American College of Gynecologists. 1994. Preembryo Research: History, Scientific Background and Ethical Considerations. Resource Center, ACOG, Washington, D.C.

7. National Institutes of Health. Transcripts of The Human Embryo Research Panel. 1994. September 27th session, p.2.

8. Moore, Keith and T.V.N. Persaud. 1993. The Developing Human. 5th ed. W.B. Saunders Co., Philadelphia.

9. Donum Vitae. 1987. Respect for Human Life. Pauline Books & Media, Boston.

10. May, K.A. and L.R. Maklmeister. 1995. Maternal and Neonatal Nursing Family - Centered Care. 3rd ed. Lippincott, Philadelphia.

11. Sadler, T.W. 1990. Langman's Medical Embryology. Sixth ed. p. 106. Williams and Wilkins, Baltimore.

12. Moore, K.L. and T.V.N, Persaud. 1993. The Developing Human. 5th ed. p. 142. W.B. Saunders, Philadelphia.

QUID SIT VERITAS?

The Odyssey of One Human Embryologist
As A Modern Diogenes

Clayton Ward Kischer, Ph.D.
Department of Anatomy
University of Arizona
Tucson, AZ   85724

Science should be revealed and evaluated by public exposure. But, when science, more specifically, human development, is being reinvented, it must be subject to analysis and critique by scientists who know the subject, so that the public might be properly informed to evaluate that science, lest it become politicized.   Without proper dialogue, public policy could be changed or invoked to dramatically affect our societal evolution, and this has already occurred.

Ignorance is no special domain of the unschooled. In the effort to make public policy, socio-legal politicos (some of them scientists) have misstated the factual knowledge of human embryology and engaged in a kind of "doublespeak". Further, the more outrageous the misrepresentations have become, the more frequent they have appeared.   This signals the desperation that revisionists of human embryology display. The overkill has often resulted in gross canards. But, where is the ordinary outlet through or by which misleading comments or outright lies can be corrected?

In 1990 Brent Bozell and Brent Baker edited a book entitled: And That's The Way It Isn't (Media Research Center, Alexandria, Virginia, 1990), which documented and confirmed what most people sensed and believed for many years: that the media have been and are heavily biased towards liberal politics and policies. The ordinary citizen expects a free press to report the truth.   But, what has actually occurred has been an eclipse of truth and a dearth of balance.

Bozell and Baker provide an example of media bias on the subject of abortion. They evaluated media labeling of proponents and opponents of abortion over the last four months of 1988. They found that proponents received positive labels 97% of the time, while opponents received positive labels only 21% of the time.

This kind of bias seemed impressive to me; but, surely, I believed, not what one would ordinarily encounter when trying to correct false statements and concepts concerning *science*, especially when made by persons who are not scientists.

I was wrong! Those in control of the major media sources are apparently unwilling to balance the cascade of false statements made with the real truth, even though they probably know the real truth, yet speak and act as though it does not exist.

In 1989 Eleanor Smeal addressed a convention of NOW (National Organization for Women) in which she made the following statement. "What makes our country great is the Bill of Rights, which says you have the freedom to do what you want". I contend that this mind set is the legacy of a judicial system gone awry. Stability of any social system is usually threatened or strained the denser the population becomes. When this occurs, more controls must be involved, sometimes with abbreviation or even loss of some freedoms. However, in our country it seems the opposite has been occurring. Our population has nearly doubled in the past 50 years. Despite this fact, I contend that since the early 1950's, whether intended or not, decisions by the Supreme Court have set a course for public behavior based on a massive experiment: *to see how much freedom the citizens of this country could exercise before the social system would come apart.* A case can be made that the right to have an abortion is borne out of this "freedom" concept.

Proponents of abortion find additional justification in errant conclusions drawn about human development in Roe v. Wade, and from other sources promoted by the major media outlets. Smeal compounded the errors in her speech by making another absurd comment, false not just by concept, but false through known biological fact: "everybody knows that life begins only after birth." At about the same time, a female candidate for a state office in New Jersey made the same statement via a political promo on cable channel WOR. I began to hear more of this kind of rhetoric. On the CNN Crossfire program of July 10th, 1990 the guest was a pediatric physician by the name of Holly Galland. The subject of the program was abortion and she made the following comment in response to a question as to when life begins: "Not even the Academy of Science (sic) can decide that." Of course, she meant the National Academy of Science.

The Prehuman Claim

Since I was trained as an embryologist, more specifically, an experimental embryologist that gravitated into the teaching and experience of human embryology soon after my Ph.D. degree, I began to take more notice of statements, such as the above, made within the public domain. I have been teaching the subject of human embryology in one form or another since 1960, mostly to medical students. Statements, such as those cited above, not only are absurd, but are politically motivated. Yet the problem was (and still is) that they were being expressed to a lay public, most of whom were most likely uninformed about human development. In the November 22nd, 1989 issue of National Review, Ernest van den Haag wrote an article titled "Is there a middle ground?" The substance of his article included several questionable statements concerning human embryology. For example, he claimed that the embryo is "pre-human". In support of this he stated that the embryo related to the human baby as a larva relates to a butterfly. This is a canard of the *primary water*. This comparison may satisfy contemporary social engineers but is biologically absurd. Even an entomologist would be grievously offended by such a notion. Van den Haag reaffirmed his claim in response to two letters sent to the National Review (February 5, 1990) but he did so by stating: "things are what they are, not what they become. That goes for concepts, too" (National Review, February 5, 1990, pages 6-8). If van den Haag really believes this, then he need not have likened human development to that of an insect. He might as well have compared it to an auto factory, more specifically, an embryo compared to a fender. It makes as much sense. The effect is to reduce and diminish the quality and status of the human during development.

No human embryologist, now or ever in recorded history, has ever referred to the human embryo as "pre-human". Is van den Haag suggesting that our science classes world-wide should now teach this *new concept?*

An Embryologist Responds

It was at this time that I took closer note as to what appeared in the print media and what was being announced via television and radio talk shows. I also noted that at this time there was no responsible retort to these wild claims that were being passed so easily and frequently through and among the lay public. I searched the literature for similar types of misrepresentations and to my surprise found numerous articles written essentially by psychologists, philosophers, and theologians which purported to invoke embryological facts but which were, in fact, misrepresentations and outright falsehoods. I found essentially no human embryologists who were answering these distorted claims. Therefore, it was at this time that I decided van den Haag's article should be rebutted. Ernest van den Haag is a political analyst. He has frequently contributed (and still does) to National Review and has authored and co-authored books on socio-legal issues. To my knowledge, he has no background whatsoever in human embryology, yet in his article in National Review he invoked a great deal of what he believes to be the science of human embryology. In fact, in that article he stated that as development proceeds "the embryo acquires human characteristics". Further, he asked "when does intrauterine life become human life?" He might defend his statements by claiming he was speaking rhetorically; but he fails to say so, or to distinguish between the biological terms and philosophical ones. As a consequence many readers have been confused, and often doubt their own common sense.

I prepared a manuscript in rebuttal essentially to the van den Haag article. I titled it: "Concerning Abortion: The Truth, The Whole Truth and Nothing But the *Biological* Truth". I sent this manuscript to National Review and specifically to an assistant editor, Mark Cunningham. My cover letter indicated that I had been teaching human embryology for more than 25 years mainly to medical students and had wished to set the record straight on the misinformation within van den Haag's article. This manuscript neither advocated an anti- or pro-view of abortion nor did it include any political appeals. It contained only statements which referred to the so-called scientific information which van den Haag used in his essay, and reviewed what is currently known within the science of human embryology and how this contradicted the statements and inferences by van den Haag. This manuscript was rejected out- of-hand and returned to me with a cover letter indicating that their policy was one of not normally accepting unsolicited manuscripts but acquiring them from a standard pool of contributors from which they normally drew for inclusions in their issues. I also sent a copy of the manuscript to van den Haag but never received a reply. I then embarked upon a virtual three year effort to get this manuscript published.

Having spent my career in a publish or perish atmosphere I have been no stranger to the mechanisms of writing and submitting manuscripts for publication and getting them accepted in various journals and dealing with reviewers and editors. Therefore, I fully expected this manuscript would be submitted for review by whichever editor of the journal to which it was submitted. The manuscript explained the need to reveal the known scientific facts about human development and was divided into four subtopics, each of which had been misrepresented, distorted or deliberately changed by many lay publications and which had been discussed on various talk shows, news programs, and by commentators, with respect to the "science" of human development. These four areas were 1) the beginning of life, 2) the quality of being human, 3) viability, and 4) sentience.

• *The beginning of life*

In brief, what this manuscript said was that those invoking a question of when life began would fail to distinguish between the biological definition of life and philosophical, religious, social or political life. At best it was disingenuous for writers or commentators to raise the question of when life began and not to include what we know as the *biological phenomenon of life*. A phenomenon of life began in the evolutionary sense approximately 4 billion years ago. From a moment in time a system of reproduction was evolved which sustained a *continuum* from that original moment. *That was the beginning of life*. But, in all the previous comments written and spoken within the public issue of abortion, of which I was aware, this concept had rarely been discussed. The consequence of this was (and unfortunately still is) that many lay people were confused and even asked themselves if in fact that issue within the womb of the pregnant woman was really alive? At the time very few scientists were speaking

103

out and answering these kinds of outrageous inferences. Physicians, especially, appeared to be conspicuously absent from the public debate. Therefore, I felt compelled to at least put forth the biological explanation of the concept of life. Indeed, in van den Haag's article in National Review he makes the following statement: "The infant is unquestionably alive, unquestionably human, and viable outside the mother, whereas the fetus might not be." He offers no further clarification, or explanation of this statement.

In an *amici curiae* brief presented to the Supreme Court, specifically cited by Justice Blackmun, in the Webster case (In the Supreme Court of the United States, October, 1988. William L. Webster, *et al.* v. Reproductive Health Services, *et al.* Amici Curiae Brief of 167 Distinguished Scientists and Physicians Including 11 Nobel Laureates in Support of Appellees) it is stated that the beginning of life cannot be determined and cannot lend itself to an empirical test such as would take place in most bench-type scientific research. This is a presumptuous statement and most unfortunate that so-called scientists would make this outrageous claim. If they are referring to the beginning of life occurring over 4 billion years ago, they are correct, because that moment in time and the environmental conditions then existing can never be repeated. But to leave the issue there is more than disingenuous. What we have seen, and see, with every case of fertilization and subsequent pregnancy is the repeated observation of life forming as a new individual by the union of a sperm and ovum. From an experimental point of view, the continuum of human life has been confirmed with every case of fertilization since the first hominid was conceived. Further, in that same brief, the *amici* state that "the essence of life cannot be determined". This is in direct contradiction to perhaps the best definition of life, and its essence, ever put forward, that by Wendell M. Stanley, discoverer of Tobacco Mosaic Virus and Nobel Prize winner in 1946, in which he said:

> "The essence of life is the ability to reproduce. This is accomplished by the utilization of energy to create order out of disorder, to bring together into a specific predetermined pattern from semi-order or even from chaos all the component parts of that pattern with the perpetuation of that pattern with time - this is life."

Stanley's definition satisfies most if not all biological scientists, and it should be satisfactory for virtually all human embryologists. But, of course it does not cut across all of the lines of esoteric definitions of life such as political, religious, financial, social, psychological, etc., and was never intended to do so. The major problem has been and continues to be the failure of many, e.g., the pro-choice advocacy, to distinguish, by what they write and what they say, between the biological distinction and the socio-legal distinctions.

• *The quality of being human*

The second topic which has been abused and which I described strictly in biological terms is *the quality of being human*. Indeed, as van den Haag stated in his article: "As development proceeds, the embryo acquires *human characteristics*." van den Haag further states the embryo lacks distinctly human characteristics which might entitle it to a social protection and then follows this by asking "when does intrauterine life become human life?"

Rivers Singleton, Jr. wrote an article published in <u>Perspectives in Biology and Medicine</u> (Paradigms of Science/Society interaction; The Abortion Controversy, 32:174-193, 1989), in which he suggested (wrongly, of course) that the human fetus contains gill slits, which would then put it in the category of a fish or an amphibian. Singleton has a Ph.D. in biochemistry. There is no indication that he has any background in anatomy or human embryology.

Carl Sagan has been a major contributor at almost regular intervals in <u>Parade</u> magazine, a nationally syndicated magazine delivered with Sunday newspapers throughout the nation. Carl Sagan (with wife Ann Druyan) wrote a solicitous article on abortion and human development in the April 22nd, 1990 issue entitled: "The Question of Abortion". Sagan is an astrophysicist and astronomer. There is no indication I have found that he has any background or training in human embryology. In this article he made several major errors concerning human development, but he also inferred that there are developmental stages in the case of the human which "resemble a worm, reptile, and a pig". In fact, Sagan and Druyan described a four week embryo with "something like the gill arches of a fish or an amphibian" and they also say it has a "pronounced tail". The real truth is that in the case of the human embryo, <u>no</u> gill slits ever appear.

Further the human embryo never develops a tail. Some embryological texts refer to the caudal area of the human embryo as having a tail process. There are elements within that tail process which if in another specie would differentiate into a tail and its component parts, but in the case of the human these elements degenerate. There is an anomalous condition in which a *caudal appendage* will appear in the case of the human but this has no intrinsic movement and no coordinated differentiation of the bony and muscular tissue which would allow for intrinsic movement. It is a different kind of tissue altogether and in no sense would represent a tail. Van den Haag's query, and the errant statements by Singleton, Sagan, and others, are essentially grounded within what was known as, the Basic Biogenetic Law. This "law" was conceived in 1866 by a developmental biologist called Haeckel and from his ideas of development the axiom was developed which stated *Ontogeny Recapitulates Phylogeny*. Literally, this means development, or the stages in human development, recapitulate (show again) the phylogeny (forms) of lesser species. Therefore, a frivolous notion followed which suggested that the adult forms of lesser vertebrates in the evolutionary tree were demonstrated in the embryonic forms of human development, a notion still found in biology texts today.

Immediately after the article appeared in Parade by Sagan and Druyan, I called the New York office of Parade and spoke to one who gave his name as Larry Smith, Managing Editor. I complained about the many errors in the article and asked if parade would publish a brief article of corrections. I was told they would not. Further, Smith became very defensive concerning the Sagans.

On August 19th, approximately 4 months later, they published a page of excerpts from letters they had received concerning the Sagans' article. Only one excerpt referred to a correction, and that one was phrased in such a way as to appear moot: "that criterion [for thought] is as arbitrary as all others mentioned . . . viability, renal function, facial characteristics, etc. . . . "

But, the editors simply ignored that *fact* with examples like the one from Governor Tommy Thompson of Wisconsin: "I thought the article's effort at building a consensus was noble and much needed on this important issue"!

The problem, of course, is that Sagan (and the Editors) attempt to build a consensus based on misrepresentations!

It is little wonder then that even today writers such as van den

Haag, Sagan and Singleton make the inference, assumed by many lay people, that human development passes through developmental stages of such lesser organisms as a worm, reptile, or a pig. The tragedy of this axiom really has been that it was obviated 38 years prior to 1866 by publication of the laws of Von Baer (1828). He stated, correctly, that developmental stages of higher organisms simply *resembled* the developmental or embryonic stages of lesser organisms. This means that the developmental stages of all vertebrates are simply similar, and that development follows an established plan, the basics of which are repeated from one species to the next. It also means that the differences between vertebrates as one ascends through the evolutionary tree are rather small, but one does not need to see major or extensive changes in order to distinguish between closely related species. For example, recently Morris Goodman of Wayne State University has shown that the DNA sequences of hemoglobin from humans and chimpanzees is approximately 98.4% identical. This is not really surprising to embryologists. That small 1.6% difference makes *all* the difference. And it is small differences which account for the uniqueness among closely related species.

•Viability

The third topic which I considered in my manuscript and which had fallen prey to the political aspects of the abortion controversy was *viability*. Roe v. Wade, decided in 1973, tentatively established the quality of *personhood* for the developing human in terms of its *viability*, which the Supreme Court defined as that time of development at which the fetus, if born, would survive. The Court indicated survivability had been recorded at 24 weeks post-fertilization. To the human embryologist, and which should be of even more significance to obstetricians, is the fact that viability is really no landmark at all for establishing the rights or equal protection under the law for a newly born "person". The reason for this is that if a fetus is born prematurely its quality of life may be compromised and this becomes less secure the earlier the birth. Indeed, in terms of its biological well-being, a full term fetus is far better off than being born at 24 weeks. Cases are on record in which born fetuses have survived, as early as 22 weeks post fertilization. Normally, a fetus born at this time, even though its subsequent care is given through an incubator, chemical additive treatments or intubation to assist its breathing, and the best nursing attendants available, its long term survival may be seriously in jeopardy and the quality of its survival is correspondingly diminished. Viability as such would be important to a pro-life advocacy since Roe v. Wade indicated that in the case of survival the fetus born at any specific time would enjoy equal protection of the law. Therefore the pro-life advocacy would prefer to see as early a birth as possible to which they could point and indicate that subsequent to that time, if it be 22 weeks or even earlier, no abortions should be allowed. But, to the human embryologist the use of viability to assign civil rights or civil protection to a born fetus is at best disingenuous and at worst a bogus issue. The quality of survival was never considered by the Roe court.

However, it was discussed in the Webster case, and the "viability" concept was reaffirmed. Blackmun stated in the Roe case that the compelling point of the state's interest in the fetus was that of "viability" and that this was so because: "the fetus then presumably has the capability of *meaningful* (sic) life outside the mother's womb"!

Blackmun references Dorland's 24th Medical Dictionary in defining *viability*, which is stated as: "can live after birth" and "capable of living outside the uterus". *Meaningful* is Blackmun's word, not Dorland's.

One must ask *meaningful* to whom? If the fetus has its say it would stay in the womb until it was full term, and prior to the court's *viability* the fetus and embryo would, of course, be carefully and methodically developing for the purpose of being born at term!

One of the more specious notions growing out of the "viability" concept is the added nonsense of capable of living (outside the womb) "on its own". This is deliberately deceitful, because not even a full term baby can "survive on its own". It needs more care than when in the womb.

• *The concept of sentience*

The fourth topic in the manuscript was devoted towards *sentience*. This term from time to time has had different definitions. However, the generally accepted definition has been, and is, "awareness of one's self". This term is not derived from any aspect of human embryology, but rather it appears it was derived from the field of psychology. Clifford Grobstein, a developmental biologist, but not a human embryologist, seized upon this term and related it to thought. Interviewed by Psychology Today in 1989 he presented six essential aspects of individuality. He related them to specific stages or times of development. *Psychic individuality*, he claimed, occurred at 26 weeks even though he admitted this was arbitrary. He identified this with sentience or thought. Sagan and Druyan in their article in <u>Parade</u> similarly claimed that sentience or "thought" occurred at 30 weeks of development post-fertilization. Likewise, van den Haag, in his article, implied that at the time of so-called sentience the brain or neural system dispensed awareness. One can only speculate at this kind of relationship. There are no definitive or conclusive data which would support the onset of thought in a human fetus. The tracings from electroencephalograms (EEGs) do not show "thought". Rather, the only conclusion we can draw, particularly in testing the neural activity in a fetus, is the reflection of "alertness of neurons". Thought is a concept and needs an historical component. No fetuses or infants relate that and, indeed, no infants can be interviewed so as to provide an historical record of having expressed thoughts which could be associated with any bodily actions or movements. Grobstein's stages are arbitrary and there is no scientific basis for them. In fact, <u>all</u> so-called *stages* are arbitrary and are important to only embryologists and obstetricians in the taxonomic sense. This is because all of development subsequent to initial contact of sperm and oocyte under conditions which we have come to understand as normal, is a *fait accompli*. All of development, therefore, is part of the *continuum* of human life. Sentience is not a topic taught in basic embryology courses by embryologists. Newborns do not respond to vocal commands. Therefore whether or not thought is part of the expressions of a newborn infant is moot and specious. Neonatologists who are used to producing and interpreting EEGs from newborns will admit to the many difficulties in interpreting the wave patterns. Usually there is a problem of background noise plus the lack of symmetry on the tracing patterns, and the irregularities involved in those patterns are normally reflecting what is called anarchy. A correlated and symmetrical tracing only gradually appears in electroencephalograms as development, post-birth, and maturing eventually occur.

The Rejections

This then was the substance of the manuscript which I had prepared in rebuttal to van den Haag's article in <u>National Review</u> and which was summarily rejected by Assistant Editor Cunningham. The manuscript was then submitted in succession to both lay and scientific publications, including abbreviated versions to newspapers. In each case the substantive portions of the manuscript which I have just described were kept intact. However, the format and style was changed, although not significantly, according to the journal or media source to which I submitted it for consideration.

Over the course of the next three years this manuscript was submitted to 13 lay publications and 5 scientific publications, each time being rejected and in virtually every case never submitted for review.

Following the rejection by <u>National Review</u> I wrote to <u>Reader's Digest</u> and as per their instructions received by telephone I included in my letter a brief description of the manuscript and why I had written it. I then asked if they would be interested in the article. Their reply included the following sentence: "After careful consideration we have decided your material would not work as an original article in <u>Reader's Digest</u>." They went on to say that most of their articles "are prepared on assignment by staff writers or *regular contributors* to the magazine." Next, I submitted it to the <u>Atlantic</u>. Their reply was "I am afraid one of the two articles on abortion we just published, *though different from the piece you propose,* must preclude us from taking up the subject again for some while." Following this, I sent the manuscript to <u>New Republic</u>, <u>Family Circle</u>, and <u>The Saturday Evening Post</u>. Rejections followed each of these submissions even though the <u>New Republic</u> and <u>Family Circle</u> had previously published articles on abortion with false and misleading statements about human development. <u>Family Circle</u> replied that the manuscript "just isn't right for us". <u>The New Republic</u> replied with a form letter of rejection. The <u>Saturday Evening Post</u>, even though it is the official organ of the Benjamin Franklin Literary and Medical Society was similarly not interested. Their form letter of rejection included the comment "we feel this article is inappropriate for our readership". During this time I rewrote and reduced the manuscript in size so that it would conform to a newspaper Op-Ed piece. I then sent it to the Los Angeles Times, the New York Times, the Chicago Tribune, and the Arizona Republic. Each Op-Ed editor quickly rejected the article. I wrote another abbreviated form concentrating only on the origin of life and sent it to the Arizona Daily Star, which, to my surprise, published it. Subsequently I condensed all four of the topics within this manuscript to the format of another newspaper Op-Ed piece and submitted it to the Tucson Citizen, which published it. But the larger manuscript was still in limbo and I was still having great problems getting it accepted for publication. I submitted it to The New England Journal of Medicine as an unsolicited editorial opinion or special article, and, specifically, it went to the desk of Marcia Angell, M.D., Executive Editor. Apparently, it remained on her desk for approximately six weeks. Within that time I had attempted to call the Journal office and requested information as to the disposition of that manuscript. Finally, during the sixth week and after the fifth phone call I succeeded in talking to Dr. Angell about the manuscript. She had not sent it out for review and she had rejected it. The conversation went like this:

> Angell: *If facts are misstated they don't necessarily have or those misstatements don't necessarily have any implications for an argument that involves a value judgement as the abortion argument does - and we are just not going to publish something on this issue that really using facts or not using facts or correcting facts or putting facts in a different perspective . . .*
> Me: *You are an M.D.?*
> Angell: *Yes*
> Me: *Do you believe in the biological basis for the practice of medicine?*
> Angell: *What are you talking about?*
> Me: *If a surgeon intervenes in a uterus to remove an embryo or a fetus it seems to me that surgeon ought to know whether or not whatever is being removed is alive, and whatever . . .*
> Angell: (talkover) *Why?*
> Me: *. . . whatever is being removed whether or not it is human!*
> Angell: *Why? Why does he have to know that?*
> Me: *If you want to question that - why wouldn't you*

want to question elements in the Hippocratic Oath . . .
for example, do no harm?
Angell: *I would!*

The New England Journal of Medicine publishes routinely on
the subject of abortion, *in vitro* fertilization, fetal tissue research and
other socio-legal issues, as well as social policies. A cursory review of
the table of contents of The New England Journal of Medicine over the
past several years will confirm these facts. Following this rejection I
next sent the manuscript to Perspectives in Biology and Medicine.
Again, the manuscript lay on the desk of the Editor, Richard Landau,
for approximately six weeks. I eventually was able to talk to him on
the telephone at which time he admitted the manuscript had not been
sent out for review and told me "two's enough". I inquired of him what
that meant since I knew of only one article in his journal published on
abortion and that was by Rivers Singleton, Jr. I reminded him of
several errors that Singleton had made in that paper, which I was trying
to correct on the basis of factual and scientific knowledge in human
embryology. Landau informed me that there was another manuscript
that had been accepted for publication and would be published within
the next several issues of the journal. Further, in the course of the
conversation he said: "You should know that I am pro-abortion.
Violently so!" Recognizing the futility of any further discussion I
simply requested the return of the manuscript copies. I also discovered
that Clifford Grobstein was, at that time, a member of the editorial
board of Perspectives in Biology and Medicine. The second
manuscript Landau referred to, that eventually was published in his
journal, indeed, concerned abortion and the abortion controversy and
was a very pro-abortion article in which the author, Robert T. Muller, a
psychologist, justified abortion on the basis that our society executes
convicted criminals and therefore the paradigm for killing was already
embedded in our society (1991. In Defense of Abortion: Issues of
Pragmatism Regarding the Institutionalization of Killing. Perspectives
in Biology and Medicine, 34:315-325). This is at best a bizarre way to
look at the justification for abortion. But, Muller was prophetic! On
April 13, 1991, Judge Michael J. Noonan delivered a wholly odious
opinion in the State of New Jersey vs. Alexander Loce *et al.* It seems
Loce and friends were found guilty of trespassing while protesting
around and about an abortion clinic in the effort to prevent the abortion

of an embryo, which he had fathered. Noonan's decision included: "Roe v. Wade is still the law of the land and this court is bound by it. Therefore, I find that the 8 week fetus (sic) in this case was a living human being that was *legally executed* (sic) pursuant to the United States Supreme Court decision in Roe v. Wade." Is this what we now should be teaching in classes of Human Embryology? Incidentally, the judge erred in identifying the 8 week *embryo* as a fetus.

Noonan was simply amplifying what the Supreme Court had already decided. Brennan, for example, has publicly stated his position on the death penalty for born adults: "the best way in which we choose who will die reveals the depth of moral commitment among the living." (Are not the embryo and the fetus living?) Blackmun, when interviewed on 3 December, 1993, by Ted Koppel on the death penalty, said his concerns, with regard to equal protection, are: "the disturbing statistics that come in when one considers race"! Moral posturing by the likes of Justices Brennan and Blackmun are out of character. Obviously, Blackmun is not concerned when considering age, e.g. up to 24 weeks after conception. It is apparent that these two Justices would drown if caught in the shallow waters of moral outrage.

I then sent the manuscript to BioScience, the official publication of the American Institute of Biological Sciences. Again, it was rejected without review. The Editor, Julie Anne Miller, included a comment in the cover letter stating that a returned copy contained reviewer comments. In fact, there were three comments, only, written on the manuscript, two of which were corrected typos, and did not constitute a *bonafide* review. The third comment concerned my correction of the fact that Singleton in his article in Perspectives had inferred that the human embryo displayed gill slits and a tail. In my manuscript I corrected that by indicating that gill slits never appear in humans, and the embryos never display a tail, but that, unfortunately, the caudal area is referred to as a tail *process*. The so-called reviewer for BioScience had written after that sentence "snide, again". After receiving the manuscript back from Dr. Miller and BioScience, I wrote to her that one comment written in a phrase on one copy of my manuscript did not constitute a *bonafide* review. I requested a copy of a review commentary and that not being available I requested that the manuscript be reconsidered and this time sent out for a real review. I never received a reply from her. Following this I retitled the manuscript to: "In Defense of Human Development" and submitted it to Issues in Science and Technology, then to Policy Review. Again, it was summarily rejected in both cases. Next, the manuscript went to Pharos, which is the official publication of the Alpha Omega Alpha Honor Medical Society. Their reply, another rejection, included the following comments: "We have had this paper for a much longer time than in the case with other manuscripts. The delay in our getting back to you reflects the fact that there was considerable debate among the various members of the Editorial Board to whom we sent the paper regarding its suitability for publication. Everyone agreed that the paper was well written and it obviously deals with a topic of importance in our current society. Taking into account the pros and cons, however, I regret to say that we have come out on the side of not accepting the paper."

To date, not a single *major* publication, lay or scientific, has published any article correcting the plethora of false statements about human development which have burdened the literature for the past 15 or more years. I next sent the manuscript to the Western Journal of Medicine. The letter of rejection included the following statement: "It is the policy of the Western Journal of Medicine to send (to the author) any available comments from the board's reviewers. This is intended to assist authors to rework manuscripts before submitting them to another publication." Rubber stamped in bold black letters at the bottom of this letter were the words "No comments received". This Journal returned my manuscript with the letter of rejection within 10 days.

I also sent the manuscript to Human Life Review, but again it was returned with a brief cover letter indicating that it was essentially "inappropriate" for publication in Human Life Review, but one year later an article appeared on abortion with a somewhat romanticized approach. Thus, in all, this manuscript, essentially, was rejected, in one form or another, a total of eighteen (18) times.

A Second Manuscript

While I was struggling to get this manuscript published a paper appeared in The Kennedy Institute of Ethics Journal. It was the lead article in the very first issue of this journal, authored by Richard A. McCormick, a Jesuit priest. The title of the article was "Who or What is the Pre-Embryo?" In this article the Reverend McCormick called for a reconsideration of the time for ensoulment based upon Grobstein's so-called stage of *developmental individuality*. In essence, this "stage" was described as that point after which the embryonic mass could no longer divide and form a copy or multiple copies (twins or multiple identical individuals). This would be a time from 5 to 6 days and perhaps up to 14 days post-fertilization. The fallacy of this definition lies in the facts that monozygotic twins occur in only 10 of every 2700 live births, and at least 30% of all monozygotic twins (arising from one fertilized oocyte), occur within the first two or three mitotic cell divisions post-fertilization. Still further, the origin of monozygotic twinning is not known. It does not appear to be familial in origin, and therefore, is not predictable. Therefore, if ensoulment were to be withheld until after the inner cell mass stage, assuming that one could indeed tell at that stage that twinning had occurred, it would be withheld for approximately every 385 individuals until 1 had been determined. It seems this would constitute a major problem in ethics, especially for any religion or church.

The editorial Statement of <u>The Kennedy Institute of Ethics Journal</u> states that it "publishes opinion and analysis dealing with social, ethical, and public policy aspects of bioethics and related areas of 'applied' ethics. It presents varied points of view and *encourages open debate of critical issues*." Encouraged by this lofty and noble objective I wrote a reply to McCormick's article and submitted it to the Journal.

•The story of the preembryo

In this article I reviewed all of the previous and contemporary textbooks used in human embryology, none of which used the term *pre-embryo*. It appears that this term, *per se*, was conceived by Clifford Grobstein in a 1979 article from Scientific American. It is most unfortunate that the newest, fifth edition (1993), of Keith Moore's textbook <u>The Developing Human</u> uses the term *pre-embryo*. However, Moore uses the term in a contradictory way. In subsequent correspondence which I have had with Keith Moore protesting the use of this term in his text, he replied that he understood the objection and offered to remove it for the next subsequent printing of that text. There has never been a historical record of the use of that term. Indeed, the renowned dean of human embryology, Bradley Patten, used the term *embryo* for every stage subsequent to the fertilized ovum (zygote). Further, the author of a new textbook, Human Embryology And Teratology, Ronan O'Rahilly, indexes the term *pre-embryo* but this is what he states in his text in a footnote: "The ill defined and inaccurate term pre-embryo which includes the embryonic disk is said either to end with the appearance of the permanent streak or (in the *Nomina Embryologica*) to include neurulation. The term is not used in this book." While it is true that the current issue of *Nomina Embryologica*, the taxonomy of language for human embryology, does not *per se* use the term *pre-embryo*, it does use as a heading <u>pre-embryonic period</u>. <u>Pre-embryonic period</u> implies a period of the <u>pre-embryo</u>. Because Keith Moore is currently a member of the nomenclature committee for the American Association of Anatomists, and a member of the committee on nomenclature for human embryology, I wrote to him in protest about the inclusion of the term *pre-embryo* in the third edition of *Nomina Embryologica*. His reply to me was: "The term pre-embryo does not appear in the third edition of *Nomina Embryologica*. This is at best disingenuous because, as stated above, there is no difference between the terms pre-embryonic and pre-embryo. In correspondence with Dr. O'Rahilly inquiring as to how this term found its way into *Nomina Embryologica*, Dr. O'Rahilly replied that he did not know and that even though he was a member of the International Anatomical Nomenclature Embryology subcommittee and a human embryologist, he was never solicited for his opinion. Then, how did "pre-embryonic" become incorporated into the current *Nomina Embryologica* nomenclature? Perhaps, a statement at the beginning of the manual (page ix) may provide a clue: "1985 Twelfth International Congress of anatomists in London: Discussions at this *and thereafter* led to the present . . . *Nomina Embryologica*"! Looking at the list of members of the last committee for *Nomina Embryologica* this membership was comprised of individuals the world over. It may be that very few of these individuals were human embryologists. Indeed, Moore's text is the first one to include the term *pre-embryo*. However, predating this is a book advertised *"for course consideration*: <u>Embryo Experimentation,</u> (subtitled): Ethical, Legal and Social Issues" (1992, Cambridge University Press). It is edited by six faculty members from the Monash University Centre for Human Bioethics (Australia). Interestingly, the senior editor, Peter Singer has authored other books including, *Practical Ethics, Marx, and Should the Baby Live?* This book uses the term *pre-embryo* liberally, and advocates *continuing* "human pre-embryo research". Included are recommended guidelines on embryo experimentation. How can one avoid the feeling that the fox is running the chicken coop? Political correctness, deceit and fraud have found their way into the science of human embryology.

The term *preembryo* in on the verge of having wide popular acceptance. On a February 4th, 1994 CNN broadcast of Sonya Live, which discussed genetic testing of *in vitro* fertilized embryos, Dr. William Gibbons, a Gynecologic surgeon from Eastern Virginia Medical College in Norfolk, Virginia, defended the term *preembryo* and freely (and without interruption) defined early stages of human development using such terms as <u>trophoblast</u>, etc.

But, when a bioethecist, Dr. Diane Irving, protested, declaring the term *preembryo* a myth and attempting to use the identical terminology in her rebuttal as Dr. Gibbons had used, she was abruptly interrupted by Sonya, who declared such scientific terms as unsuitable for her listening audience.

Currently, the National Institutes of Health are holding hearings on proposals involving *in vitro* fertilization of donor ova. Of course, a significant amount of testimony is centering on the unethical and immoral use of zygotes, which some witnesses regard as allowable based on the early developmental stages as not constituting the new individual, thus, a *preembryo*.

More Rejection, Then Finally Acceptance

In spite of the stated objective to publish articles on both sides of an issue, <u>The Kennedy Institute for Ethics Journal</u> rejected my manuscript without review. I protested to the Editor, Renee Shapiro, and subsequently she apparently did seek a kind of review which, again, as in the instance of <u>BioScience</u>, came back with a handwritten comment on a manuscript copy that I was "fossilized". The scientific data in this manuscript was not reviewed and not commented upon. I then sent this manuscript to <u>Cross Currents</u>, the official organ of the Association for Religion and Intellectual Life (ARIL), College of New Rochelle (New York). Again, the manuscript was rejected without review and without comments.

Finally, I sent both manuscripts to The Linacre Quarterly, the editor of which is John P. Mullooly, M.D. The Linacre Quarterly accepted both and eventually they were published. The first one, "In Defense of Human Development" appeared in the November 1992 issue, volume 59, number 4, pages 58-76. The second manuscript: "Human Development and Reconsideration of Ensolement" appeared in the February 1993 issue, volume 60, number 1 pages 57-63.

The problems of publishing the truth about human development are not just manifest in the difficulties related here. They can also be observed in some subsequent events, for example, in attempting to deliver the history of these rejections at a recent conference sponsored by the Journal of the American Medical Association which took place in Chicago in September, 1993. When I was informed that there was to be a conference sponsored by the JAMA in Chicago in September of 1993 on *Peer Review*, which would be the perfect forum to relate the problems described above, I wrote to the organizer of that conference, Dr. Drummond Rennie, but, at the same time I called the Chicago office of the JAMA and made an inquiry about the meeting. I was told by Cheryl Manno, the person assigned to collate the abstracts and send them out for review that "We are still sending abstracts out for review." I then asked, if that is the case may I fax to her an abstract of the paper I would like to deliver from the podium. She said yes. I wrote the abstract and faxed it that afternoon and she confirmed by telephone the next morning that she indeed had received the abstract. The abstract I faxed was essentially the history of rejections including biased statements by some editors of the article on the misuse and false statements of the known science of human embryology within the abortion controversy. I waited several days and received a reply of my original letter to Drummond Rennie, the organizer of the conference, who said in the letter that the program had already been established and to allow me on the program would mean bumping someone off. I found Rennie's letter to be disconcerting since I had been told that abstracts were still being sent out for review.[*]
I wrote him back indicating that I had been told that the program had

---

[*]Even more disconcerting is the fact that Dr. Rennie has recently been appointed to a newly formed commission on Research Integrity by HHS Secretary Donna Shalala.

not yet been put together and asked him to reconsider. He replied and again refused my request, but did not reply to my claim that I had been told the program had not yet been established. It was interesting to me in the meantime to have received a flyer on the program to see the various sessions scheduled for the program and the names of the session chairmen. It was no small observation to me to see that the session to which my abstract would have been sent and in which I would have delivered my presentation was chaired by none other than Marcia Angell, the Executive Editor of the New England Journal of Medicine. If the abstract I faxed to the JAMA office had, indeed, been sent to review, it would seem logical that Dr. Angell would have reviewed it.

The First Casualty Of The Cultural War

I believe Patrick Buchanan is right when he stated at the Republican National Convention in 1992 that "our society is engaged in a cultural war". I also believe that the first and most significant casualty of this war has been, and continues to be the human embryo and human fetus. This casualty is not dead but severely wounded. Only total care and treatment with every resource in the armamentarium of truth can bring this wounded soldier back to full and vibrant life.

Human embryology is a subject which is fast becoming incorporated into daily communication, but in a distorted "New Wave" form. It is not well understood by the lay public because the truth has not been given to them. But it is not just the lay public which has trouble interpreting the facts or science of human development. One can find this kind of problem within medical students (as well as physicians, e.g. Holly Galland). For example, a third year medical student called in to an afternoon radio talk show on KNST, Tucson Arizona, on April 17, 1993 in which he made the following statement: "In the emergency room, we pronounce a person dead when the heart stops beating, I would like to propose we just reverse that, that life begins when the heart starts beating." Clearly, there is a problem here, not just in communication, but in education, particularly that of medical students.

119

The College of Medicine at the University of Arizona, and many other medical schools, does not offer a credit achieving course in human embryology to the medical students. It never has. When it had been proposed in the past to do this, the curriculum committee rejected the proposal on the basis that it would provide one more course with a potential failing mark for the medical student, which they were loath to do. We now know the importance of knowledge about human embryology and it's relevancy in such profound elective social pursuits such as *in vitro* fertilization, abortion, fetal tissue research, human embryo research, *in utero* fetal surgery and fetal farming. It should be incumbent upon every medical school in this country to provide a thoroughly grounded course in human embryology to medical students. It should further be the mission of every school or college of medicine in the United States to provide a service of education concerning human development with the lay public through seminars, public lectures and forums and through published communications by appropriate news services. Only in this way are we going to alert the lay public to the gravity of the condition of our wounded casualty in this cultural war. It is not an easy task, particularly when the ground work has been laid to obviate many of the scientific facts known about human embryology for the sake of political correctness (PC) and expediency. One such example of PC lies in the fact that many medical schools, the University of Arizona included, no longer require their graduates to take the Hippocratic Oath. Rather, a modified Hippocratic oath or a substitute oath is given to the graduates, or at least offered as an alternative to the traditional Hippocratic Oath. One of these alternatives is called the Oath of Lasagna. In this oath the reference to abortion has been removed, which is incorporated in the Hippocratic Oath. In the Oath of Lasgna it is stated *"It may also be within my power to take a life, this awesome responsibility must be faced with great humbleness and awareness of my own frailty."* This is more politically correct and in tune with our times, apparently, although in direct contradiction to everything that is taught in medical school to the student. It seems paradoxical in view of the fact that the prevailing concept taught in medicine today is that the human fetus is a second patient.

This is where science has been clearly separated from the law. The "second patient" is recognized medically from the point of diagnosis of pregnancy, but the court (Roe v. Wade) only recognizes it at 24 weeks post-fertilization. Why is this so? The legal "choice" pundits say the rights of the mother cannot be superseded. Why? Why are not the rights of the mother and that of the conceived at least equivalent? After all, the mother is no longer living for one, but for two, and a good mother will, no doubt, sacrifice habits and conduct to effect proper care of the "second patient". Some states have already prosecuted pregnant alcoholic or cocaine addicted mothers for abuse in cases where there have been compromising effects (which are permanent) on the fetus or newborn. The Supreme Court decisions, indirectly, do not support the states' caveats.

The embryo and early fetus are exceedingly small, cannot protest or produce an outwardly recognizable sign that they are in danger, and, therefore, cannot signal to third parties that something is threatening or wrong. In the final distillation of the Court's (and other's) decision can be found the answer to *WHY?*: *It is a matter of arrogance!*, a characterization to which the court (and others) would be loathe to admit.

Quid Sit Veritas?

This chronicle is a revelation of the attempts to bring scientific knowledge of human development before the public, which has been exposed (and still is) to an excess of misrepresentations. Generally, it has been the case that the truths within science have been sought and revealed by those who know the subject best. Sadly, this has not been true in the case of human development. Political imperatives have allowed other than human embryologists to speak for human embryology and to gain credibility through acceptance by the media.

Science in its purest form is the pursuit of truth, and repeated confirmations, over time, can produce absolute truths. But, truth is often obscured by relevancy. To be politically correct in our present time one often is driven to qualify the truth and declare that there are no absolutes. In the absence of absolutes, quality and status become arbitrary, and value can be redefined at will. The consequence of this to human embryology is that the value of the human embryo is now being reduced to the surgeon's instrument and the research bench.

Nevertheless, no amount of revisionism can obscure the fact that one of the great absolute truths is that LIFE has been a gift, provided in virtual perpetuity in the form of a *continuum* renewed through a system called reproduction, which is the *essence* of life.

> *"All truths pass through three stages.*
> *First, they are ridiculed; second, they are*
> *violently opposed; third, they are accepted as*
> *being self evident."*
>
> *- - - Arthur Schopenauer (Philosopher)*

Addendum

A Brief Journey Through the Home of
Human Embryology: Human Anatomy

I have been a long time member of the American Association of Anatomists. Through the years of their annual meetings their programs often have included sessions on the History of Anatomy. In the spring of 1994 I conceived the idea to organize a Symposium on The History of Human Embryology, and attended the annual meeting in Anaheim, California in order to propose such a Symposium to the incoming President, Charles Slonecker. I met with Slonecker and issued my verbal proposal on the basis that Human Embryology was in danger of losing its base in Human Anatomy because the language of Human Embryology was being preempted by Developmental Biology. A case in point is the "preembryo", conceived specifically for the human embryo by an amphibian embryologist, Clifford Grobstein. Slonecker agreed the term was at least "unfortunate".

He was sympathetic but wanted to make sure the proposed symposium would not be used as a political forum. I assured him it would not be, that my interest was in reclaiming the correct and true science.

Slonecker advised me to write him the proposal (for the next year's April meeting) by summer (sometime before the end of July) and include the topics I would plan. He would submit the proposal to the Executive committee for a decision.

I did that, and had tentatively obtained speakers in three areas:
1. the history of early embryology
2. a comparison of the characteristics of human embryology, obtained through traditional studies, with *in vitro* fertilization procedures, and
3. the history of development of the brain and nervous system, including the validity of studies involving electroencephalograms on fetuses, (or, as some have claimed, on embryos) and the concepts of "sentience" and "brain birth".

I also had intended to find another speaker on the history of the fetus as a "second patient".

This was submitted to Slonecker in early July, and despite a follow up letter requesting a reply, I never received any response from Slonecker. In mid-October I requested intercession from a friend of mine who was an officer of the Association. Slonecker then called and simply said he would submit my proposal. But, by that time the Symposia had already been selected and their schedule published and distributed to the Association.

Needless to say, it seemed there had not been any intention to accept my proposal and it further appeared that the gravity of the situation with human embryology never really registered with Slonecker. As expected, a letter of denial followed shortly thereafter.

One may explain this sequence of events in procedural terms according to the traditional workings of a scientific society. On the other hand, it ought to be clear that the problems of exhibiting the truth concerning human embryology are significantly compounded by the pusillanimous regard to a profound component of the moral crisis in our culture, even within the structure of the very body (American Association of Anatomists) which ought to set right the heart of the problem: the true science!

SECTION TWO: THE PHILOSOPHY

From the foregoing accounts, it is clear that for many years much of the "science" published concerning the early development of the human being is scientifically erroneous. Incorrect human embryology (and other science) has been used for years by scientists, philosophers, bioethicists and theologians as their starting points to determine different arguments about the "moral status" of the early human embryo and fetus. Obviously, if their scientific starting points are incorrect, then their conclusions about the moral status or ethical treatment of these developing human beings are automatically incorrect as well, regardless of which philosophical system they use. It is doubly fallacious when the "philosophy" used is also incorrect.

It is important to understand the proper connection between science and ethics. "What" something is, or its "nature" (natural philosophy and philosophical anthropology) will determine to a large extent how we "ought" to treat it (philosophical ethics). If one questions, for example, whether or not it is ethical to use living human embryos or fetuses in destructive experimental research, the answer in large measure depends on "what" the living human embryo or fetus is. Obviously, if it is a cabbage or a frog, or just skin cells, then one's answer to the ethical question would be quite different than if it is a human being. That there is such an integral connection between science and ethics is just common sense and common practice.

The question as to when the life of a human being begins is a scientific question; when a "person" begins is a philosophical question. In the substantially updated article, "Scientific and Philosophical Expertise: An Evaluation of the Arguments on 'Personhood'", the author analyzes the accuracy of both the science and the philosophy used by many in bioethics who argue for "delayed personhood." Rather than acknowledge the scientific fact that at fertilization a new, unique, individual human being exists, they incorporate inaccurate "scientific claims" into their philosophical or bioethical theories, to argue that until some later biological marker event during human embryogenesis there is no human being existing as yet. Or similarly they will argue that maybe there is a human being, but there is no human "person" there as yet. In other words, they conceptually make a "split" between a human being and a human person, in effect rendering early human embryos and fetuses merely "pre-embryos," "pre-persons," or "possible" or "potential" persons. This in turn allows them to argue for a "delayed" ethical and legal status for human embryos and fetuses. In fact, many bioethicists, such as Peter Singer, Helga Kuhse, Steven Buckle, Michael Tooley, R.M. Hare and Tristram Englehardt, use their bioethics theories of "delayed personhood" to argue for the moral permissibility of the infanticide of normal, healthy human infants and young children. Richard Frey extends Singer's argument on abortion to suggest that mentally retarded human beings (as well as other handicapped human beings) are not "persons" and should be substituted for the higher primate animals (who are persons) in destructive experimental research—only one of many logical extensions of the "philosophy" used.

In analyzing these arguments, the author finds that, in virtually every case, incorrect science is used, and that none of the conclusions follow logically from their premises. Furthermore, the philosophical or bioethical theories used to determine the "moral status" or "personhood" of the early human embryo and fetus are either historically wrong, or so theoretically compromised that one has to wonder why any *bonafide* philosopher, having studied the history of philosophy would every want to use them. Theories about "delayed personhood" are not a function of science, but rather are conceptual "artifacts" derived from philosophy and bioethics. Such theories need to be rigorously evaluated and defended – not just simply posited and accepted. The philosophical and bioethical theories being used to determine the "moral status" and "personhood" of developing human beings are refuted and rejected by the author.

It is to be stressed that regardless of one's position on abortion or on the "personhood" of the early human embryo or fetus, those scientifically and philosophically deficient and invalid concepts of "delayed personhood" are transferable and applicable to millions of adult human populations - rendering them "non-persons" too. Just as scientists must be the ones to correct the scientific misinformation in their own fields, philosophers, especially bioethicists, need to take a hard look at the quality of their own literature, and do the same.

A further source of philosophical misinformation is the claim that there are certain ethical theories which are somehow "neutral", and therefore useful in our "pluralistic" democratic society. But there is really no such thing as a "neutral" ethics, including "utilitarianism," relativism, consensus ethics and communitarianism. In the second article, "Which Ethics for Science and Public Policy?", the author addresses specifically the scholarly quality and defensibility of certain ethical theories which are being used by many in medicine, biomedical research and public policy. Of particular concern are the recent theories of bioethics, especially that theory known as "principlism" (otherwise known as the "Belmont Principles", or the "Georgetown mantra" of principles - autonomy, beneficience, non-maleficience and justice). These "neutral" bioethics principles were originally developed by the National Commission for the Protection of Human Subjects ... "of Biomedical and Behavioral Research (The Belmont Report, 1978)", and subsequently passed on to various other private and governmental public policy documents, as will be noted in our following section. These bioethics principles have been used almost exclusively for years to determine what is "ethical" or not, particularly in the fields of clinical medicine, biomedical research, and public policy.

In the preface to a recent book highly critical of "principlism", it is interesting that Albert Jonsen, one of the originators of these principles, reported that, having abandoned their traditional philosophical disciplines, they and others on the National Commission in effect made up these "ethical principles." Even Daniel Callahan, the long-time Director of the Hastings Center which has fostered and elaborated "principlism" for over 25 years, has admitted recently in his publications that "principlism doesn't work" and should be abandoned. Although some good has come of their use, there is an ever-growing body of literature that is very critical of "principlism," both here and abroad. But ideas have consequences when applied, and extensive damage has already been done through their application. Despite the rising tide of criticism and the recognition that these "ethical principles" are no longer valid, they continue to determine the basic premises for "what is

127

ethical" in many other fields and in may public policy regulations, guidelines and decisions – nationally and internationally.

The burning question is: if these "ethical principles" are now invalid, then wouldn't all documents and public policy decisions based on them be invalid as well?

Scientific and Philosophical Expertise: An Evaluation of the Arguments On "Personhood"

Dianne N. Irving, M.A., Ph.D.

I. Introduction

All too often lately we hear or read the lament, "We just don't or can't know what a human being or a human person really is", or, "There just is no consensus or agreement on what the definition of a "human being" or a "human person" is, so why should one person's or one group's definition be preferred over any other. The definition of a "human being" or of a "human person" just cannot be objectively determined, and so must remain a relative one."

The aim of this paper is to debunk these current myths concerning the relativism of what a human being or a human person is, and to at least raise the question at the end of how these "myths" came about even at the level of scientific and philosophical professional "expertise". What I will argue is that we can and do have an objective and empirically-based definition of a human being and a human person, and that, other than conceptually, one cannot really split a human being from a human person. "Personhood" begins when the human being begins - at fertilization.

Toward this end I will address some of the kinds of major scientific and philosophical arguments used to support the sudden appearance of "personhood" at different biological "marker events", indicating that such arguments are arbitrarily grounded on scientific data which is incorrect or misapplied; and that the philosophical claims of these arguments are arbitrarily grounded in systems of philosophy which are themselves very problematic, as any historian of philosophy well knows,[1] with highly indefensible definitions of a "human being" or of a "human person". Such definitions are actually remnants of those philosophical systems in which conceptual mind/body splits are still sustained, even today. It is important to understand that the question of "personhood" is not simply restricted to some wild-eyed academic's preferred theoretical ramblings, but that the issue has now been translated into the quite practical question of whether or not these "tiny" human beings are as protected ethically, socially and legally as are more "mature" human beings. The really "burning" question is: if the early human embryo is a human *being*, is it also a human *person*?

II. General scientific and philosophical background of the issues

Before addressing the specifics of the science and philosophy, some general charts are provided for an over-all view of the issues. Only a few of the major marker events will be covered, as the actual list is quite long. I refer you, however, to my own analysis of 26 arguments which goes into much greater detail.

Fig. 1 indicates some of the suggested biological marker events during embryological development - from just before fertilization to about 14-days.[2] During this period the major philosophical issues include whether the early human embryo is an individual (a prerequisite for personhood), and/or if he/she actually possesses the genetic or formal capacity of a human being or human person. It is during this period also when mass-confusion reigns on the philosophical misuse of the terms "possibility", "probability", "potentiality" and "potency". These positions are generally arguing for either the actual *capacity* for, or the actual *exercising* of either "rational attributes" or "sentience".

Daly[3] represents the type of argument which claims that "personhood" begins at the time when the sperm has penetrated the ovum. Examples of positions arguing for "fertilization" are my own, or Ashley and O'Rourke[4] (although within the advocates of "fertilization", much ambiguity exists as to which point during the process of fertilization itself "personhood" begins). Suarez[5] will argue for the 2-cell stage. And a great deal of the current literature consists of arguments for the 14-day stage.[6] In these latter arguments a general distinction can be made between those which contain elements concerning the pre-condition for the exercising of so-called "rational attributes" - e.g., self-awareness, self-consciousness, interaction with the environment, etc. - and those concerning the pre-condition for sentience, or the ability to feel pain or pleasure. For those unfamiliar with philosophy, let me just point out that such distinctions - as well as those that will follow - are grounded in different philosophical schools of thought.

130

Some of the suggested biological marker events range from 14-days and after, as indicated in Fig. 2.[7] During this period the major philosophical issues include: individuality, the biological substrate as the precondition for the capacity for "rational attributes", or for "sentience" - or for the actual exercising of those capacities. The full integration of those substrates and capacities are also at issue.

As noted, writers such as Bole[8] argue that individuality and ensoulment are not possible until after 2-6 weeks, whereas Singer and Wells[9] argue that only after 6 weeks is sentience possible. At 8 weeks Lockwood[10] argues for the beginning of "personal identity", and Shea[11] for that point where the brain actually controls bodily functions as a whole. Finally, there are those who focus not on the mere capacity but the actual integration and exercising of "rational attributes" and/or sentience as a condition for true personhood, such as Hare[12], Engelhardt[13] or Singer[14].

As these and similar distinctions made between a human being and a human person are really philosophical distinctions, I have sketched the major historical philosophical sources of a mind/body split in Fig. 3 (although one could go back to Plato and beyond).[15] The major point I want to indicate is that some philosophical schools of thought define a human being as *one* whole substance, and thus there is no mind/body split inherent in their theories. Such theories define a human being in terms of the actual nature of the human substance. Characteristics such as "rational attributes", sentience, moral autonomy, etc., are only activities of powers which are of secondary consideration, because they are consequent to or follow upon the actual nature of that substance.[16] Other "schools" do maintain a mind/body split inherent in their theories; a human being is defined as *two* independent and separate substances. Interestingly, most of the theories addressed here are derivative of these modern philosophies, especially that of Descartes.[17]

An entire paper - or even a book - could be dedicated to explaining the theoretical and practical consequences of such mind/body splits, especially in the present context. Suffice it to point out that where there is such a split - where the mind (or even the whole "soul") is an independent substance in and of itself, separate or apart from the "body" (which is seen as an independent and separate substance in and of itself), then it is impossible either theoretically or biologically to "piece them back together again", as Humpty Dumpty might have said. Nor could one explain any interaction between these separate "substances" of mind and body. We can see the effect of such Cartesian dualism - and the consequent historical breaking-off to either rationalism or empiricism - in the distinctions writers make here between a human being and a human person.

III. Biological marker events of personhood

There are enumerable points along the continuum of embryological development at which different writers claim the appearance of so-called "personhood". These are claimed as "biological marker events of personhood" - before which there is only a human being (at best); and after which there is a human person. Before that biological point, then, the human embryo or human fetus is considered as only an "object", a "thing" which may be used or dealt with according to the personal objectives or desires of a human person. After that particular biological marker event we suddenly have a human person, who is now considered a "subject" or an entity deserving of protections against the interests, objectives or desires of another human person.

A. Fertilization as the beginning of personhood

In order to identify the major issue quickly, a few questions might be posed so as to clarify at the start exactly what is at stake when we define a human being or a human person in one way or another. If our definition is incorrect - even in part - then the consequences of this incorrect definition are long-ranged and potentially profound. Aristotle reminds us of something we all know too well. To paraphrase him: a small error in the beginning leads to a multitude of errors in the end.[18] In this case, if one's definition of a human person is incorrect, then one might find one's self experimenting on or euthanizing something which one thought was not a human being or a human person - but which in fact really is.

So I pose the question - how would you yourself define a human person? Would you consider any of the following a human person: a rock; a head of cabbage; a giraffe; ...those who are old and senile in a nursing home; Alzheimer's patients; Parkinsonian patients; stroke victims; comatose patients; drunks and alcoholics; drug addicts; the homeless, poor; prisoners; the emotionally ill and depressed; mothers-in-law; teenagers; the physically handicapped; the mentally ill; children under 7 years of age; a new-born baby; the fetus before the mother has given birth (or, at 6 months, 8 weeks, 35 days, 14 days, 6 days, 2 days, fertilization, or the egg or the sperm). These latter examples actually constitute some of the different biological markers at which various writers variously claim that there is present a human person. Obviously there is some disagreement about exactly when we have, definitionally, a human person present. And that period of time between fertilization and 14 days is the grayest area, i.e., the seemingly most difficult and most controversial stage.

What, then is a human being or person - and when does he or she begin? I will argue that at the biological marker of fertilization a *substantial* change (or a change in natures) has taken place - and a new, unique, living, individual embryonic human being who is simultaneously a human person is present. I will also argue that from fertilization onward - including the zero to 14-day old embryonic human stage - until the death of the adult organism - *accidental* change (or a change only in accidents) has taken place, in which a human being/person is continuously present.[19]

1. The connection between science and philosophy

First, although a question about "natures" seems to be fundamentally a philosophical one, I would argue that any philosophical reflections, analyses or accounts about the nature of a human being or person must begin or start with the empirically observable biological facts.[20] Otherwise our philosophical concepts actually bear little or no relation or resemblance to the real world which we are trying to understand and explain by those philosophical concepts. Instead, I would suggest, we are left with multiple half-truths or fantasies - or wishful thinking! Epistemologically, the starting point of our philosophical questions and investigations about reality must be grounded in that empirical and scientific reality. Only in this way can we have a realistic or objectively-based definition of a human being - one that is not relativistic.

Operationally, what is the connection between a thing's nature and the biological facts? Put briefly, the answer is that we can know *what* a thing is (i.e., its nature) *by observing its actions and functions* - how it behaves, what it does. We know that a thing acts according to the kind of thing it is, i.e., its nature. That is simply an empirically observable fact. In first-year chemistry or in microbiology students are given "unknowns", the nature of which they must identify by means of the kinds of actions or reactions exhibited by these "unknowns" as observed in the lab. Indeed, this is the obvious principle behind any basic or experimental research. The research biologist first observes the actions, reactions, functions of a biological entity and reasons from these specific kinds of actions back to the specific kind of nature it possesses. It is this nature which *directs and causes* such characteristic actions. As biology texts themselves discuss it: function follows form.[21] Thus Na burns orange, and cobalt burns blue/green - or beta-hemolytic streptococcus can only be grown on specific culture medium containing blood, but not on other mediums. Further, a thing is not only characterized by its nature, which determines the specific kinds of actions it can do - but that same nature limits the kinds of actions it can do. That is, there are certain actions which a thing can not do because it does not have the specific kind of nature it would need to do it. For example, birds have wings and so can fly - but stones, dogs or human beings can't fly; corn stalks produce ears of corn and corn proteins and corn enzymes - but acorns, tomato plants or asteroids do not and cannot produce corn or corn proteins. Frog embryos direct the formation of frog tissues and organs - but they cannot direct the formation of human tissues and organs.

Apply these considerations to the point at hand. To determine what a human being or person is is really not all so difficult as is often claimed. We are not Gods or angels - but embodied human beings.[22] We do have bodies - don't we? At least I have never seen a simple "soul" wandering aimlessly around the labs, manipulating a computer, cooking dinner or playing soccer without a body. In fact, I have never seen even a Platonic or a Cartesian philosopher "thinking" without his or her body! As Aristotle noted, the whole man thinks; the whole man knows; and the whole man acts.[23] There are voluminous biological facts which we do know already about the human body and its embryological development. Clearly by observing and studying these known biological facts - how the human being begins his or her

134

biological existence as a specifically *human* zygote, and the kinds of specifically *human* functions and human actions that take place during embryological development - we can then determine to a very sophisticated extent the nature of a human being or a human embryo - or "what" it is. So I will turn now to a brief consideration of the well-known, well-referenced biological facts concerning when the life of a human being begins to exist and how it then merely grows and develops during embryogenesis, without changing "natures".

2. The scientific facts

Before fertilization there exist a human sperm (containing 23 chromosomes) and a human ovum (also containing 23 chromosomes - the same number, but different kinds of chromosomes).[24] Neither the sperm nor the ovum, singly, by itself, can become a human being - even if implanted in the womb of the mother. They are only gametes - they are not human embryos or human beings. In contrast, the single-cell embryonic human zygote formed after fertilization (the beginning of the human being and the embryonic period)[25] contains 46 chromosomes (the number of chromosomes which is specific for members of the human species) - and these 46 chromosomes are mixed differently from the 46 chromosomes as found in either the mother or the father - that is, they are unique for that human individual. And at the single-cell embryonic human zygote stage that unique individual human being is already genetically a girl or a boy.[26] If allowed to "do his or her own thing", so to speak, this embryonic human zygote will biologically develop continuously without any biological interruptions, or gaps, throughout the embryonic, fetal, neo-natal, childhood and adulthood stages - until the death of the organism. And with the advent of in vitro fertilization techniques, we can see that the early human embryo can develop in vitro on his or her own without the nutrition or protection of the mother for quite a while - someday, perhaps, even until "birth"!

I want to reiterate that a human gamete is not a human being or a human person. The number of chromosomes is only 23; it only acts or functions biologically as an ovum or as a sperm, e.g, it only makes ovum or sperm enzymes and proteins, etc., not specifically human enzymes and proteins; and by itself it does not have the actual nature or potency yet to develop into a human embryo, fetus, child, or adult. And in that sense gametes are only *possible* human beings (i.e., human beings who do not exist as yet). Only after the sperm and the ovum chromosomes combine properly and completely do we have a human being. Individually, the nature of a sperm is different from the nature of an ovum - and both are different from the nature of the embryonic human zygote which is formed when their chromosomes combine.

Thus from perhaps an Aristotle-the-biologist's point of view, one would say that before fertilization there are two natures - i.e., the nature of an ovum and the nature of a sperm. After fertilization there is a human zygote with one nature, i.e., the nature of a human being. Thus, in fertilization there is *substantial* change,[27] (i.e., a change in substance or nature - or "what" it is). The substances or natures of the ovum and the sperm have changed into the nature of a human being. This is, in fact, known empirically by observing the number and kinds of chromosomes present before and after fertilization, and by empirically observing the different characteristically specific actions and functions of the ovum, the sperm, and the human zygote. Once fertilization has taken place and the new human being has formed, only *accidental* change[28] occurs (e.g., a change in weight, height, size, shape, etc.), and we know this empirically as well. We can observe that the nature of the human being does not change (e.g., into a cabbage or a giraffe), only its human accidents change.

Thus embryological development does not entail substantial change, but only accidental change. Once it is a human being it stays a human being, and acts and functions biologically as a human being. The human zygote produces specifically human enzymes and proteins; he or she forms specifically human tissues and organ systems, and develops humanly continuously from the stage of a single-cell human zygotic embryo to the stage of a human adult.[29]

This is observed empirically. A human zygote does not produce cabbage or carrot enzymes or proteins, and does not develop into a rock, an ear of corn, nor into a cat, a horse, a chicken, or a giraffe. Empirically it is observed that a human zygote produces specifically and characteristically human proteins and enzymes at the moment of fertilization - as demonstrated recently, for example, by experiments using transgenic mice[30] - and that he or she develops continuously throughout embryological development in a specifically and characteristically human way.

In short - the biological facts demonstrate that at fertilization we have a real human being with a truly human nature. It is not that he or she will become a human being - he or she already is a human being. We know that empirically. And this nature or capacity to act in a certain characteristic way is called, philosophically, a nature or a *potency*.[31] Thus a human zygote or embryo is not a possible human being;[32] nor is he or she a potential human being;[33] he or she is already a human being. A human zygote, embryo or fetus does not have the potency to become a human being, but already possesses the nature or capacity to be at that moment a human being. And that nature will direct the accidental development, i.e., the embryological development, of his or her own self from the most immature stage of a human being to the most mature stage of a human being.

Now, this is strongly convincing empirical evidence that at fertilization there is present a human being (the well-referenced unequivocally agreed upon answer to the scientific question); but is there also a human person (a philosophical question) - or not? These are two different questions - one scientific, the other philosophical. It is in this shifting from the paradigm of a human being to that of a human person where the philosophy - and the confusion - come into play. Is a human being also a human person; or are they different things? Which philosophy is adequate to cope with this biological data?

3. The matching philosophical concepts

(Fig. 3) With even only a cursory rummaging through the history of philosophy, there is one major "realistic" philosophical "ball-park" which would in fact deny that there was any real (as opposed to conceptual) essential distinction between a human being and a human person. That is, in the real world which we experience empirically, they cannot really be split or separated - except perhaps only conceptually. This philosophy was part of a 2500 year old tradition which was the bath water, so to speak, that was "thrown out with the baby". It is the philosophical ball-park, for example, of Aristotle-the-biologist.[34] For Aristotle - as well as for others, such as Thomas Aquinas - his major metaphysical and anthropological treatises argue consistently for a single human substance with no mind/body split (although there is evidence of a serious Platonic streak in his *De Anima* - that atypical and historically problematic treatise of Aristotle's so often quoted by contemporary scholars - as well as historians who researched for *Roe* vs *Wade*). As Aristotle argues, "...'nature' has two

137

senses - matter and form. If one considers 'nature' as the form, then it would be the shape or form (not separate except in statement) of things which have in themselves a source of motion"[35] (emphasis added). Again, he says, ..."the physicist is concerned only with things whose forms are separable [in the mind], indeed, but do not exist apart from matter."[36] And similarly, matter cannot exist apart from the form. For Aristotle, the human being is defined as one composite substance - the vegetative, sensitive and rational powers of the "soul" together with the human "body".[37] The whole soul, he wrote, is homogenous, and in each part of the body as one whole composite:

> In each of the bodily parts there are present *all* the parts of the soul, and the souls so present are *homogenous with one another and with the whole*; this means that the several parts of the soul are *indisseverable from one another*.[38] (emphasis added)

And in contrast to his opposite view in the very same *De Anima*, Aristotle addresses the very possibility of a "being-on-the-way", or an "intermediate" human being, railing against the anthropological consequences of Plato's or Pythagoras' mind/body split when he very sarcastically retorts: "Yet how are we to *believe* in such things?" (emphasis in the original).[39] Although Aristotle-proper did not actually use the term "person", he clearly would have to concur that a human being is always a human person, for neither form nor matter can exist on their own as two different things or independent substances.

Thomas Aquinas, to give another example, puts an even finer gloss on Aristotle's anthropology, by affirming his own adamant rejection of Plato's anthropology. To paraphrase Thomas: the name of "person" (and he uses that term) does not belong to the rational part of the soul, nor to the whole soul alone - but to the entire human substance (or, subsistens).[40] This means that the whole soul, whole body and its act of existing constitute one substance entire - with no separate and troublesome independent "parts" each of which are claimed to be true and independent whole substances. And it is worth noting that Aquinas is one of the only philosophers who includes undesignated matter in his formal definitions of natural things - of which man is one.[41]

For Thomas a human being is a human person, and the later characteristics which we will look at in these debates, such as "rational attributes", autonomous willing or sentience, are only consequential and secondary or accidental actions which follow upon certain powers (not "parts") which themselves follow upon the essential nature of the human being itself.[42] That nature is defined as the single, whole, formal, material and existential human substance. As Thomas states:

> ...*the soul must be in the whole body* [and therefore not just in the brain], and in each part thereof ...for to the *nature of the species* belongs what the *definition* signifies; and in natural things, the *definition* does not signify the form only, but the form *and* the matter...so it belongs to the *notion of man* [definition] to be composed of soul, flesh and bones.[43] (emphasis added)

These philosophical precisions force at least two major questions on any of the several types of Aristotlean/Thomistic frameworks used in these debates. First, if it is claimed that the "rational" soul - which "organizes and directs embryological development" - is not infused until about the third month,[44] then what explains the specifically *human* organization of the human embryo and human fetus up to that point? Hasn't the work of this supposed "delayed rational soul" *already been done* - as empirically verified? If so, then this biological evidence of specifically human organization which we do empirically observe must be accounted for by the presence of the human soul right from the beginning. In addition to the specifically human structural organization from the beginning, we also empirically observe specifically human functions and activities from the beginning - e.g., the production of specifically human proteins, enzymes, etc. If so, then this biological evidence of specifically human functions and activities which we do empirically observe must be accounted for by the presence of the human soul right from the beginning.

Second, for both Aristotle and Thomas the "rational soul", or more properly, power, *includes virtually* the vegetative and sensitive powers,[45] and for neither is there such a thing as a "rational soul" alone, or even a whole soul alone - or a whole soul without a body (except in some sections of the *De Anima*). The whole existing human complex (body and soul - and for Thomas, *esse*) must be present together at once.

Apart from the biological and conceptual absurdity of an "intermediate man" walking down the street, if there were only a "vegetative" soul present at first, how do we explain the production of specifically human enzymes and proteins - instead of carrot or corn enzymes - from the very start? If there were only a "vegetative and sensitive" soul present, how do we explain the production of specifically human tissue and organs - instead of only giraffe or gorilla organs and systems? If the human soul cannot be split (and must contain all three powers at once), and if specifically human enzymes, proteins, tissues, organs and structures are empirically observed - which they are - then the human rational soul must be present at the very beginning along with the human vegetative and sensitive "powers" (not "parts") of the human soul. And this "soul" - or, more properly, these powers - must exist as a composite with the human body which it is organizing and whose functions and activities it is directing from the moment of fertilization - which we know empirically.

Thus, at fertilization, I would argue, the "matter" (i.e., the newly combined fertilized ovum or embryonic single-cell zygote) is already appropriately organized as human - since we empirically observe it as specifically human and as developing humanly from the beginning.[46]

So far the scientific facts and the philosophical concepts match. At this point I want to take a closer look at the biological facts after fertilization, i.e., those of human embryological growth and development. Along the way I will point out several other different biological "marker events" of personhood which have been variously argued by others. All of these writers will make a real distinction between a human being and a human person - supposedly based on these biological marker events. The use of certain biological data which they will use to support their arguments will also be addressed. (The use of their problematic philosophies with mind/body splits, which seem to be imposed upon their problematic biological facts, will be discussed later in this paper).

B. Zero - 14-days

As noted above, the newly formed single-cell embryonic human zygote consists of 46 chromosomes and non-nuclear DNA in which are coded the specific directions for virtually all of the processes of embryological development. The content of this initial pool of genetic information never changes throughout embryological development.

(1) Yet it has been argued by Bedate, Cefalo[47] and Bole[48], for example (Fig. 1), that not all of the "information" needed is present in this single original cell, that some of the information comes from "molecular information" in later stages of development, and some even comes from "molecules" originating from the mother. Thus they conclude that the original human zygote does not contain all of the "information" needed to be a self-directing, human individual, and therefore it is not a human person.

I would question this biological data. First, "molecular information" or "positional information" is not the same as genetic (chromosomal) information. Yet they seem to gloss over this very important scientific distinction, and imply that the two are the same. Second, "molecular information" itself is coded in the original single-cell human zygote. As the embryologist Moore discusses at great length, the genetic information in the original human zygote determines what "molecular information" will be formed, which in turn determine what proteins and enzymes will be formed, which determine which tissues and organs will be formed. In genetics this is called the *"cascading"* effect.[49] That is, the information in the original single-cell embryonic human zygote "cascades" throughout embryological development - each previous direction causing the specific formation of each succeeding direction. Thus, all "positional" or "molecular" information or direction is already determined itself by the information which preceded it, and ultimately by the original genetic information in the single-cell human zygote.[50]

Third, although the genetic information in the human zygote may direct the absorption of molecules from the mother, that hardly means that the maternal molecules or the mother herself determines the very nature of the growing embryo or fetus which she is merely nurturing. (This argument is also rejected by Suarez[51]). The nature of the embryo or fetus, as is empirically known, is determined by the formal biological

141

genetic make-up of the zygote from which he or she continuously develops; and the directing of this absorption of maternal molecules is done by the genetic information within the embryo or fetus - not by the mother or any genetic or "molecular" information from the mother.[52] Those are simply the correct biological facts. As Jerome Lejeune, the internationally prominent prize winning geneticist has testified:

> ...each of us has a unique beginning, the moment of conception... As soon as the twenty three chromosomes carried by the sperm encounter the twenty-three chromosomes carried by the ovum, the *whole information* necessary and sufficient to spell out all the characteristics of the new being is gathered... (W)hen this information carried by the sperm and by the ovum has encountered each other, then *a new human being is defined* which has never occurred before and will never occur again.... [the zygote,and the cells produced in the succeeding divisions] is not just simply a non-descript cell, or a "population" or loose "collection" of cells, but a very specialized individual, i.e., someone who will *build himself according to his own rule.*"[53] (emphasis added)

Finally, Bedate and Cefalo[54] also argue that the developing embryo can give rise to biological entities which are not human beings, e.g., hydatidiform moles and teratomas. But hydatidiform moles and teratomas do not arise from genetically normal human embryos, but from abnormal entities (usually caused, e.g., by dispermy), which are not therefore genetically normal human beings to begin with.[55]

(2) Next, it is argued by some that this original single cell divides neatly first into 2 cells, then into 4 cells, then into 8 cells, etc.[56] This biological data too is questionable, (and has consequences in understanding the argument about "totipotency"). As known and published in human embryology textbooks for over 60 years (as Lejeune[57] points out), human embryogenesis immediately following fertilization is asynchronus (unlike amphibian or mouse embryology). The original single cell divides into 2 cells - and then only one of those

cells divides, giving 3 cells . After a time the other cell divides, making it 4 cells, and then 8 cells, etc.

Part of what happens at this three-cell stage is that one can observe empirically the process of methylation. This observation is important philosophically. Many argue that these very early cells - including the original single-cell zygote up to the 8-cell stage - are "totipotent".[58] They explain totipotent cells as the most vaguely directed and least differentiated cells in all of embryological development. Each cell, they claim, is not yet determined enough to be classified as an individual human being or a part of an individual human being. These cells, they say, have not yet "made up their minds" what they want to be. They can become any number of things. These cells are not differentiated or specialized enough yet. What happens in early development, they claim, is that there is a gradual change from total unspecialization to greater and greater specialization or differentiation. For example, at first we have a cell that could become any kind of human cell. Progressively a cell becomes specialized so that it can only become a kidney cell, or a stomach cell, or a muscle cell, i.e., it becomes more and more determined and differentiated.

This portrayal of differentiation is backwards, as Lejeune notes. The original single-cell human zygote is the most determined and specialized cell in all of embryological development. Progressively he or she loses, in fact, the ability to use information. A kidney cell, for example, contains virtually all of the genetic information that was in the original single human zygote cell, but can now use only a small portion of that information. So the kidney cell has not lost any of this information - only the ability to use it. This ability to use or not use the information that is present is partially determined by the process of methylation (which itself is coded in the original single-cell zygote). Through methylation and other processes during embryogenesis, genes are turned on or turned off. When the cell wants to control the use of cellular information, it methylates a molecule to silence that gene, to block or stop its use at a certain point in development. No information is progressively lost; only its use is lost. Thus a specialized kidney cell cannot be prodded to become an entirely new human being - not because it does not have all of the necessary information (it does), but because all of the information other than that of being a "kidney cell" has been methylated, or silenced.[59]

Thus to be so differentiated as a kidney cell is actually a negative in such arguments. The kidney cell cannot direct anything but a small minuscule part of the development of the human embryo or fetus; whereas the original single-cell human zygote contains and can use all of the genetic information only partially used by the later cells. So there is nothing vague, undirected or undecided about it. It is the human zygote which represents the greatest fullness of human content and useable information, of directedness and decisive action - more than that found in any of the later cells. The human zygote will "decide" what reactions and formations take place. He or she will direct all of the processes and formations during the entire embryological process.[60] Furthermore, "totipotency" is even suppose to happen - it is a normal part of human embryogenesis, and is indeed encoded in the original genetic information of the human zygote. Differentiation is also encoded in the original human zygote, and is partly explained by methylation. Differentiation, then, really represents the restricted ability to make any "decisions".

(3) Next, Suarez argues for the 2-cell stage, with, as he claims, the completion of the first division and of the genetic input. "The two-cell stage already is, like the adult, a moment in the execution of the program 'man'". And besides, he argues, the two-cell stage is already the same living being as the human adult arising from it.[61] However, we already know that the genetic input is complete at the single-cell zygote stage, and that the zygote in fact is the source of the genetic input of the two-cell stage and is the same living being as both the two-cell stage and the adult stage. Thus Suarez's own argument actually argues for personhood for the zygote rather than for his two-cell stage.

(4) But to continue, the cells will proceed to divide until about 5 or 6 days, when two cell layers are formed in the blastocyst - the trophoblast or outer cell layer, and the embryoblast or inner cell layer. Some writers, such as Grobstein and McCormick, have stated that this stage is significant because they can demonstrate empirically that there can be no true human individual present at this time - we have only a genetic individual, not a developmental individual. A person can be present, they claim, only if there is a developmental individual - and this cannot take place until 14-days:

I contend in this paper that the *moral status* - and specifically the controversial issue of personhood is related to the attainment of *developmental individuality* (being the source of one individual)... It should be noted that at the zygote stage the genetic individual is not yet developmentally single - a source of only one individual. As we will see, that does not occur until a single body axis has begun to form, near the end of the *second week* post fertilization when *implantation* is underway.[62] (emphasis added)

It is to be noted that the moral status of the developing human being explicitly hinges directly on what developmental stage he or she is at. Note also that they make implantation (5-7 days) co-extensive with two weeks (when the primitive streak begins to form) - also scientifically incorrect.

But to continue, these early cells, they claim, are only "collections" of undifferentiated, "totipotent" cells, and they name them, or designate them collectively, as only comprising a *"pre-embryo"* (a term, by the way, which is specifically rejected by human embryologists[63] - only amphibian and mouse embryologists, philosophers, theologians and bioethicists use the term). Further, the term was rejected by the judge in the Davis vs Davis frozen embryo case.

The scientific facts which they give to support these claims are the following. They claim that only the cells from the inner layer of the blastocyst (the embryoblast), eventually become the adult human being. The cells from the outer trophoblast layer, they write, are all discarded after birth as the sac and the umbilical cord, etc. Thus, developmentally, the implication is, that we are not dealing exclusively with those "important cells" which will become the adult human being, i.e., the embryoblast, but rather a mixture of "essential" and "non-essential" cells, i.e., a PRE-embryo. A pre-embryo, then, is not a human person, yet:

> This multicellular entity, called a blastocyst, has an outer cellular wall, a central fluid-filled cavity and a small gathering of cells at one end known as the inner cell mass. Developmental studies show that the cells of the outer wall become the trophoblast

145

(feeding layer) and are precursors to the later placenta. Ultimately, *all these cells are discarded at birth*[64] (emphasis added)

But, again, these scientific "facts" are questionable, and necessarily lead to questionable philosophical concepts. It simply is not true that all of the cells from the trophoblast layer are discarded after birth and do not contribute cells to the inner cell layer; nor is it true that only the cells from the inner layer become the later adult or that none of the cells from the inner cell layer contribute to the outer layer. As can be found in virtually all embryology texts, including Moore's text from which they quote, many of the cells from this trophoblast layer become an integral and essential part of the constitution of the later fetus, newborn and adult human being. For example, the cells from the trophoblast layer known as the yolk sac cells become part of the adult gut. And cells known as the allantois cells become part of the adult ligaments, blood cells and urinary bladder.[65]

Thus these "scientific" facts used by Grobstein and McCormick are scientifically incorrect - and therefore so also are their philosophical conclusions about "pre-embryos" and "developmental individuals" which are grounded on those incorrect scientific facts.

Yet McCormick and Grobstein continue. It is impossible, they claim, for a human person to be present until at least the 14-day marker event, at which point the primitive streak forms in the embryo. The philosophical significance of this marker, it is claimed, is that until the formation of the primitive streak it is possible for twinning to take place. The totipotent cells "do not yet know whether to be one or two individuals". After 14-days, they claim, twinning is not possible, and thus the organism is finally determinantly developmentally one individual - an essential pre-requisite for personhood.[66]

But, again, this science is incorrect. As Karen Dawson[67] points out in these debates - and as is found in every human genetics textbook - it is possible for monozygotic twinning to take place after 14-days and the formation of the primitive streak. For example, fetus-in-fetu twins can be formed up to 2 and 3 months after fertilization, and Siamese twins even later. Also, it is known that "twinning" is sometimes genetically determined and coded in the original human single-cell zygote (as, indeed, is totipotency and differentiation).

146

There is nothing magical, it turns out, about this 14-day stage as far as the concept of individuality and personhood is concerned. (Even the Warnock Report, which encouraged the use of the term "pre-embryo", admitted that the 14-day marker event or any other was totally arbitrary, as did the NIH Human Embryo Research Panel).[68] If a 2-cell, 8-cell, implantation stage, 14-day primitive streak stage embryo or 4 month fetus splits into twins, that simply means that the original entity was one individual - and now there are simply two individuals. The fact of twinning says nothing about the individuality of the first individual, i.e., the single-cell human zygote.[69] Indeed, the history of all living organisms is of one individual giving rise to another individual - but one would certainly not then conclude that there were therefore no individuals ever present, or that the former individual was hopelessly "undecided".

C. Ward Kischer, a human embryologist, argues that the scientific data of McCormick and Grobstein is highly selective and that they leave out a majority of other relevant data:

> It is not a question as to whether science can or cannot decide the question of personhood. Science is not interested in deciding personhood. However, if the socio-legal status of personhood cannot be decided without invoking what is known scientifically, then the whole of scientific data should be used and *not arbitrarily selected bits and pieces of data.* (emphasis in original)
>
> ... Human embryology is now in danger of being rewritten as a stratagem statement of current socio-legal, but also of late, even *theological* issues. Unless the errors are corrected now, we will be in danger of entering a protracted period of *false concepts* concerning our own development.[70]

Unfortunately, Grobstein later publicly admitted before a scientific conference that he had knowingly substituted amphibian embryology for human embryology.[71] Yet this "science" continues to be promoted. For example, there are the claims by Robertson (a lawyer) that "personhood" is only a social construct and that the early human embryo has only "symbolic value" to the parents and society.[72]

But Robertson bases his argument almost exclusively and exhaustively on the "embryology" of Grobstein, even in his court cases. And recently, the N.I.H. Human Embryo Research Panel issued its Recommendations to the Director of N.I.H. Ron Greene and Carol Tauer, the Ethics Co-Chairpersons of that Panel, grounded the "reduced moral status" of the early human embryo on the published work of Grobstein and McCormick, and most of the writers considered here[73] - concluding that certain kinds of destructive experimental research could ethically be performed on these early live human embryos because of their "reduced moral status". Furthermore, certain pharmaceutical companies have argued that the F.D.A. should allow them to market oral contraceptives because there is "no embryo there until two weeks", and therefore their product is not abortifacient. Their source for this scientific claim is the Australian theologian Fr. Norman Ford's book (below), grounded on the "science" of Grobstein and McCormick.[74] Obviously, if Grobstein's embryology is incorrect, then Robertson's argument, the N.I.H.'s Recommendations, and the claims by the pharmaceutical industry and advocates which are all based on Grobstein's "embryology" are also invalid.

(5) Ford[75] also argues for the 14-day stage, based primarily on the same science from Grobstein, although Ford claims there is an individual present at fertilization - but it is only a biological individual. Rational ensoulment cannot take place until after 14 days, at which point there is, he claims, an ontological individual, i.e., when differentiation is completed and there is a distinct individuality.[76] But aside from the problems with the science of Grobstein and McCormick on which Ford basis his own conclusions, we know empirically that complete differentiation does not actually take place until well after birth. As the embryologist Moore states:

> Human development is a *continuous* process that begins when an ovum from a female is fertilized by a sperm from a male. *Growth and differentiation* transform the zygote, a single cell formed by the union of the ovum and the sperm, into a multicellular adult human being. Most developmental changes occur during the embryonic and the fetal periods, but important changes also occur during the other periods of development:

childhood, adolescence, and adulthood... Although it is customary to divide development into prenatal and postnatal periods, it is important to realize that birth is merely a dramatic event during development resulting in a distinct change in environment. Development does not stop at birth: important developmental changes, in addition to growth, occur after birth... *Most developmental changes are completed by the age of 25.*[77] *(emphasis added)*

Obviously, then, a 14-day embryo is nowhere near being "completely differentiated". Once again, the incorrect science on which a philosophical claim is based actually negates the validity of that philosophical claim.

C. <u>After 14-days</u>

(1) Sometimes Wallace,[78] too, wants to argue for 14-days, but he is inconsistent and seems more to argue for a point after 14-days. He bases his own position on what he calls an "Aristotelean-Thomistic" theory of "natural law". This "natural law theory" grounds his distinction between transient natures (or seeds, or beings-on-the-way) as applied dubiously and analogously to the transition from plant, animal, to human natures during human embryological development; and stable natures, as applied to the actual embryological development of individual systems of plants, animals and human beings. This "transition" from plant, animal to human substances during human embryological development for Wallace is, then, actually a series of substantial changes within human embryogenesis itself; and once again he bases much of his argument on the science of Grobstein and McCormick, and a rather neo-Platonic rendition of Aristotle and Aquinas, as well as a distinctively physicist's rendition of "science".

Two points out of many which are problematic are his descriptions of his "Aristotelean-Thomistic" grounding, and the blatant contradictions in his analogies. First, Wallace subscribes to the Aristotle of the historically problematic *De Anima*, and attributes to both Aristotle and Thomas a theory of the "eduction" of these substantial forms from "proto-matter", substantial forms which Aristotle, he says, would call "natures", and which Thomas, he says, would define as (quantity + proto-matter) - a definition of substance with which neither Aristotle-proper nor Thomas would agree. Wallace renames this as "mass-energy", to bring Aristotle and Thomas "up to date with modern physics".[79]

However, Wallace is really elucidating a very neo-Platonic interpretation of both Aristotle and Thomas, one with which neither the historic Aristotle nor Thomas can be reconciled. Neither of them gave any real existence to "proto-matter", or what I think Wallace confuses with "prime matter". And, indeed, for both of them "prime matter" was only a conceptual construct, and by definition, was totally without forms[80] - in fact, that was the whole point! As Klubertanz states:

> Of itself, prime matter is *not actually any kind of thing; nor does it have quantity*, or any kind of qualities or other accidents. Hence prime matter *cannot exist in itself*; it cannot be found as such in direct or indirect sense experience; it cannot even be understood separately from substance or substantial form. It is an *intelligible* co-principle...[81] (emphasis added)

Thus no substantial forms can be educed from "proto-matter" for either Aristotle or Thomas, because there were no forms there to begin with. And Thomas, like Aristotle, actually argued against this sort of theory:

> Creation does not mean the building up of a composite thing from pre-existing principles; but it means that the *composite is created* so that it is brought into being *at the same time with all its principles.*[82] (emphasis added)

Further, "quantity" for both Aristotle and Thomas was an accident of substance, not a concrete substance itself.[83] Thus neither would even equate their "quantity" with the modern concept of "mass". And finally, Wallace also never once includes *esse* (the act of existing) - which is the hallmark of Thomas' definition of any existing substance - in any of the definitions of "substance" which he attributes to Thomas. In fact, he simply never mentions *esse* at all.

Second, his concept of "transient natures" is drawn from rather shaky chemistry and biology. He claims, for example, that when Na and Cl react together they each actually change their natures. But Na and Cl are only sharing electrons, not protons (which determine the "nature" or kind of element it is, and which place the element in a specific place in the periodic chart). He also fails to mark the critical differences between the nuclei of radio-isotopes and those of living cells. Nor does he mark the critical differences which distinguish the generation of a radioisotope from that of a plant; nor that of an animal from that of a human being. He also builds a "model" of what he calls "transient natures", yet admits that they probably are really "stable natures"! Inexplicably he will call them "transient natures" anyway.[84] He then applies his own theory of transient natures, questionable even to himself -to plant and animal generation - all the while acknowledging that real plants and real animals have stable natures which are descriptive of the mature individuals only - not to the developmental stages of those individuals.[85] How credible is such a theory? Should it be applied to determine the real moral status of real live human beings?

(2) A final marker event I will point out is 8 weeks or several time-markers after that (Fig. 2) - although there are many others with equally troubling science invoked. Personhood, it is claimed, does not begin until the dawning of or the maturation of the physical substrate of human consciousness, self-consciousness, or sentience - i.e., the nervous system and/or the brain. Indeed, there is already a movement by some in legal jurisprudence to formalize the legal concept of "brain birth" to denote that point in time biologically when there is present a "person", as a parallel to the already legal criteria of "brain death".

One well-known criticism of this claim comes from Gareth Jones, who rejects scientific claims that we can determine the biological point of either "rational attributes" or sentience. As he states, the parallelism between brain death and brain birth is scientifically invalid. Brain death is the gradual or rapid cessation of the functions of a brain. Brain birth is the very gradual acquisition of the functions of a developing neural system. This developing neural system is not a brain. He questions, in fact, the entire assumption and asks what neurological reasons there might be for concluding that an incapacity for consciousness becomes a capacity for consciousness once this point is passed. Jones continues that the alleged symmetry is not as strong as is sometimes assumed, and that it has yet to be provided with a firm biological base.[86] A different Jones who is partaking in these debates makes the following poignant remark:

> The reproductive biologist cannot assign moral status to the sperm or the egg or the fertilized egg or any of the subsequent products that may result from this fusion ... The reproductive biologist can help, however, by assuring that other scientists or those *who wish to assert a moral status*, and use a biological term or concept to do so, *know what they are talking about!*[87] (emphasis added)

Furthermore, the empirical fact is that complete physiological brain integration is not complete until many months or years after birth,[88] just as the complete exercising of "rational attributes" is not possible until years after birth.[89] Empirically this would extend their biological marker for personhood into early adulthood (and thus the moral status as well).

VI. <u>Philosophical definitions of "personhood"</u>

I could continue, biologically, down any number of "marker events" where it is argued at different points during biological development that until that point there is only a human being and only after that point there is a human person. But virtually every single marker event claimed is also using extremely problematic scientific "data" to back up their philosophical claims of personhood. It would seem that there is more of a problem here than simply the use of incorrect science. Perhaps there is also involved - whether consciously or not - the imposition on that incorrect science of certain characteristically problematic philosophical presuppositions. What I see is the use of specific metaphysical and anthropological presuppositions which result in a classic mind/body - or even sometimes a body/body split - that are imposed upon the scientific data.

A rough consideration of just how different philosophical schools of thought have defined a "human being" or a "human person", then, is in order. Especially in light of the obvious biological continuity present throughout the entire course of embryological development, as well as the specifically human development which we know empirically takes place, how adequately do the various philosophical definitions of a human person reflect the correct biological facts as we empirically know them?

I will focus on the definition that is most generally agreed upon these days, i.e., one that is basically "derived" from Descartes[90] or Locke.[91] Generally, a human person is someone who is actually acting at the time in a rational manner (Fig. 3). That is, he or she is self-conscious, self-aware, competent, autonomous, logical, mature, conversant, and interacts with the environment and other rational beings around him or her. In short, if one is acting rationally one is a person. If this is true, then 99% of the possible examples of human persons I gave you at the beginning of this paper are - by definition - not persons. Those examples include the mentally ill and retarded, drug and alcohol addicts, patients with Parkinson's and Alzheimer's diseases, and the comatose (medical conditions which especially effect a considerable percentage of the elderly population).

This is the sort of philosophical definition that in fact has been used for many years by writers such as Engelhardt,[92] Tooley,[93] Kuhse[94] and Singer[95] (yes, the animal rights person) who argue in the literature for infanticide of even normal healthy infants. If, they argue, a normal new-born baby cannot act rationally (as described above), then it is not a "subject" but only an "object" - and we can therefore use it in destructive experimental research if we rational agents so chose. In Singer's own words:

> Now it must be admitted that these arguments apply to the newborn baby as much as to the fetus. A week-old baby is *not* a rational and self-conscious being, and there are many non-human animals whose rationality, self-consciousness, awareness, capacity to feel pain (sentience), and so on, exceed that of a human baby a week, a month, or even a year old. If the fetus does not have the same claim to life as a person, it appears that the *newborn baby is of less value than the life of a pig, a dog, or a chimpanzee.*[96] (emphasis added)

And philosopher Richard Frey (presently a Senior Scholar at the Hastings Center), pushing Singer's logic (correctly) one step further, suggests that mentally ill human beings are therefore also not "persons", and therefore they might be used in purely destructive experimental research in place of the higher animals who are "persons".[97]

Would you agree that the killing of normal healthy human infants, or the substitution of mentally ill human beings for the higher animals in destructive experimental research, is morally justifiable? If not, then we have to question, at least, such very rationalistic definitions of a human person, and the metaphysical and epistemological foundations on which they are grounded. If one argues from the rationalistic premise that a "human person" is defined only in terms of active "reason" (or only the rational part of the soul), and if only normal older children or adults exhibit such active "rational attributes", then even a normal newborn infant, or a 15-year old child is not a person - and to be logically consistent, you must agree with Singer's or Engelhardt's arguments for infanticide, and with Frey's conclusions about the mentally ill in research. To be even more logically consistent, you might also have to agree that my partial list of human beings who are not presently exercising their "rational attributes" could also be used for the "greater good" in experimental research, be denied medical help or costs, or be euthanized.[98] After all, these populations of human beings have a "reduced moral status" - they are no longer human persons - no longer "subjects", but "objects".[99]

On the other hand, sometimes a "human person" is defined only in terms of the whole soul - i.e., the vegetative, sensitive and rational "souls" all together. Once this soul unites with a body, we then have a human person. It doesn't matter, they say, whether this person is presently acting rationally. What is important is that the rational nature or capacity is present. But if we think about it, we run into similar problems as mentioned earlier. If there are no vegetative, sensitive, or rational directions injected until about 3 months - how did a specifically **human** biochemical, tissue, organ system get built before 3 months?

Or perhaps we should restrict ourselves to a purely material definition of a "human person". The human person is simply a complex system of molecules, tissues and organs. But this definition has continuously failed in explaining our experience of thoughts, ideas, and concepts, and especially of intentionality, willing, or choosing. It is argued that a "person" is simply a more advanced sophisticated phase of a material complex human being. But aren't we really talking then

154

about a secondary or accidental quality? Surely the definition of the nature of a human person should not be put in terms of only a secondary or accidental phase - however sophisticated it may be. And again, if you are arguing from the materialist premise that a "human person" is defined only in terms of sentience, or the physical integration or functioning of the brain, then you will also have to argue for infanticide - or worse (as already indicated), because as pointed out, full brain integration and sentience is also not completed until over the age of 20 years, and parapeligics, stroke victims, advanced diabetics, and the comatose often cannot optimally feel pain.

Finally, there are some who would follow the long-discredited "scientific" theory that any individual instance of embryogenesis "recapitulates" the historical evolution of the species (e.g., that there is the formation of ancestral "gills" or "tails" during the embryogenesis of a single human embryo, somehow "recapitulating" the evolution of all of the species). Such "theories" are still attractive, especially to evolutionists, and to some "process" philosophers and theologians - leading again to a theory of delayed hominization.

However, these claims were based on scientific myths (the best they could do at the time) which have long since been discarded scientifically. There is no empirical evidence that the "gills" or "tails" of primitive animals are really formed during any individual embryogenesis of a single human embryo, and such theories are rejected (if discussed at all) even in human embryology text books. Such claims fail to make a real distinction between the historical process of the evolution of millions of different species (which takes place over millions of years) and the mere growth and development of a single individual human being within one species (which takes only nine months). In short, it confuses a "species" with an individual. As O'Rahilly succinctly puts it:

> The theory that successive stages of individual development (ontogeny) correspond with ("recapitulate") successive adult ancestors in the line of evolutionary descent (phylogeny) became popular in the 19th century as the so-called biogenetic law. *This theory of recapitulation, however, has had a "regrettable influence on the progress of embryology"* [citing de Beer]... Furthermore, during its development an animal departs more and more

from the form of other animals. Indeed, the early stages in the development of an animal are not like the adult stages of other forms, but resemble only the early stages *of those animals.*[100]

Could "process" scientists, philosophers and theologians be imposing their philosophical presuppositions on the individual processes of human embryogenesis? Does every individual process imply evolution? Just because there is a process does not mean that there is no individual there or that the very nature of that individual is changing during that process. Consider the life-long process of growth and development (embryo, fetus, infant, child, adult, elderly) which any individual human being goes through. Just because there is a process taking place does not mean that there is no individual human being who retains his/her own nature throughout that process.

At any rate, if "recapitulation" were true, then we would also observe the formation of "fish" or "monkey" enzymes, proteins and tissues, which we don't. Even though there are many genes we do share in common with other species, let's not forget about the genes we do not share with them and which make us specifically human and different from them.

Once again, consider the legitimacy of the fundamental groundings on which so-called "process" scientific, philosophical or theological theories are based. Who is to say that any particular "rendition" of that "process" is either sound or valid to begin with. Can any such proponent successfully prove the validity of his or her "process" theory, or successfully defend it? Could such a "calculus" be arbitrary or abused? And once again consider the logical and practical conclusions to which one must be pushed if "moral status" is merely grounded on a "calculus of process". Literally no human beings contained within that process would be left untouched or unaffected.

The political and cultural impact of such incorrect scientific and philosophical definitions (or redefinitions) of "personhood" is potentially devastating. As Judge Robert Bork has so succinctly and brilliantly comprehended and demonstrated, such "logic", the scientific and philosophical premises on which they rest, and many of the several radical libertine and egalitarian agendas which have been derived from them, are pushing us ever more rapidly towards what he describes as "Gomorrah", the final stage or end point of the living, breathing political and cultural Slope on which we have already been and continue to be rapidly Slipping. Such "theories" or social "constructs", which inherently debase the inalienable value of newly existing unborn human lives, are now being tapped to ground the politically correct and absolutized concepts of "autonomy", perceived "social needs" and "convenience". The political and cultural consequences which he so carefully and at considerable length develops should give us immediate pause:

> The systematic killing of unborn children in huge numbers is part of a general disregard for human life that has been growing for some time. Abortion by itself did not cause that disregard, but it certainly deepens and legitimates the nihilism that is spreading in our culture and finds killing for convenience acceptable. *We are crossing lines*, at first slowly and now with rapidity: killing unborn children for convenience; removing tissue from live fetuses; contemplating creating embryos for destruction in research; considering taking organs from living anencephalic babies; experimenting with assisted suicide; and contemplating euthanasia. Abortion has coarsened us. If it is permissible to kill the unborn human for convenience, it is surely permissible to kill those thought to be soon to die for the same reason. And it is inevitable that many who are not in danger of imminent death will be killed to relieve their families of burdens. Convenience is becoming the theme of our culture. Human tend to be inconvenient at both ends of their lives.[101] (emphasis added)

V. Questions about professional "expertise"

Perhaps this is an appropriate point to at least raise the ticklish and often ignored question of both scientific and philosophical "expertise".[102] It is clear from even the few arguments presented here that there are serious problems with both the scientific and philosophical inaccuracies pervading these arguments on "personhood".

The science used is often selective, cryptic and/or simply incorrect, and does not apply to or is irrelevant to the philosophical issue it is trying to ground. Some still insist that the "science" being used is correct - although certainly to so "insist" does not make it so. We would all welcome those who support such "scientific" claims to prove them. When all of the human embryological, human genetic and other scientific texts - as well as the most recent research and assurances by the most respected researchers - state clearly and unequivocally that very different basic scientific facts are universally acknowledged which actually contradict the scientific "facts" used by many of the proponents of delayed personhood, let those proponents defend their scientific "facts" openly and publicly before an open body of their scientific peers.

What human embryologist, for example, would agree that ova and sperms are really the same as zygotes; that the zygote is not a human being or human embryo; that the early human embryo or fetus is just a "piece" of the mother's tissues; that human cells divide asynchronously and neatly into two, four, 8, etc.; that all of the cells at the two-cell stage are completely differentiated; that "totipotency" is somehow problematic, vague, or "indecisive"; that "molecular molecules" from the mother actually determine the very nature of the developing human embryo; that hydatidiform moles or teratomas derive from normal human embryos; that scientifically there is any such thing as a "pre-embryo", a "developmental individual" or an "ontological individual"; that none of the cells from the trophoblast layer ever find their way into the fetus or even the adult human being - or that none of the cells from the embryoblast layer ever find their way into the placenta, etc.; that twinning never takes place after 14-days; that implantation takes place at two weeks; that the physical brain is parallel to the physical nervous system or primitive nerve network, or that either is fully integrated by the eighth week; or that full sentience or rational attributes are present anytime before birth (or beyond)?

What chemist would agree that the sharing of electrons when Na and Cl combine changes the very natures of these elements, or that the nucleus of a radioisotope is physically or chemically analogous to the nucleus of a living plant or animal cell?

158

Such basic scientific inaccuracies are academically difficult to explain.[103] Why don't other scientists publicly or privately refute such scientific mis-information? Might they lose much needed research grants if they did? At what point does such scientific mis-information become unethical - especially when it degrades and corrupts these very sciences, and is then applied and used to determine the moral status of certain human beings?

The philosophy that is often invoked is just as selective and problematic. Sometimes the "philosopher" apparently has had no background in the history of philosophy, and seems to be totally (or conveniently) oblivious to the theoretical problems inherent in any philosophical position with a mind/body split, or with rationalistic or empiricist philosophical presuppositions. Nor does there seem to be the least awareness that these philosophies are not really viable - but interesting today mostly from an historical or propadeutic perspective, i.e., examples of how such systems historically have failed. Sometimes an historical philosopher is depicted with grosse imprecision, or completely out of context - making that historical philosopher "say" things he never would or could conclude to.

There is no way many "quotes" from Aristotle, Aquinas or Descartes can be sustained academically. And it is hardly a new academic insight that the Aristotle of the *De Anima* is and has been (for centuries) highly problematic and contradictory to his main-stream metaphysical doctrines on substance and anthropology.[104] Nor did Aristotle or Thomas even mention "proto-matter", and both argued that "prime matter" doesn't even really exist. Neither would have defined "substance" as "mass-energy"; nor equated "quantity" with "mass". And Thomas would have always included *esse* in his definition of any "substance". Nor are the proper academic distinctions made among the several different kinds of Thomists (e.g., neo-platonic, aristotelean, suarezian, transcendental, maritainian, rahnerian, process, etc.),[105] many of whom read St. Thomas differently and conclude to different theories on these issues.

Descartes' philosophy was abandoned hundreds of years ago because of its multitudinous theoretical problems - not only because of its mind/body split, belief in innate ideas and that there were only two substances in the entire universe (Mind and Extension), and neo-platonic epistemology - but also because of the blatantly erroneous and absurd scientific theories to which it led (e.g., his theory of the

159

"vortex").[106]   These basic philosophical are likewise difficult to explain.[107] Again, let the "philosophers" in these "personhood" debates defend their philosophical positions with their mind/body splits, as well as their historical philosophical "depictions" and interpretations, openly and publicly before a body of philosophical scholars. Or would that be considered too "uncollegial"? At what point does "collegiality" become unethical - e.g., when it corrupts and degrades the history of philosophy, and is then also applied to determine the moral status of certain human beings?

This observation has serious implications for the assumed "professional" status of researchers, philosophers, ethicists and bioethicists - issues which have received too little attention, especially in light of the current movement of the theories of these writers out of the "ivory towers" of academia into the domaine of public policy. Scientific, philosophical, ethical or bioethical "experts" are being used more and more as "expert witnesses" - for example, in the media, courtrooms, Congressional hearings, and federal panels - to help to determine health care and medical research issues in public policy. It would seem that they should at least be held to the same standards of professional activity as are other "professionals" who have as significant an impact on the public welfare. Interestingly, these four "professions" are not even listed in the *Codes of Professional Responsibility*[108] - although physicians are. I do not consider myself an "expert" in any of these fields at all, and surely I am fallible as well. But given their impact on public policy, certainly there must be some bare minimum of standards in these fields below which one can not go without expecting to be held professionally accountable.

As "food for thought", consider the above-mentioned *Codes*. Among the criteria used as standards for "professionals" in that work are: accountability and responsibility; competence and qualifications; education, training and experience; law and legal requirements; licensing, certification, and accreditation; and other codes, bylaws, policies and technical standards - to name but a few. A glance down the list of "professions" included under these standards of behavior reveals some interesting examples:

1. Accountability and responsibility (p. 479): these professions state specific "codes of professional conduct" or "codes of ethics": accountants, arbitrators, architects, bankers, business executives,

clinical social workers, counselors, dental hygienists, dentists, engineers, financial planners, government lawyers, hospitals, insurance agents, journalists, lawyers, legal assistants, lobbyists, mediators, neutrals, nurses, personnel consultants, physicians, prosecutors, psychiatrists, psychologists, public administrators, real estate agents, social workers, and trial lawyers.

Note that researchers, philosophers, ethicists and bioethicists have no formal professional code of ethics, and no formal professional standards of behavior.

2.   <u>Competence and qualifications</u> (pp. 485-486):   these professions state specific requirements which must be met before practicing, including the mastery of a defined body of knowledge and the attainment of professional degrees which reflect similar requirements; many require testing on local, state or national levels: accountants, advertising agencies, arbitrators, bankers, business executives, clinical social workers, counselors, dental hygienists, dentists, direct marketers, engineers, financial planners, hospitals, insurance agents, journalists, law librarians, lawyers, legal assistants, mediators, neutrals, nurses, physicians, prosecutors, psychiatrists, psychologists, public administrators, real estate agents, social workers, and trial lawyers.

On the other hand, biological researchers are allowed to use radioisotopes without having a course in nuclear chemistry, or chemists are allowed to use infectious microbes without having a course in microbiology or sterile technique. Also, one finds metaphysicians teaching bioethics with no previous course work, ethicists teaching metaphysics with no previous course work, and bioethicists teaching metaphysics and ethics with no previous course work. Wouldn't it be odd to find a lawyer teaching organic chemistry with no previous course work in organic chemistry? As someone once aptly put it, "you can't teach what you don't know". And although philosophers, ethicists, and bioethicists must meet the idiosyncratic requirements of their degree institutions, there are no local, state or national testing requirements or standards to meet in order to assure the public of any common degree of competence or mastery of a similarly defined body of knowledge.

161

3.   Education, training and experience (p. 492):   these professions go beyond the above standards by requiring constant professional up-dating of information under formal, systematic conditions, as well as competence in specific training and a clear demonstration of effective experience: accountants, advertising agencies, arbitrators, architects, bankers, business executives, clinical social workers, counselors, dental hygienists, dentists, engineers, financial planners, hospitals, insurance agents, journalists, law librarians, lawyers, legal assistants, lobbyists, mediators, neutrals, nurses, personnel consultants, physicians, prosecutors, psychiatrists, psychologists, public administrators, real estate agents, social workers, and trial lawyers.

Note that researchers are not required to take courses in research ethics; nor do physicians or nurses necessarily know how to do basic or clinical research.   Nor do philosophers, ethicists, or bioethicists have uniform requirements for course work, yet alone even agree on how to define the subject-matters of their disciplines.   There are no requirements for updating their bodies of knowledge, there are variable degrees and levels of post-degree training - if any - and there are no determinable formal and global professional oversights or requirements for any experience.

Of particular interest is the fact that many public policy issues discussed here (and others) have been grounded on bioethics and its three basic principles of autonomy, justice and beneficence ("principlism").[109] But if "principlism" is no longer acknowledged as a viable basis on which to ground even bioethics,[110] then how can all of those local, national and international regulations, guidelines and documents - which were explicitly grounded on "principlism" - any longer be valid themselves?

4.   Law and legal requirements (pp. 500-501):   these professions go even further and require their members to practice their professions within certain local, state and federal legal requirements: accountants, advertising agencies, arbitrators, architects, bankers, business executives, clinical social workers, counselors, dental hygienists, dentists, direct marketers, engineers, financial planners, government lawyers, hospitals, insurance agents, journalists, law librarians, lawyers, legal assistants, lobbyists, mediators, nurses, personnel consultants, physicians, prosecutors, psychiatrists,

psychologists, public administrators, real estate agents, social workers, and trial lawyers.

There are virtually no local, state or federal legal requirements restricting the practice of philosophers, ethicists or bioethicists.

5.   Licensing, certification and accreditation (pp. 501-502): these professions require that their members obtain local, state or federal licensing, certification and/or accreditation before they are even allowed to practice: architects, clinical social workers, counselors, dental hygienists, dentists, engineers, financial planners, hospitals, insurance agents, lawyers, legal assistants, mediators, nurses, personnel consultants, physicians, prosecutors, psychiatrists, psychologists, real estate agents, and trial lawyers.

Although physicians and nurses are required to be licensed as care givers, they are not required to be licensed as clinical researchers; nor are bench scientists required to be licensed to do basic research. Clearly philosophers, ethicists and bioethicists are not required to be licensed or certified to practice on any local, state or federal level.

In these times of specialization, many "insist" that we must rely on the "professional expertise" of others. But if this and other studies on the arguments for "personhood" indicate anything, it is that one still must question the kind of "expertise" abounding today. If one prefers to propound a scientific/philosophical/ethical/ bioethical theory that the world is made up of "quadrads" or "zeta particles", for example, and that a human being is defined in such terms, such a theory use to be academically entertained "indulgently". But today, when such theories are taught as fact to thousands of students, and further incorporated into local, state, national and international public policies and guidelines which effect the health, welfare and very lives of multi-millions of innocent human beings, then such theories, as well as those who espouse and promote them, ought to bear serious accountability to the public who eventually bears the brunt of such theoretical mis-information.

VI. Conclusion

Given the scientific and philosophical problems inherent in the positions which argue for the various biological marker events of "personhood", can we really accept their various conclusions? Can we accept either the "science" that is used or the rationalistic or empiricist philosophical definitions of human beings or human persons which are incorporated into those arguments? Or is it even possible to reconcile the correct biological facts with a philosophical definition of a human being or a human person?

What I am leading to is a definition which does not split the human being from the human person, and which does not consist of only a part of the human beings of which we have experience. Can you really have a human person without simultaneously having a human being? And vice-versa, can you really have a human being without also simultaneously having a human person?

I would argue no - you really can't split them - except conceptually, as rationalistic or empiricist philosophers are wont to do. But if you do define a human person as only a part of the whole complex - i.e., only in terms of matter, or sentience, or soul, or a part of the soul, or rational attributes - then you will also logically have to argue not only for delayed hominization, but for the infanticide of even normal healthy infants or young adolescents, the substitution of the mentally ill in destructive experimental research, and the abuse and possible euthanizing of many sick human beings (especially the elderly) as well. And delayed hominization simply does not match up with the correct empirical facts.

Philosophically what has occurred is that a "part" of a whole has been turned into a whole thing itself (e.g., the "soul" alone, or the "body" alone are considered separate independent substances in themselves). And, of course, this leads to the chronic Platonic or Cartesian problems of a mind/soul, soul/body, or even a body/body split - with all of the accompanying *chorismos* or "separation" problems latent in those philosophical position (such as no possibility of any interaction between the separated "body" and the "mind" or "soul").

However, if we look closely at the earlier Aristotelean-Thomistic ball-park definition of a human person I would submit that - oddly enough - it matches the most contemporary body of scientific facts that are available today. For example, at fertilization substantial change has taken place, resulting in an embryonic human zygote possessing 46 chromosomes, and a human nature or potency which contains all of the information needed to effect or cause specifically human accidental or embryological change or development. And this original information is not lost until the death of the adult human being. Biological

164

phenomena, such as totipotency, "positional molecules" and even twinning are really normal phenomena which are suppose to happen, and are explained by the human genetic information in the original single-cell human zygote. Once the biological facts are correctly understood it is not difficult to define a human being.

From empirical observations we can then draw our objectively based philosophical concepts of personhood, and these philosophical concepts should surely reflect or match those biological facts as accurately as possible - or else we are not philosophizing about the real world at all.

I have attempted to demonstrate, however briefly, that to define a "human being" or a "human person" in terms of only a part of the whole leads to counterintuitive and incomplete expressions of what we actually experience about human persons, as well as a miss-match with the correct empirical facts. The definition of a "human being" or a "human person" does not have to be relative - as long as the correct science is employed, and our philosophical definitions actually match that reality. I leave it up to you to decide which of the proffered definitions make that match.

"Biological Marker Events"

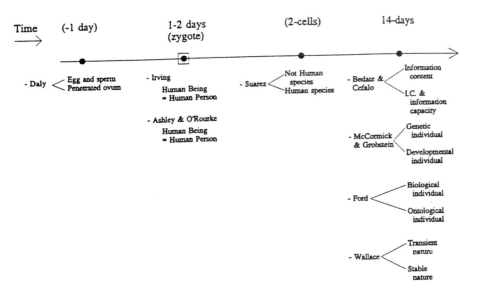

(Figure 1)

"Biological Marker Events"

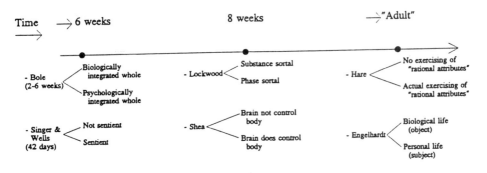

(Figure 2)

Philosophical Definition of a
"Human Being" or a "Human Person"

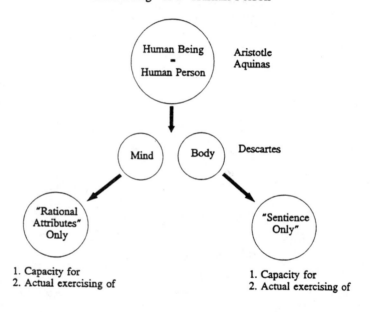

(Figure 3)

REFERENCES

1. See Etienne Gilson, Being and Some Philosophers (Toronto: Pontifical Institute of Mediaeval Studies, 1949); also, Frederick Copleston, A History of Philosophy (New York: Image Books, 1962).

2. See Dianne Nutwell Irving, Philosophical and Scientific Analysis of the Nature of the Early Human Embryo (Doctoral dissertation: Washington, D.C., Department of Philosophy, Georgetown University, April 1991), pp. 267-273 (includes charts of 26 of the arguments).

3. Fr. Tom Daly, "When does a human life begin? The search for a marker event", in Karen Dawson and Jill Hudson (eds.), Proceedings of the Conference: IVF: The Current Debate (Clayton, Victoria, Australia: Monash Center for Human Bioethics, 1987), 79.

4. Irving, Philosophical and Scientific Analysis of the Nature of the Early Human Embryo (1991), particularly Chap. 5.. In addition to the writers I have referenced infra, for an non-exhaustive list of other writers who basically argue similarly with the scientific and/or philosophical critiques presented here include (see also Note 15): [arranged in "rough" categories, as there is usually substantial over-lapping] Science: C. Ward Kischer, "A new-wave dialectic: The reinvention of human embryology", Linacre Quarterly (1994), 61:66-81; C. Ward Kischer, "In defense of human development", Linacre Quarterly (1992), 59:68-75; P. McCullagh, The Foetus As Transplant Donor: Scientific, Social and Ethical Perspectives (New York: John Wiley & Sons, 1987), 483-502; E.F. Diamond, "Abortion? NO!", Insight (Feb. 1972) 36-41. Philosophy: W. Quinn, "Abortion: identity and loss", Philosophy and Public Affairs 13 (1984): 24-54; B. Brody, "On the humanity of the fetus", in Tom Beauchamp and LeRoy Walters, (eds.), Contemporary Issues in Bioethics (California: Wadsworth, 1978), 229-240; R. Werner, "Abortion: the moral status of the unknown", in Social Theory and Practice, 3 (1974): 202; R. Wertheimer, "Understanding the abortion argument", Philosophy and Public Affairs (1971), 1:67-95. Science/Philosophy: Laura Palazzani, "The nature of the human embryo: philosophical perspectives", Ethics and Medicine (1996), 12:1:14-17; C. Ward Kischer and D.N. Irving, The Human Development Hoax: Time To Tell The Truth (Clinton Township, MI: Gold Leaf Press,1995), pre-marketing edition; Antonio Puca, "Ten years on from the Warnock Report: Is the human embryo a 'person'?", Linacre Quarterly (May 1995), 62:2:75-87; Agneta Sutton, "Ten years after the Warnock Report: Is the human neo-conceptus a person?", Linacre Quarterly (May 1995), 62:2:63-74; A. Zimmerman, "I began at the beginning", Linacre Quarterly (1993), 60:86-92; A.A. Howsepian, "Who or what are we?", Review of Metaphysics (March 1992), 45:483-502; S. Heaney, "Aquinas and the presence of the human rational soul in the early human embryo", The Tomist (Jan. 1992), 56:1:19-48;

Anthony Fisher, "Individuogenesis and a recent book by Fr. Ford", Anthropotes (1991), 2:199ff; Stephen Schwarz, The Moral Question of Abortion (Chicago: Loyola University Press, 1990), esp. Chapters 6 and 7; S. Schwarz and R.K. Tacelli, "Abortion and some philosophers: A critical examination", Public Policy Quarterly (1989), 3:81-98; T. Iglesias, "In vitro fertilization: The major issues", Journal of Medical Ethics 10 (1984): 32-37; J. Santamaria, "In vitro fertilization and embryo transfer", in M.N. Brumsky, (ed.), Proceedings of the Conference: In Vitro Fertilization: Problems and Possibilities (Clayton, Victoria: Monash Center for Human Bioethics, Clayton, Vic., 1982), 48-53. **Science/Philosophy/Theology:** Mark Johnson, "Quaestio Disputata: Delayed Hominization; Reflections on some recent Catholic claims for delayed hominization", Theological Studies (1995), 56:743-763; B. Ashley and A. Moraczewski, "Is the biological subject of human rights present from conception?", in P. Cataldo and A. Moraczewski, The Fetal Tissue Issue: Medical and Ethical Aspects (Braintree, MA: The Pope John Center (1994), Chapter Three; B. Ashley and K. O'Rourke, Ethics of Health Care (2nd ed.)(Washington, D.C.: Georgetown University Press, 1994), pp. 149-151; B. Ashley, "Delayed hominization: Catholic theological perspectives", in R.E. Smith (ed.), The Interaction of Catholic Bioethics and Secular Society (Braintree, MA: The Pope John Center, 1992), esp. pp. 165, 176; A. Regan, "The human conceptus and personhood", Studia Moralis (1992), 30:97-127; W.E. May, "Zygotes, embryos and persons", Ethics and Medics, Part I (Oct. 1991), 16:10; G. Grisez, "When do people begin?", Proceedings of the American Catholic Philosophical Association (1990), 63:27-47; T.J. O'Donnell, "A traditional Catholic's view", in P.B. Jung and T. Shannon, Abortion & Catholicism (New York: Crossroad Publishing Co., 1988), pp. 44-47; Benedict Ashley and Kevin O'Rourke, Health Care Ethics: A Theological Analysis (St. Louis: Catholic Health Association, 1987, 2nd ed.), pp. 2-6, 218-233; Jean de Siebenthal, "L'animation selon Thomas d'Aquin: Peut-on affirmer qui l'embryon est d'abord autre chose qu'un homme en s'appuyant sur Thomas d'Aquin?", in L'Embryon: Un Homme. Actes du Congres de Lausanne 1986 (Lausanne: Societe suisse de bioethique, 1986, 91-98); M.A. Taylor, Human Generation in the Thought of Thomas Aquinas: A Case Study on the Role of Biological Fact in Theological Science (Ann Arbor: University Microfilms International, 1982); Benedict Ashley, "A critique of the theory of delayed hominization," in D.G. McCarthy and A.S. Moraczewski, (eds.), An Ethical Evaluation of Fetal Experimentation: An Interdisciplinary Study (St. Louis: Pope John XXIII Medical-Moral Research and Education Center, 1976), 113-133; G.C. Grisez, Abortion: The Myths, the Realities and the Arguments (New York: Corpus Books, 1970). **(Science)/(Philosophy)/Law:** D.N. Irving, amicus curiae brief, Alexander Loce vs The State of New Jersey (1994)(No. 93-1149); S. Heaney, "On the legal status of the unborn", The Catholic Lawyer 33:4:305-323; J.J. Carberry and D.W. Kmiec, "How law denies science", Human Life Review (1992), 18:4:105; G.T. Noonan, "An almost absolute value in history", in J.T. Noonan (ed.), The Morality of Abortion (Cambridge, MA: Harvard University Press, 1970), 1-59.   On related issues, several recent writers have criticized the legal validity of Roe vs Wade: "Testimony of Douglas W. Kmiec, Professor of Constitutional Law, University of Notre Dame, Straus Distinguished Visiting Professor, Pepperdine University, Before the Subcommittee on the Constitution, Committee of the Judiciary, U.S. House of Representatives" April 22, 1996;   "Testimony of Mary Ann Glendon, Learned Hand Professor of Law, Harvard University, Before the Subcommittee on the Constitution, Committee of the Judiciary, U.S. House of Representatives", April 22, 1996;   M.A. Glendon, Abortion and Divorce in Western Law: American Failures, European Challenges (Cambridge MA: Harvard University Press, 1987);   C. Crandall, "Failed predictions", First Things (June/July 1996), pp. 62ff;   C. Forsythe, "The effective enforcement of abortion law before Roe vs Wade", Part V: "Legal Perspectives", in Brad Stetson (ed.), The Silent Subject (Westport, CN: Praeger Publishers, 1996);   P. Cunningham and C. Forsythe, "Is abortion the 'first right' for women?: Some consequences of legal abortion", in J.D. Butler and D.F. Walbert, Abortion, Medicine and the Law (4th ed.)(New York: Facts on File, Inc, 1992).

     Several well-known documents also argue for personhood at "fertilization":   Congregation for the Doctrine of the Faith, "Instruction on Respect for Human Life in its Origin and on the Dignity of Procreation," [Donum Vitae] reprinted in L'Osservatore Romano (Vatican City: 16 March 1987), 3;   Commonwealth of Australia, Senate Select Committee on the Human Embryo Experimentation Bill 1985, (Official Hansard Report), (Canberra: Commonwealth Government Printer, 1986), 25;   Parliamentary Assembly of the Council of Europe, "On the use of human embryos and foetuses for diagnostic, therapeutic, scientific, industrial and commercial purposes", Recommendation 1046 (1986), 1;   and Davis v Davis, 641 1 (D. Tenn. 1989).

     For a non-exhaustive list of arguments counter fertilization in addition to those infra, see: Science: H.J.Morowitz and J.S. Trefil, The Facts of Life: Science and the Abortion Controversy (Oxford: Oxford University Press, 1992);   Karen Dawson, "Fertilization and moral status: A scientific perspective", in P. Singer, Embryo Experimentation (1990), 43-52. Science/Philosophy: Stephen Buckle, Karen Dawson and Peter Singer, "The syngamy debate: when precisely does a human life begin?", in Peter Singer et al (eds.), Embryo Experimentation (New York: Cambridge University Press, 1990), 214-215.   Science/Theology: Jean Porter, "Individuality, personal identity, and the moral status of the preembryo: A response to Mark Johnson", Theological Studies (1995), 56:763-770;   L. Cahill, "The embryo and the fetus: New moral contexts", Theological Studies (1993), 54:124-42;   Shannon and A.B. Wolter, "Refelctions on the moral status of the pre-embryo", Theological Studies (1990), 51:603-26;   C. Tauer, "The tradition of probabilism and the moral status of the early embryo", in P.B. Jung and T.A. Shannon (eds.),

Abortion & Catholicism (New York: The Crossroad Publishing Co., 1988), pp. 54-84; Michael J. Coughlan, "'From the moment of conception...': The Vatican instruction on artificial procreation techniques", Bioethics 2(4), 1988, p. 294-316; Karl Rahner, "The problem of genetic manipulation", in Theological Investigations 9 (New York: Herder and Herder, 1972), p. 226, n. 2; J. Donceel, "Immediate animation and delayed hominization", Theological Studies 31 (1970), p. 75-105. **Science/?:** Clifford Grobstein, Science and the Unborn: Choosing Human Futures (New York: Basic Books, 1988); Clifford Grobstein, "A biological perspective on the origin of human life and personhood", in M.W. Shaw and A.E. Doudera (eds.), Defining Human Life (Washington: Association of University Programs in Health Administration, 1983). **British document:** Dame Mary Warnock, Report of the Committee of Inquiry into Human Fertilization and Embryology (London: Her Majesty's Stationary Office, 1984), esp. p. 17.

5. Antoine Suarez, "Hydatidiform moles and teratomas confirm the human identity of the preimplantation embryo", Journal of Medicine and Philosophy, 15 (1990): 627-635.

6. Carlos Bedate and Robert Cefalo, "The zygote: to be or not be a person", Journal of Medicine and Philosophy 14 (6), 1989: 641; Richard McCormick, S.J., "Who or what is the preembryo?", paper presented at the Andre E. Hellegers Lecture (Washington, D.C., Georgetown University: May 17, 1990) (pre-publication manuscript); see also Richard McCormick, S.J., "Who or what is the preembryo?", Kennedy Institute of Ethics Journal 1(1), 1991, 1; Norman Ford, "The case against destructive embryo research", in Proceedings of the Conference: IVF: The Current Debate, 90-95; also Ford, When Did I Begin? (New York: Cambridge University Press, 1988); William Wallace, "Nature and human nature as the norm in medical ethics", in Edmund D. Pellegrino, John Langan and John Collins Harvey, (eds.), Catholic Perspectives on Medical Morals (Dordrecht: Kluwer Academic Publishing, 1989), 23-53.

7. D.N. Irving, Philosophical and Scientific Analysis of the Nature of the Early Human Embryo (1991); note 2 supra, pp. 267-273.

8. Thomas J. Bole, III, "Metaphysical accounts of the zygote as a person and the veto power of facts", Journal of Medicine and Philosophy 14 (1989): 647-653; also, "Zygotes, souls, substances, and persons", Journal of Medicine and Philosophy 15 (1990): 637-652.

9. Singer and Wells, in D. Gareth Jones, "Brain birth and personal identity", Journal of Medical Ethics 15 (1989): 175.

10. Michael Lockwood, "When does life begin?", in Michael Lockwood, (ed.), Moral Dilemmas in Modern Medicine (New York: Oxford University Press, 1985), 10; also Lockwood, "Warnock versus Powell (and Harradine): When does potentiality count?", Bioethics 2 (3), 1988: 187-213.

11. M.C. Shea, "Embryonic life and human life", Journal of Medical Ethics 11 (1985): 205-209.

12. R.M. Hare, "When does potentiality count? A comment on Lockwood", Bioethics 2 (3), July 1988: 214.

13. H.T. Englehardt, The Foundations of Bioethics (New York: Oxford University Press, 1985), 111.

14. Peter Singer, "Technology and procreation: How far should we go?", Technology Review (Feb./Mar. 1985).

15. See Dianne N. Irving, "Science, philosophy, theology - and altruism: the chorismos and the zygon", in Hans May, Meinfried Striegnitz, Philip Hefner (eds.), Loccumer Protokolle (Rehburg-Loccum: Evangelische Akademie Loccum, 1996); Etienne Gilson, Being and Some Philosophers (Toronto: Pontifical Institute of Mediaeval Studies, 1949); Frederick Copleston, A History of Philosophy (New York: Image Books, 1962); Leonard J. Eslick, "The material substrate in Plato", in Ernan McMullin, ed. The Concept of Matter in Greek and Medieval Philosophy (Indiana: University of Notre Dame Press, 1963); Frederick Wilhelmsen, Man's Knowledge of Reality (New Jersey: Prentice-Hall, Inc., 1956), esp. Chaps. 2 and 3.

16. For an excellent explanation of the difference between Boethius' and Aquinas' definitions of a "human being" or "human person", see Kevin Doran, "Person - a key concept for ethics", Linacre Quarterly 56 (4), 1989, 39.

17. See J. Cottingham, R. Stoothoff, D. Murdoch (trans.), The Philosophical Writings of Descartes (Cambridge: Cambridge University Press, 1989).

18. Aristotle, in his De Coelo (1.5.271b, 9-10), in Richard McKeon (ed.), The Basic Works of Aristotle (New York: Random House, 1941).

19. See Irving, Philosophical and Scientific Analysis... (1991); esp. pp. 83-125, and Chap. 5.

20. Aristotle, Categories, in Sir David Ross, Aristotle (New York: Random House, 1985), p. 20-21; also, Aristotle, Analytica Posteriora 2.19, 100a 3-9, in Richard McKeon (ed.), The Basic Works of Aristotle (New York: Random

House, 1941); for **Aquinas'** similar position, see: <u>The Division and Method of the Sciences</u>, Q6, a.1, reply to 1st Q, pp. 65-66; ibid., Q6, reply to 3rd Q, pp. 71-72; ibid., Q6, a.2, pp. 176-178; ibid., Q6, a.4, p. 90; ibid., Q5, a.3, p.35 (also quoted there in note 21: <u>In I Post. Anal.</u> lect. 1-3, and in <u>De Veritate</u> 1.1); see also George Klubertanz, <u>Introduction to the Philosophy of Being</u> (New York: Appleton-Century-Crofts, 1963), pp. 293-298.

21. Benjamin Lewin (ed.), <u>Genes III</u> (New York: John Wiley and Sons, 1987), pp. 11-13,17-19, 30, 32, 33, 35, 37, 79, 91, 93-94; also Alan E.H. Emery, <u>Elements of Medical Genetics</u> (New York: Churchill Livingstone, 1983), pp. 25, 34, 65, 101-103.

22. **Aristotle**, <u>Categories</u> 5. 2a, 11-13, (McKeon, 1941), p. 9; also (Ross, 1985), p. 24; also (McKeon, 1941): <u>Metaphysica</u> 7.11.1036b, 3-7, p. 800; 8.1.1042a, 30-31, p. 812; even in his <u>De Anima</u> (McKeon, 1941) Aristotle argues for the composite: 2.1.412b, 6-10, p. 555 and 2.1.413a, 3-4, p. 556; for Thomas **Aquinas**, see his <u>Summa Theologica</u>, Fathers of the English Dominican Province (trans.) (Westminster, Md.: Christian Classics, 1981, Vol. 1): Ia.q29,a.1,ans., ad2,3,5, p. 156; ibid., a.2, ans., p. 157; see also Kevin Doran, "Person - a key concept for ethics", <u>Linacre Quarterly</u> 56(4), 1989, p. 39.

23. **Aristotle**, <u>De Anima</u> (McKeon, 1941): 1.4.408b, 13-15, p. 548; also, 1.4.488b, 25-26, p. 548; for **Aquinas** see ST Ia.q75, a.2, ad.2, p. 365; also see Frederick Wilhelmsen, <u>Man's Knowledge of Reality</u> (New Jersey: Prentice-Hall, Inc., 1956), pp. 78-79 and 103-105.

24. Keith L. Moore, <u>The Developing Human</u> (Philadelphia: W.B. Saunders Company, 1982, 3rd. ed.), pp. 14ff; also Benjamin Lewin, <u>Genes III</u> (New York: John Wiley and Sons, 1987), pp. 24ff.

25. K. Moore, <u>The Developing Human</u> (Philadelphia: W.B. Saunders Company, 1982), p. 1; W.J. Larsen, <u>Human Embryology</u> (New York: Churchill Livingstone, 1993), p. 1; Bruce M. Carlson, <u>Human Embryology and Developmental Biology</u> (St. Louis, MO: Mosby, 1994), pp. 3,33-34; R. O'Rahilly and F. Muller, <u>Human Embryology and Teratology</u> (New York: Wiley-Liss, 1994), pp. 19, 23.

26. Bruce M. Carlson, <u>Human Embryology and Developmental Biology</u> (St. Louis, MO: Mosby, 1994), p. 31.

27. **Aristotle**, <u>Physica</u>, (McKeon, 1941): 1.7.191a, 15-18, pp. 232-233; also 2.3.194b, 23-35, pp. 240-241; see also, Henry B. Veatch, <u>Aristotle: A Contemporary Approach</u> (Indiana: Indiana University Press, 1974), Chaps.

2,3; for **Aquinas**, see George Klubertanz, The Philosophy of Human Nature (New York: Appleton-Century-Crofts, 1963), pp. 124ff; also Klubertanz (Philosophy of Being, 1963), pp. 98-100, 116 (and Thomas Aquinas, Commentary on Aristotle's Metaphysics, Bk. VIII, lect.1, (ed.) Cathala, Nos. 1688-1689, as quoted p. 118).

28. Ibid.

29. See Moore (1982) and Lewin (1987), note 26 *supra*.

30. Irving, Philosophical and Scientific Analysis...(1991), see notes pp. 78-80. There is a rapidly increasing volume of this kind of work, e.g., Kollias, G; Hurst, J; deBoer, E. and Grosveld, F. "The human beta-globulin gene contains a downstream developmental specific enhancer", Nucleic Acids Research 15(14) (July, 1987), 5739-47; R.K. Humphries et al, "Transfer of human and murine globin-gene sequences into transgenic mice", American Journal of Human Genetics 37(2) (1985), 295-310; A. Schnieke et al, "Introduction of the human pro alpha 1 (I) collagen gene into pro alpha 1 (I) - deficient Mov-13 mouse cells leads to formation of functional mouse-human hybrid type I collagen", Proceedings of the National Academy of Science - USA 84(3) (Feb. 1987), pp. 764-8.

31. See note 27 *supra*.

32. *pace* R.M. Hare, "When does potentially count? A comment on Lockwood", Bioethics 2(3), 1988.

33. *pace* Michael Lockwood, "Warnock versus Powell (and Harradine): When does potentiality count?", Bioethics 2(3), 1988.

34. For brevity I will designate Aristotle's theory of substance as a composite, which is the pre-dominant one in his Categories, Physics, the first half of the Metaphysics, and even in many parts of his De Anima, as "Aristotle - proper". Aristotle's theory of substance as form alone - or as only the "rational" part of the form, and the succession of souls as found predominantly in the second half of his Metaphysics and in parts of the De Anima, contradicts the former theory. (See 150-page Appendix A, "Aristotle: A question of substance", in my dissertation, Philosophical and Scientific Analysis ..., pp. 296-381). There is also some degree of contradiction in Thomas - insofar as he sometimes "unblushingly" follows Aristotle's theory of separate form (see, for example, the differences between the definition of a human being and that of a human soul in the De Ente et Essentia in Chapter Two and Chapter Four). Also see note 100 for come contemporary criticisms of Aristotle's inconsistencies on "substance". It is worth noting that for both of them the state of human

embryology and chemistry was still rather primitive (e.g., both still held for only 4 physical elements - air, earth, fire and water).

35. Aristotle, Physica 2.1.193b, 3-5, (McKeon, 1941), p.238.

36. Ibid., 2.2.194b, 12-14, p. 240; see also 2.2.193b, 33-37, p. 239.

37. Aristotle, De Anima 1.5.411b, 14-18, (McKeon, 1941), p. 554.

38. Aristotle, De Anima, 1.5.411b, 24-28, (McKeon, 1941), p.554.

39. **Aristotle**, Metaphysica, 3.2.997b18-998a10, (McKeon, 1941), p. 721; see also 11.1.1059a34-1059b14. pp. 850-851; for **Aquinas**, see ST, Ia.q.45, a.4, ad.2, p. 235.

40. Thomas Aquinas, ST, Ia.q29, a.1, ans., ad.2,3,5, p. 156; ibid, a.2, ans., p. 157; also ST, IIIa.q19, a.1, ad.4.2127; see also, Kevin Doran, "Person-a key concept for ethics", Linacre Quarterly 56(4), 1989, p.39.

41. See notes 22 and 40 *supra*; also Thomas Aquinas, On being and Essence, Armand Maurer (trans.), (Toronto: Pontifical Institute of Mediaeval Studies, 1983), Chap. 2; also The Division and Method of the Sciences, Armand Mauer (trans.), (Toronto: Pontifical Institute of Mediaeval Studies, 1986), p. 14, 29, 39, 40.

42. Thomas Aquinas, ST, IIIa. q19, a.1, ad.4.2127; see also Kevin Doran (1989), p. 39.

43. Thomas Aquinas, ST, Ia.q75, a.4, ans., p. 366.

44. For example, Suarez, McCormick, Ford, Wallace and Bole, *infra*.

45. **Aristotle**, De Anima, 1.5.411b, 14-18, (McKeon, 1941), p. 554; also, 1.5.411b, 24-28, p. 554; for **Aquinas**, see notes 41 and 39, *supra*.

46. As the Thomist Klubertanz has expressed it, the human soul, being a form, cannot be divided. The ovum and sperm unite, "thus giving rise to a single cell with the material disposition required for the presence of a soul": Klubertanz, The Philosophy of Nature, 1953, p. 312. Also see B. Ashley and K. O'Rourke, Ethics of Health Care: An Introductory Textbook (Washington, D.C.: Georgetown University Press, 1994), pp. 149-151.

47. Carlos Bedate and Robert Cefalo, "The zygote: to be or not be a person", Journal of Medicine and Philosophy 14(6), 1989, p. 641 -645.

48. Thomas J. Bole, III, "Metaphysical accounts of the zygote as a person and the veto power of facts", Journal of Medicine and Philosophy 14, 1989: 647-653; also, "Zygotes, souls, substances, and persons", Journal of Medicine and Philosophy 15, 1990: 637-652.

49. Benjamin Lewin (ed.), Genes III (New York: John Wiley and Sons, 1983), p. 681; also Alan E.H. Emery, Elements of Medical Genetics (New York: Churchill Livingstone, 1983), p. 93.

50. In addition to the references on "information cascading", see also those in note 25 *supra*.

51. Antoine Suarez, "Hydatidiform moles and teratomas confirm the human identity of the preimplantaion embryo", Journal of Medicine and Philosophy 15, 1990, 630.

52. H. Holtzer, J. Biekl and B. Holtzer, "Induction-dependent and lineage-dependent models for cell-diversification are mutually exclusive", Progress in Clinical Biological Research 175:3-11 (1985); Mavilio, F. et al, "Molecular mechanisms of human hemoglobin switching: selective under-methylation and expression of globin genes in embryonic, fetal and adult erythroblasts", Proceedings of the National Academy of Sciences USA 80:22:664-8 (1983); C. Hart et al, "Homeobox gene complex on mouse chromosome II: molecular cloning, expression in embryogenesis, and homology to a human homeo box locus", Cell 43:1:9-18 (1985).

53. Jerome Lejeune (Nobel Prize, genetics), testimony in Davis v Davis, Circuit Court for Blount County, State of Tennessee at Maryville, Tennessee, 1989; as reprinted in Martin Palmer, A Symphony of the Pre-Born Child: Part Two (Hagerstown, MD: NAAPC, 1989), 9-10.

54. Bedate and Cefalo (1989), p. 641.

55. A.E. Szulmann, U. Surti, "The syndromes of hydatidiform mole. I. Cytogenic and morphologic correlation", American Journal of Obstetrics and Gynecology 131:665-671 (1978); M.S.E. Wimmers, J.V. Van der Merwe, "Chromosome studies on early human embryos fertilized in vitro", Human Reproduction 7:894-900 (1988). See also Suarez, note 61 *supra*.

56. See, e.g., Richard McCormick, S.J., "Who or what is the preembryo?", paper presented at the Andre E. Hellegers Lecture (Washington, D.C. Georgetown University: May 17, 1990) (pre-publication manuscript); see also, McCormick, "Who or what is the Preembryo?", Kennedy Institute of Ethics Journal 1(1), 1991, p. 3; also see reference to Lejeune, p. 14, note 53 *supra*.

57. Lejeune, 1989, p. 14; also, Bruce Carlson, Human Embryology and Developmental Biology (St. Louis, MO: Mosby), p. 33.

58. For example, Grobstein and McCormick, Ford, Wallace *infra*.

59. Lejeune, 1989, p. 17, 20; also see article by Mavilio, where he explains that the modulation of the methylation pattern represents a key mechanism for regulating the expression of human globin genes during embryonic, fetal and adult development in humans. Mavilio et al, "Molecular mechanisms of human hemoglobin switching: selective undermethylation and expression of globin genes in embryonic, fetal and adult erythroblasts", Proceedings of the National Academy of Sciences USA, 80(22) (1983): p. 690;7-11; see also Alan E.H. Emery, Elements of Medical Genetics (New York: Churchill Livingstone, 1983), p. 103.

60. See references on "cascading" in note 49, *supra*; also "transgenic mice" in note 30, *supra*.

61. Antoine Suarez, "Hydatidiform moles and teratomas confirm the human identity of the preimplantation embryo", Journal of Medicine and Philosophy 15 (1990): p. 631.

62. McCormick, p. 3, note 56 *supra*.

63. Ronan O'Rahilly and Fabiola Muller, Human Embryology and Teratology (New York: John Wiley & Sons, 1994), footnote p. 55: "the ill-defined and inaccurate term *pre-embryo* ... is not used in this book". See also C. Ward Kischer, "Human development and reconsideration of ensoulment:, Linacre Quarterly (Feb. 1993), 60:1:57-63; also Kischer (1992, 1993, 1994) in note 4 *supra*.

64. McCormick, p. 3, note 56 *supra*.

65. Keith L. Moore, The Developing Human (Philadelphia: W.B. Saunders Co., 1982), p. 33, 62-63, 68, 111, 127; Ronan O'Rahilly (1994), p. 51; William Larsen, Human Embryology (New York: Churchill Livingstone, 1993), p. 19. 33; Bruce Carlson, Human Embryology and Developmental Biology (St. Louis, MO: Mosby), pp. 34-35. See also see K. Chada et al, "An embryonic pattern of expression of a human fetal globin gene in transgenic mice", Nature (1986), 319:6055:685-9; also G. Migliaccio et al, "Human embryonic hemopoiesis. Kinetics of progenitors and precursor underlying the yolk sac - liver transition:, Journal of Clinical Investigation 78(1), 1986: 51-60.

66. McCormick, p. 4, note 56 *supra*.

67.   Karen Dawson, "Segmentation and moral status", in Peter Singer et al, Embryo Experimentation (New York: Cambridge University Press, 1990), p. 58; see also Keith Moore (1982), p. 133.

68.   Dame Mary Warnock, Report of the Committee of Inquiry into Human Fertilization and Embryology (London: Her Majesty's Stationary Office, 1984), p. 17;   National Institutes of Health: Report of the Human Embryo Research Panel (Washington, D.C.: NIH, Sept. 27, 1994), pp. 45ff.

69.   E.g., see Larsen (1993), p. 1: "... gametes which will unite at fertilization to initiate the embryonic development of a new individual [i.e., the zygote]"; Kischer (1993), note 63 supra; A. Fisher, "Individuogenesis and a book by Fr. Ford", Anthropotes (1991), 2:199f.

70.   C.   Ward   Kischer,   "Human   development   and   reconsideration   of ensoulment" Linacre Quarterly (Feb. 1993), 60:1:57-63.

71.   During taped participation at the "Ethics in Research Conference", FIDIA (Georgetown University, Washington, D.C., April 1991).

72.   E.g., John A. Robertson, "Extracorporeal embryos and the abortion debate", Journal of Contemporary Health Law and Policy 2:53:53-70 (1986). Significantly, he used this argument while representing the father in the Davis vs Davis frozen human embryo appeal - and won the appeal.

73.   National Institutes of Health: Report of the Human Embryo Research Panel, September 27, 1994; pp. 47, 50, 51; available free of charge from Division of Science Policy Analysis and Development, National Institutes of Health, Bldg. 1, Room 218, 9000 Rockville Pike, Bethesda, MD 20892; phone 301-496-1454.   Interestingly, these N.I.H. Recommendations referenced their "human" embryology chart and their list of scientific definitions on the book by Australians Peter Singer (a philosopher), Helga Kuhse (an ethicist), Kasimba (a lawyer) and Karen Dawson (a geneticist).   In that book, [Human Experimentation, (New York: Cambridge University Press, 1990)] the chart and scientific definitions have no references.   There was no human embryologist on that N.I.H. Panel. See also, D.N. Irving, "Testimony before the NIH Human Embryo Research Panel", Linacre Quarterly (1994), 61:82-89.

74.   See personal communications from different pharmaceutical companies to Judie Brown, President, American Life League, April 30, 1996, and August 30, 1996.   Also used and defended recently in T.V. debates by representatives of The Center For Reproductive Law and Policy: Cable Network New York, "News Talk Television", July 2, 1996, 11 A.M.;   CBS News, "Up to the Minute", July 1, 1996, 3 and 5 A.M.   These advocates redefined several

embryological terms, including "abortifacient = contraception", "pregnancy begins at implantation", and that we don't know when the life of a human being begins because that is a philosophical or theological question. They also claimed that the American Medical Association and the World Health Organization supported their claims - which they do not.

75. Norman Ford, When Did I Begin? (New York: Cambridge University Press, 1988), p. 298.

76. Ibid., p. 156.

77. Keith L. Moore, The Developing Human (1982), p. 1.

78. William A. Wallace, "Nature and human nature as the norm in medical ethics:, in Edmund D. Pellegrino, John P. Langan and John Collins Harvey (eds.), Catholic Perspectives on Medical Morals (Dordrecht: Kluwer Academic Publishing, 1989), 23-53.

79. Ibid., p. 30.

80. Aristotle, Metaphysica VI, 1029 a.20, Ross (trans.), in Klubertanz, Philosophy of Being (1963), p. 115 (note 27); for Aquinas see ST, Ia.q6, a.1., ad.3, p. 330; also Commentary on Aristotle's Metaphysics, Book VIII, lect. 1 (ed. Cathala, No. 1686), in Klubertanz (1963), p. 100, and 124-125.

81. Klubertanz (1963), p. 100.

82. Thomas Aquinas, ST, Ia.q.45, a.4, ad.1 and 2, p. 235; also, Ia.q6, a.1., ad.3, p. 330; also Ia q.65, a.3, ans., p. 327; also ibid, a.4, sed contra, p. 327; also ibid, ans., p. 328-329; also, Ia.q.76, a.7, ans., 381.

83. Aristotle, Categories, in Ross (1985), p. 20-21; Thomas Aquinas, The Division and Method of the Sciences (Mauer, ed., 1986), pp. 37-38.

84. Wallace (1989), p. 43-44.

85. Ibid., p. 33.

86. D. Gareth Jones, "Brain birth and personal identity", Journal of Medical Ethics 15(4), 1989, 178.

87. Howard W. Jones and Charlotte Schroder, "The process of human fertilization: implications for moral status", Fertility and Sterility 48(2), Aug. 1987: p. 192.

179

88. G. Gareth Jones (1989), p. 177.

89. See arguments relying on this fact by Singer and Englehardt, *infra*

90. Rene Descartes, <u>Meditations on First Philosophy</u>, in John Cottingham, Robert Stoothoff and Dugald Murdoch (trans.), <u>The Philosophical Writings of Descartes</u> (New York: Press Syndicate of the University of Cambridge, 1984), 2nd Meditation, 12ff.

91. John Locke, <u>An Essay Concerning Human Understanding</u>, A.D. Woozley (ed.) (London: Fontana/Collins, 1964), Book Two, Ch. XXXI, pp. 211-12.

92. H.T. Englehardt, <u>The Foundations of Bioethics</u> (New York: Oxford University Press, 1985), p. 111.

93. Michael Tooley, "Abortion and infanticide", in Marshall Cohen et al (ed.), <u>The Rights and Wrongs of Abortions,</u> (New Jersey: Princeton University Press, 1974), pp. 59, 64.

94. Helga Kuhse and Peter Singer, "For sometimes letting - and helping - die", <u>Law, Medicine and Health Care</u> 3(4), 1986: pp. 149-153; also Kuhse and Singer, <u>Should the Baby Live?</u> The Problem of Handicapped Infants (Oxford: Oxford University Press, 1985), p. 138; Peter Singer and Helga Kuhse, "The ethics of embryo research", <u>Law, Medicine and Health Care</u> 14(13-14), 1987. For one reaction, see Gavin J. Fairbairn, "Kuhse, Singer and slippery slopes", <u>Journal of Medical Ethics</u> 14 (1988), p. 134.

95. Peter Singer, "Taking life: abortion", in <u>Practical Ethics</u> (London: Cambridge University Press, 1981), p. 118.

96. Peter Singer, "Taking life: abortion" (1981), p. 118.

97. Richard G. Frey, The ethics of the search for benefits: Animal experimentation in medicine", in Raanan Gillon (ed.), <u>Principles of Health Care Ethics</u> (New York: John Wiley & Sons, 1994), pp. 1067-1075.
For some arguments counter, see: Adil E. Shamoo and D.N. Irving, "The ethics of research on the mentally disabled", chapter in D.C. Thomasma and J. Monagle (eds.), <u>Health Care Ethics: Critical Issues for the 21st Century,</u> 1997 (forthcoming); Shamoo, Irving and Langenberg, "Comparison of U.S. and non-U.S. studies from psychiatric literature on schizophrenia", <u>Cambridge Quarterly on Health Care Ethics</u> 1997 (forthcoming); J. Katz, "Ethics in neurobiological research with human subjects", <u>Accountability in Research</u> (1996), 4:277-283; Shamoo and T.J. Keay, "Ethical concerns about relapse studies", <u>Cambridge Quarterly on Health Care Ethics</u> (1996), 5:373-386; D.N.

Irving, "Background paper: Washouts/relapses in neurological research using human subjects", in Shamoo (ed.), Proceedings of the First Baltimore Conference on Ethics: Ethics in Neurobiological Research With Human Subjects (New York: Gordon and Breach Science Publishers, 1996); D.N. Irving, "Psychiatric research: Reality check", The Journal of the California Alliance for the Mentally Ill (Spring 1994), 5:1:42-44 (see also similar articles there by Hassner, Shamoo, Becker, Caplan, and the Journal's "Postscript"); Shamoo and Irving, "Accountability in research with persons with mental illness", Accountability in Research (Nov. 1993), 3:1:1-17; Shamoo and Irving, "The PSDA and the depressed elderly: Intermittent competency revisited", Journal of Clinical Ethics (Feb. 1993), 4:1:74-80; R. A. Destro, "Quality-of-life ethics and constitutional jurisprudence: The demise of natural rights and equal protection for the disabled and incompetent", Journal of Contemporary Health Law and Policy (Spring 1996), pp. 1-11.

For a more historical background, see: B. Muller-Hill, Murderous Science (Oxford: Oxford University Press, 1988); R. Proctor, Racial Hygiene-Medicine Under the Nazis (Cambridge, MA: Harvard University Press, 1988); J. Lifton, The Nazi Doctors (New York: Plenum Press, 1986); B. Barber, Research On Human Subjects (New York: Russell Sage Foundation, 1993); H. Jonas, The Imperative of Responsibility (Chicago: Chicago University Press, 1984); Jay Katz, Experimentation With Human Beings (New York: Russell Sage Foundation, 1972); A.C. Ivy, "The history and ethics of the use of human subjects in medical experiments", Science (1948), 108:1-5.

98. M.M. Uhlmann, "The legal logic of euthanasia", First Things (June/July 1996), 39-43.

99. Similar to my concern with the use of the terms "pre-embryo" and "person" used in these bioethics "personhood" debates, see the exquisite work demonstrating historically the abuses perpetrated on "vulnerable" populations by means of redefining them as in some way "sub-human" beings, by William Brennan, Dehumanizing the Vulnerable: When Word Games Take Lives (Chicago: Loyola University Press, 1995).

100. O'Rahilly and Muller (1994), pp. 8-9.

101. Robert H. Bork, Slouching Towards Gomorrah: Modern Liberalism and American Decline (New York: Harper-Collins [Regan Books], 1996), p. 192, also pp. 174ff. See also notes 72, 73, 74 supra.

102. E.D. Pellegrino, "Character and the ethical conduct of research", Accountability in Research 2(1), 1992: pp. 1-11; E.D. Pellegrino "Trust and distrust in professional ethics", in E.D. Pellegrino, R. Veatch, J. Langan, Ethics, Trust, and the Professions (Washington, D.C.: Georgetown University

Press, 1991), pp. 69-85; E.D. Pellegrino "Character, virtue and self-interest in the ethics of the professions", Journal of Contemporary Health Law and Policy 5 (Spring 1989), pp. 53-73.

For works more focused on bench research science, see: D.N. Irving, "The impact of scientific 'misinformation' on other fields: Philosophy, theology, biomedical ethics and public policy", Accountability in Research (April 1993), 2:4:243-272; A.E. Shamoo, "Role of conflict of interest in public advisory councils" (Chapter 17), in D. Cheney, Ethical Issues in Research (Frederick, MD: University Publishing Group, Inc., 1993); A.E. Shamoo, "Role of conflict of interest in scientific objectivity: A case of a Nobel Prize work", Accountability in Research (1992), 2:55-75; A.E. Shamoo, "Policies and quality assurance in the pharmaceutical industry", Accountability in Research (1991), 1:273-284; A.E. Shamoo, "Policies and quality assurance in the pharmaceutical industry", Accountability in Research (1991), 1:273-284; A.E. Shamoo, "Role of conflict of interest in public advisory councils", Fidea Research Foundation Proceedings (1991); John C. Bailar III, Marcia Angell, Sharon Boots et al, Ethics and Policy in Scientific Publication (Bethesda, MD: Council of Biology Editors, Inc., 1990); A.E. Shamoo, "Organizational structure and function of research and development" (Chapter 4), in A.E. Shamoo (ed.), Principles of Research Data Audit (New York: Gordon and Breach, 1989); Peter McCullagh, The Foetus as Transplant Donor: Scientific, Social and Ethical Perspectives (New York: John Wiley and Sons, 1987); A.E. Shamoo and Z. Annau, "Ensuring scientific integrity", Nature (1987), 327:550; Gerhard Portele, "Moral development and education", in David Gosling and Bert Musschenga, Science, Education and Ethical Values (Geneva: World Council of Churches Publications; and Washington, D.C.: Georgetown University Press, 1985), pp. 31-36; for a feminist view see Evelyn Fox Keller, Reflections of Gender and Science (New Haven: Yale University Press, 1985); Gerrit Manenschijn, "Reasoning in science and ethics", in Gosling (1985), pp. 37-54; for an historical view, see Crombie, Medieval and Early Modern Science (New York: Doubleday Anchor Books, 1959).

103. D. N. Irving, "Politization of science and philosophy", C.E.R.P.H. Newsletter no. 2, p. 4 (Poitiers, France: Centre d'Etudes sur la Reconnaissance de la Personne Humaine, 1995); D.N. Irving, "'New age' embryology text books: 'Pre-embryo', 'pregnancy' and abortion counseling; Implications for fetal research", Linacre Quarterly (May 1994), 61:2:42-62.

104. Mary Louise Gill, Aristotle on Substance (Princeton: Princeton University Press, 1989); Charlotte Witt, Substance and Essence in Aristotle (New York: Cornell University Press, 1989); Marjorie Grene, A Portrait of Aristotle (Chicago: The University of Chicago Press, 1963). Also see note 34 supra.

105. J. M. de Torre, "Transcendental Thomism and the encyclical Veritas Splendor", Fellowship of Catholic Scholars Newsletter (April 1995), pp. 21-24; G.C. Reilly, "The empiricism of Thomistic ethics", Proceedings of the American Catholic Philosophical Association (Washington, D.C.: The Office of the Secretary of the Association, The Catholic University of America, 1956), pp. 1-36.

106. Paul Edwards, ed. The Encyclopedia of Philosophy (New York: Macmillan Publishing Co., 1967); Vol. 1, pp. 341-352.

107. D. N. Irving, "Academic fraud and conceptual transfer in bioethics: Abortion, human embryo research, and psychiatric research", in J.W. Koterski (ed.), Life and Learning IV: Proceedings of the Fourth University Faculty For Life Conference (Washington, D.C.: University Faculty For Life, June 1994), pp. 193-215.

108. Rena A. Gorlin (ed.), Codes of Professional Responsibility (Washington, D.C.: The Bureau of National Affairs, Inc., 1991).

109. E.g., to name but a few: the current legislation pending in the State of Maryland for the use of incompetent mentally ill patients in experimental research; National Commission for the Protection of Human Subjects of Biomedical and Behavioral Research, The Belmont Report (Washington, D.C: U.S. Department of Health, Education, and Welfare, 1978) (the explicit basis for all of these documents); President's Commission for the Study of Ethical Problems in Medicine and Biomedical and Behavioral Research, several individual Reports including Summing Up (Washington, D.C., U.S. Government Printing Office, 1983); United States Code of Federal Regulations: Protection of Human Subjects 45 CFR 46 (revised Jan. 12, 1981, Mar. 8, 1983; reprinted July 1989 - now in the Common Rule for all departments of the federal government) (Washington, D.C.: DHHS); National Institutes of Health: Report of the Human Fetal Transplant Research Panel (Washington, D.C.: NIH, December 1988); NIH Guide for Grants and Contracts (Washington, D.C.: NIH, 1990); NIH Revitalization Act, Public Law 103-43 (June 1993); Office for the Protection from Research Risks (OPRR), Protecting Human Research Subjects: Institutional Review Board Guidebook (Washington, D.C. NIH, 1993); NIH Guidelines on the Inclusion of Women and Minorities as Subjects in Clinical Research, Federal Reg. 59 FR 14508 (Washington, D.C.: NIH, March 28, 1994); NIH Outreach Notebook On the Inclusion of Women and Minorities in Biomedical and Behavioral Research (Washington, D.C.: NIH, 1994); National Institutes of Health: Report of the Human Embryo Research Panel (Washington, D.C.: NIH, Sept. 27, 1994); the CIOMS/WHO International Ethical Guidelines for Biomedical Research Involving Human Subjects (Geneva: CIOMS/WHO, 1993).

110. To mention but a few: B. Ashley and K. O'Rourke, <u>Ethics of Health Care</u> (St. Louis, MO: The Catholic Health Association, 1996), pp. 250-251; T. Engelhardt, "Christian bioethics: A non-ecumenical rebirth", <u>Bioethics Research Notes</u> (Dec. 1995) (Australian), 7:4:37-38; J. F. Kilner, N.M. Cameron and D.L. Schiedermayer, <u>Bioethics and the Future</u> (Grand Rapids, MI: William Eerdmans Publishing Co., 1995); D. Brodeur, "Guidance for a failing system", <u>Health Progress</u> (Sept./Oct. 1995), 30-30-40; Daniel Callahan, "Bioethics: private choice and common ground", <u>Hastings Center Report</u> (May-June 1994), 28:31; Albert Jonsen, "Preface", in DuBose et al, <u>What About Principles? Ferment in U.S. Bioethics</u> (Valley Forge, PA: Trinity Press International, 1994); D.N. Irving, "Testimony before the NIH Human Embryo Research Panel", <u>Linacre Quarterly</u> (1994), 61:82-89; D.N. Irving, "Quality assurance auditors: Between a rock and a hard place", <u>Quality Assurance: Good Practice, Regulation, and Law</u> (March 1994), 3:1:33-52; see the many writers who reject bioethics "principlism" in Raanan Gillon (ed.), <u>Principles of Health Care Ethics</u> (New York: Wiley & Sons, 1994); D.N. Irving, "Which ethics for science and public policy?", <u>Accountability in Research</u> (1993), 3:2:3:77-99; D.N. Irving, "Philosophical and scientific critiques of "autonomy-based" ethics: Toward a reconstruction of the 'whole person' as the natural ground of ethics and community", The International Bioethics Conference: Beyond Autonomy: New International Perspectives for Bioethics (San Francisco, CA; April 16-18, 1993). A. Sharpe, <u>How the Liberal Ideal Fails As a Foundation for Medical Ethics</u> (Doctoral dissertation)(Washington, D.C.: Georgetown University, 1991), Chapters 1-3.

Which Ethics for Science and Public Policy?

Dianne N. Irving, M.A., Ph.D., and Adil E. Shamoo, Ph.D.

ABSTRACT

The problem of inaccurate, misapplied or fraudulent data could be addressed by government regulations, or by self-regulation from within science itself. To many, self-regulation implies the grounding of research activities in some "neutral" standard of "ethics" acceptable in a "pluralistic" society. Yet, there is no such thing as a "neutral ethics"; and many "contemporary" theories contain such serious theoretical deficiencies and contradictions that they are practically inapplicable. As a viable alternative to these theoretical and practical problems, an objectively based realistic framework of ethics is considered, and used to ground both the individual scientific and the collective public policy decision making processes. This is an ethics of properly integrated relationships. It is then applied to an analysis of many of the causes of incorrect data, as well as of many of the internal and external pressures and abuses often experienced by scientists today. This approach respects the integrity of each decision maker as a human being and as a moral agent - which in turn better insures the integrity of the protocol, the data, and the public policy decisions which follow - and ultimately, the integrity of the scientific enterprise itself. The alternative is government regulations.

INTRODUCTION

Contemporary science is, in many respects, big business. It consumes hundreds of billions of dollars annually from our national treasure. The structure of science and its fueling energy - the research and development operations - consume tens of billions of dollars with over 1 million scientists involved in the process (Shamoo, 1989).

Many individuals are attracted to scientific careers because of a desire to be useful, the excitement of exploring new territory, the hope of finding order, or the desire to test established knowledge (Kuhn, 1970). Additionally, the reward system is an important fuel component that can enhance enthusiasm and creativity. Even deep ideological drives find expression in the scientific enterprise. As the U.S. National

Academy of Science has noted: "... a strong personal attachment to an idea is not necessarily a liability. It can even be essential in dealing with the great effort and frequent disappointments associated with scientific research" (U.S. National Academy of Science, 1989) (Hopefully ideology will not inadvertently cause the scientist to "prejudice" his or her data). In effect the scientific enterprise will also necessarily reflect the various ethical principles and social values espoused by the multitude of individuals involved in the scientific enterprise. In acknowledging the even more basic "humanity" underlying each of these individuals, Arthur Kornberg, the Nobel Laureate biochemist, perceptively quipped: "Science is great, but scientists are still people" (Kornberg, 1992). At times it would seem that contemporary science has lost sight of the "person" behind the starched white lab-coat.

One of the more serious concerns of contemporary science is how to deal with inaccurate, misapplied or fraudulent data (Irving, 1991, 1993A, 1993B; Kischer, 1993). That such data exists, or is problematic, or that some form of over-sight is necessary is no longer the issue. The scientific community no longer debates whether some form of oversight should be exercised over the scientific enterprise, but rather how much and in what form" (Shamoo, 1992A)? In other words, what is the balance to be struck between self-regulation and federal regulations? Kornberg, for example, does recognize "laxity and negligence", but he opposes any "bureaucratic procedures" (Kornberg, 1992). Others insist that scientists are incapable of any meaningful "self-regulation", and so the only real alternative to scientific fraud is governmental regulation.

Several of the causes of such problematic data include: the inevitable conflicts of interests, the very complexity of the information, the remoteness of the information from its sources (Shamoo and Annau, 1990; Shamoo, 1991), the lack of quality control and of quality assurance, the proliferation of information and data, and its reliance on the computer (Shamoo and Davis, 1990). Other serious influences on the scientist include the institutional pressures to "publish or perish"; to obtain funding - in industry, university settings, governmental agencies and in Congress; and media pressures.

However, our question here concerns a broader cause or source of error - that is, the presence of intellectual artifacts in decision-making processes - on both the individual and the institutional levels - which ultimately impact and more subtly influence how we design our protocols, produce data, or analyze public policy. It is with a view toward the development of a viable theoretical and practical structure for scientific "self-regulation" that we attempt to articulate and clarify here some of these intellectual artifacts. The intent is neither to debunk nor ensconce any particular individual philosopher or his teaching - but rather to examine briefly some of the major ethical frameworks available for our consideration and evaluation.

NO SUCH THING AS A "NEUTRAL ETHICS"

Often we are told that one sure way to insure the integrity of our data as well as the integrity of our policies is by being "ethical". If we are only "ethical" we can relax, be accountable, responsible, and assure good data and good policies - thus also avoiding over-reaching governmental regulations. And in a democracy, where no one's values should be imposed on others, the best ethics to employ is a "neutral" ethics. But, unfortunately, and incredibly, what is usually not explained by ethicists is that there is no such thing as a "neutral" ethics. Even risk/benefit analysis is grounded on variations of a utilitarian theory - which by definition is a normative ethical theory - i.e., it takes a stand on what is right and what is wrong, just as any other normative ethical theory does (Beauchamp and Childress, 1979; Beauchamp and Walters, 1978, 1982, 1989). As any good historian of philosophy will tell you, there is even no such thing as a "neutral" logic (Gilson, 1963; Copleston, 1962).

So what are we to do? If no ethical theory is "neutral", then which ethics is to be used for science and for public policy - especially in a democratic society? No one likes the "god-squad" - particularly scientists and public policy makers! But what we want to convey is that someone is playing "god" - regardless - on every level of our collective decision-making - even if it sounds "neutral". And so the question is no longer whether science and public policy should be ethical - but rather, which ethics should be used? To even begin to address this question we will explore briefly the individual and institutional integrity essential for decision making concerning scientifically sound protocols, accurate data, and responsible public policy. Clearly, if scientists are really serious about "self-regulation", they need to consider "integrity" seriously as well. The alternative is

187

governmental regulation.

RECENT HISTORY OF THE PROBLEM IN ETHICS

There are several problems with some of the present theories of ethics which are likely candidates for use in science and public policy. Generally they are currently theories borrowed from bioethics. As recently pointed out (Irving, 1993C), the early "classic" bioethics texts basically restricted our considerations (for all intents and purposes) to ethical theories questionably derived from Kant or Mill. Renditions of Kant's theory - or deontology - was suppose to represent the defense of the interests of the individual; Mill's theory - or utilitarianism - was suppose to represent the defense of the interests of society. From primarily variations of these "theories" were derived the basic guiding theoretical ethical principles so often quoted and elaborated today: autonomy, beneficence and justice (Beauchamp and Childress, 1979, 1989; Beauchamp and Walters, 1978, 1982, 1989) - often referred to fondly as the "Georgetown Mantra" (a reference to the Kennedy Institute of Ethics, Georgetown University).

Although perhaps the intentions were good, and given that the field was in its infancy - as is your field right now - over the years a sort of "empirical ethics" has slowly been taking place. Often the identification and application of these theoretical ethical principles in routine daily medical practice did indeed help to clarify otherwise murky issues. But cracks began to form. For example, these three ethical principles were held to be prima facie (Beauchamp and Childress, 1989; Beauchamp and Walters, 1978, 1982, 1989) - that is, no one principle held precedence over either of the others. Yet in real-life medical situations, these theoretical principles would often come into conflict (Pellegrino, 1993; Shamoo and Irving, 1993B) - with no theoretically structured means by which to resolve the conflict, or to really balance them.

Soon each of these principles began to take on a life of its own, each one approaching an "absolute", and separated or split from the other two. For example, autonomy was claimed as the "ethical" ground for a patient to insist on extraordinary and often extremely expensive medical care, because it was his - or his family's - free autonomous choice. Or, a physician could rationalize the use of certain

188

care for her patient against the patient's wishes because it was clearly medically indicated and the doctor knows best what is beneficent or good for her patient. Or again, institutionalized mentally ill patients could be used in experimentation for the benefit of others in their "class" of diseases (Shamoo and Irving, 1993C), or in purely experimental research for the sake of obtaining knowledge in general or for the "greater good of society" (see Tannenbaum and Cook, 1978; U.S. Code of Federal Regulations 45 CFR 46, 1989) because in justice they owed society for providing them with shelter, food and care, or because this is one way in which the mentally ill could presume to want to help to "share" the burdens of society (McCormick, 1974).

However, through daily empirical observations by practitioners in the field, the inadequacies and inconsistencies in these theoretical "ethical principles" began to show. There has been a steady growing uneasiness with their formulation and application, which somehow seems sometimes counter-intuitive; and newer attempts to move beyond this original formulation and stage of the field have begun (Irving, 1993C; Hamel, DuBose and O'Connell, 1993).

THE HISTORY OF PHILOSOPHY REVEALS AN ARTIFACT

However, there is an even more fundamental problem with these ethical theories, although in order to see this requires consulting the history of philosophy itself [Fig. # 1]. Briefly, each of the major philosophers in the history of philosophy have defined "being" or reality differently (Gilson, 1963). If one defines "being" differently, then one defines "human being" differently, and then the ethics are different. Or they then define "material being" differently, and then the science is different (Crombie, 1959). The major common source of the errors and inaccuracies which follow from some of these definitions is what is known in philosophy as a "mind/body split" (Wilhelmson, 1956; Fox, 1989; Meilander, 1987).

Closely related to these metaphysical and anthropological differences are the methodological (or, epistemological) differences [Fig. # 2]. The starting point of knowledge for some philosophers is outside the mind, i.e., the things they are investigating. Information about these things is induced through the senses, worked on by the intellect, and finally checked back with the things outside the mind which have been experienced in order to determine if there is a correspondence between the information or concepts formed in the intellect with the things outside the mind - their criteria for the truth or falsity of their information or concepts. The limited validity of both sense and intellectual cognition is acknowledged (Irving, 1992; Veatch, 1974; Klubertanz, 1963).

For others [Fig. # 3], the starting point of knowledge is inside the mind, e.g., a concept or a hypothesis; and information about reality is deduced from this internal rational starting point, and checked with the original store of knowledge systems in order to determine if the "information" or concepts cohere with, or fit in with, these systems - their criteria for the truth or falsity of their information. Only intellectual cognition is acknowledged as truly valid; the validity of sense cognition is generally rejected. Thus the major sources of error in methodology usually concern the starting points of the investigation, and the reliability of the check-backs for truth and falsity (Gilson, 1963; Wilhelmson, 1956; Irving, 1992).

All of these theoretical differences eventually trickle down to cause very different and often contradictory conclusions - not only throughout the history of philosophy, but also throughout many other fields as well. This is only a very quick and brief indication of from where, we would argue, these intellectual artifacts originate. Regardless of how objective we try to be concerning our observations or the information which we use, these intellectual artifacts constitute a much more subtle machine that is driving our scientific and public policy decisions, and more difficult to rout out (Irving, 1993A, 1993B).

What are some of the general implications of all of this [Fig. # 4]? If, like Plato (Jowett, 1937; Vlastos, 1978; Gilson, 1963), a human being is defined as two separate substances - soul and body - and if the body (as matter) is non-being - then there is not only a separation or split between the soul and the body, and therefore no interaction possible or explainable; but a human being is defined only in terms of the "rational" part of the soul, since his body (as non-being) isn't. Even Plato himself acknowledged that this mind/body split was theoretically devastating to his own philosophy and wouldn't work.

But despite Plato's own self-effacing warnings, philosophers throughout the history of philosophy have perpetuated these metaphysical and anthropological artifacts - which, in turn, have seriously influenced their ethics (as will be noted later).

The modern counterpart of Plato was Descartes (Gilson, 1963; Wilhelmson, 1956; Copleston, 1962), who also defined a human being as two separate substances - mind and body - but ultimately, again, only as mind. If you want to see a philosopher sweat once he has painted himself into a theoretical corner, you might want to consult his Sixth Meditation (Cottingham, 1984). There Descartes is trying to explain how the pain in a physical leg is expressed or "felt" in the immaterial mind. But because he has a mind/body split, he cannot explain any interaction between the immaterial mind and the physical body because they are separated. Even his attempt with the pineal gland in the brain will not work, because the penial gland, too, is really only a part of the physical body.

To indicate how Descartes-the-physicist's metaphysical and anthropological presuppositions - or, intellectual artifacts - impacted or influenced his ability to even do science (Edwards, 1967), consider the following. The very validity of the fundamental laws of physics and mathematics depended on his proving the truth of the "cogito" ("I think, therefore I am") and on the existence of God - neither of which he was successful in doing. And because he rejected the existence of a void, Descartes' material substance, i.e., Extension, is continuous. These metaphysical presuppositions, in turn, had serious consequences for his physics - especially his scientific theory of the vortex.

For example, the material world for Descartes is therefore not composed of ultimate atoms, but only volumes, which must then move as a whole, i.e., a simultaneous movement of matter in some closed curve. Planetary motion must be explained as one infinite three-dimensional continuous and homogenous extended body. If there is only one continuous extended substance which constitutes the whole material universe, then he can only distinguish one body from another body in terms of differential volumes and secondary qualities. Therefore he cannot have a definition for density, or for viscosity.

Descartes omits "matter", therefore, from his definition of motion. Motion = speed x size; but "size", for Descartes, is a continuous volume of body. Therefore his laws of impact are actually in error. Also, he cannot isolate a particular force, e.g., gravity, in terms of how a body would move if it were free from resistance, because to imagine it moving without resistance is to imagine it in a void - the existence of which he had rejected.

Animals have no penial glands, for Descartes, and therefore no souls. Therefore they cannot feel any pain, or any other kinds of sensations - as sensations were really only modes of thought. Animals are only physical bodies, i.e., "machines", and the only sense in which they can be hurt is to "damage" them.

Thus, not only can Descartes not explain any interaction between his immaterial Mind and his material Body; he also cannot guarantee the very laws of physics and mathematics he was so anxious to protect. He cannot substantially distinguish one body from another, correctly define planetary motion, density, viscosity, motion, size, gravity, and his laws of impact are in error. Even animals are incapable of feeling any pain.

Well - so where does all this "theorizing" leave us? Amazingly, our "man" (including the scientist-man) is no longer a whole man; and our knower or investigator (including the scientist-investigator) can no longer know the real world! Such a fractured broken remnant of a human being can no longer even formulate or ask the appropriate questions necessary for survival - much less those questions needed for performing basic research.

From Descartes came the later rationalists [Fig. # 5], who took one of Descartes' substances, i.e., "Mind", and defined a human being only in terms of "rational attributes". The later empiricists took Descartes' other substance, i.e., Extension, or matter, and defined a human being only in terms of matter or sentience (or the ability to feel pain or pleasure)(Irving, 1993A).

And here one meets up once again with the contemporary bioethical theories, using primarily variations on Kant (the rationalist) or variations on Mill (the empiricist). The inherent theoretical and practical problems in these two current approaches have already been noted earlier. Now one can see that many of these problems stem from the fact that these theories retain from their historical predecessors very definite and problematic metaphysical, epistemological and anthropological presuppositions - specifically their definitions of a human being, and how that human being comes to know material reality. Now consider the impact of these philosophical presuppositions on their ethics. What is "ethical" is now based on variations of either "Kant's" pure rational autonomy - or on variations of "Mill's" pure materialistic (although more sophisticated) utilitarian calculus of pain and pleasure (the ultimate philosophical ground of risk/benefit analysis).

But if "Kant" is right, and human persons are not to be defined with a material body, but only in terms of "rational attributes"; and if only rational "autonomous" human beings are "persons" - and therefore due ethical respect and protection; then non-autonomous human beings are not persons, e.g., Alzheimer's and Parkinson's patients, persons with mental illness, drunks, drug addicts, the comatose - even very young children. Therefore one would logically have to argue that they have no ethical standing as human persons, and perhaps no legal or social protections as well, as many bioethicists, lawyers and public policy makers do argue. These writers even conclude that therefore the infanticide of normal healthy human infants and young children is ethically permissible (Englehardt, 1985; Tooley, 1974; Robertson, 1989; Hare, 1988). Well, I would argue, that leaves a great number of human beings in serious trouble.

If "Mill" is right, and human persons are to be defined and ethically protected only in terms of "sentience" (or a material substance capable of feeling pain or pleasure); and if what is ethically relevant is only degrees of pain and pleasure; then many higher mammals which are highly sentient (e.g., dogs or chimpanzees) are persons, and many human beings (e.g., newborn human infants) are not persons. And if we do know empirically that in human beings full "rational attributes" or "full sentience" are not present until years after birth (Moore, 1982), then one would again have to conclude that the infanticide of perfectly normal healthy human infants and young children is ethically permissible - as is argued by many bioethicists, lawyers and public policy makers today (Singer, 1981; Kuhse, 1986; Lockwood, 1988).

These reality checks should be taken quite seriously. Consider the conclusions and consequences for all of us human beings today if "Kant" or "Mill" were correct. Consider what is at stake. If these theories theoretically don't work, and lead to such counter-intuitive and drastic conclusions, then why use them? Can we even justify using them? Should they be used to ground the ethics of research or public policy formulation? These are just some of the intellectual philosophical artifacts which have found their way down into the medical and scientific communities, and on which much public policy is already presently being based (Irving, 1993B).

A MORE OBJECTIVELY-BASED ETHICAL THEORY FOR SCIENCE AND PUBLIC POLICY DECISION MAKING

" ... for wickedness perverts us and causes us to be deceived about the starting-points of action. Therefore it is evident that it is impossible to be practically wise without being good." [Aristotle, Ethica Nicomachea, p. 1035]

If scientists are really serious about avoiding governmental regulation by means of "self-regulation" to prevent scientific fraud, this will require an equally serious consideration of how one goes about "self-regulating" in a way which both theoretically and practically maintains the integrity of both the "man" and the "institutions" of which he is a member. Presently either no really viable constructive alternatives are proposed at all, or those which are proposed fall into one of the problematic categories above. Simply because of their theoretically and practically unsolvable problems those theories are inherently unworkable and should clearly not be used as a viable ethical basis for scientific "self-regulation".

On the other hand there is at least a third viable ethical framework one might want to consider; one in which the integrity of the "man" and of the "institutions" is maintained [Fig. # 6]. Such an ethical framework was originally advanced by Aristotle the biologist (Aristotle, "Ethica Nicomachea", in McKeon 1941, p. 935; Veatch, 1974; Gilson, 1963; Bourke, 1951; Irving, 1992), and critiqued and improved on through the wisdom gained by trial and error throughout the centuries. The deeper grounds of the starting point of this theory are the investigation of everything with the induction of information from objectively based sensitive and intellectual experience of the real things in the world outside our minds - and any such information or concepts thus obtained must be referred back to those real things outside the mind in order to determine their truth or falsity (Aristotle, "Analytica Posteriora", pp. 136, 184-186, "Ethica Nichomachea", p. 1033 in McKeon 1941). This method will sound very familiar to the life research scientist - i.e., the scientific method! Here a human being is not defined as two separated substances, but only as one whole complex substance with both formal and material aspects (Aristotle, "De Anima", p. 554 in McKeon, 1941). Thus there is no mind/body split; and the human knower can both reach and know objective reality to a very sophisticated degree. The impact of these philosophical premises on one's ethics, and on one's treatment of the decision making process, is considerable.

Ethics now is not based only on pure autonomous rational choice; nor on merely physical pain and pleasure - but proximately on the whole human being, relating properly within him or herself, as well as relating properly with society and the environment with which and in which he or she must flourish and survive (Finnis, 1980; Fagothey, 1963). It is a much more complex ethical system - but then, doesn't it more accurately match the objective reality of the very complex human beings and the very complex world in which we live? It is worth placing this ethical theory under a "microscope" for just a moment.

What is probably one of the most compelling elements is its insistence on correctly identifying the proper proximate goal or good of any human being - that is, a human being's goal or good simply by virtue of his or her being human (Aristotle, "Ethica Nichomachea", in McKeon, 1941, pp. 935-947). That end or goal is variously rendered as "happiness", "flourishing", the excellence of living well, or being the "best that you can be" - as real live human beings. Common human goods have variously included: food, shelter, education, life and even recreation (Finnis, 1982). This implies, again, no mind/body split - for these various goods represent the several real aspects of a whole, unfractured human being. It is the integrity of the whole human being - and the integrity of his relationship with society and the environment - which is at issue. It is an ethics of relationships. Here ethics is about the rightness and wrongness of human actions as they relate to our proper human goal or good.

Variations on this basic framework have further examined in more detail the decision making process itself, as well as the various criteria which should be considered in evaluating the human actions which follow from that process. The ethical aspect of our actions is not determined by any one single criteria, but, more complexly, in terms of several criteria (e.g., the very nature of the action, the circumstances under which they were performed, the intention of the actor, the consequences of his or her actions, etc. (Fagothey, 1963; McInerny, 1982). What the human good is, and what brings us closer to or takes us further from it is not to be determined by relative opinions, but to be objectively determined by the daily observations and experiences of real live human beings. There is no "is/ought gap" (as the academic argument goes), if this objectively determined goal-oriented feature of Aristotle's ethics is properly understood and theoretically retained (Aristotle, "Ethica Nichomachea", in McKeon, 1941, p. 1032).

THE ROLE OF INFORMATION IN ETHICAL AND POLICY DECISION MAKING

The role that information or data play in the ethical and policy decision making processes will be considerably different within this framework. Certainly Aristotle's warning - that "a small error in the beginning leads to a multitude of errors in the end" (Aristotle, "De Caelo", in McKeon, 1941, p. 404) - captures in one sentence the gist of that role. Such a warning should give us pause here, considering that such an error in information which is embedded deep within a policy would impact thousands of scientists - as both individuals and as policy makers.

A. Individual decision making
The individual decision making process can be broken down into several distinct components. Each should be considered separately on its own merits, although each also needs to be understood as having a direct influence on the integrity of the other components as well [Fig. # 7].

1. The starting point of the decision making process that will lead to ethical actions is "objectively" correct information - of what the physical world is, of what the proper human goal is, as well as of what different sorts of intermediate things or actions we need to consider as means to reach that goal (Aristotle, "Ethica Nichomachea", in McKeon, 1941, pp. 1030-1036). Indeed, one of the most important of the intellectual virtues (as distinct from the moral virtues) is literally none other than the virtue of "science" (Aristotle, "Ethica Nichomachea", in McKeon, 1941, pp. 1022-1024; Fagothey, 1963) - or the habit of knowing correctly what the true "objective" facts of reality are (as best we can). Relative to the bench scientist's engagement in his or her experiment, we would distinguish two

196

different criteria for obtaining "objectively correct information": the unbiased and independent observation of phenomena; and the unbiased and independent selection of data.

Unfortunately, just as there is no such thing as a "neutral ethics", there is also no such thing as a "neutral observer" or a "neutral scientific analyst". For example, during the experiment itself, personal biases could cause the scientist to either "see" or "not see" phenomena or mechanical measurements which do not accurately reflect what is actually taking place. That is, such biases could immediately affect the reliability of the observations which the scientist records. Similarly, even if these observations are accurately recorded, personal biases could cause the scientist to select for analysis only those data which fit neatly into a pre-conceived explanation of these observations.

Thus every attempt must be made by the conscientious scientist to be aware of and to filter out of his or her observations and selections of data any personal biases derived from particular backgrounds, ideologies or other intellectual artifacts, pressures imposed by professional conflicts of interests, institutional and governmental demands, media and political considerations, etc. (Irving, 1993A; Shamoo, 1991, 1992; Kischer, 1993). Otherwise these biases and pressures might in fact seriously "prejudice" his or her "data" - i.e., result in both the prejudicial recording of observations, and the prejudicial selection of data to be analyzed. In effect such biases would negate any possibility of deriving any valid or real truth or understanding of the objective reality outside his or her mind that is being investigated.

In fact, if our knowledge of our proper human goal is incorrect, or if our information about the real world is incorrect, then the entire decision making process will be wrong, because the will simply accepts as true or good what the intellect presents to it as true or good, without question.

2. Once we possess the correct relevant information, then we deliberate about the several possible things or actions which would best attain our goal.

3. Next, we prudently choose and intend those actions or means which will best achieve these goals.

4. We then perform the action, under specific particular circumstances (which themselves can alter the rightness or wrongness of an action).

197

5. Finally, the habit of periodically going back to reflect on earlier decision-making processes and their outcomes is developed, evaluating them both informationally and ethically, and questioning if they were properly thought out and executed.

So this decision-making process starts (hopefully) with "objectively" correct information about the world and our proper human goal as human beings. This information is presented to the will as objectively true and good. Ways and means of achieving that goal (or intermediate goals) are weighed and measured or deliberated about. One means is chosen and intended - and then we execute the action under particular circumstances. Finally, earlier decisions, conclusions and actions are reflected on and evaluated informationally and ethically. Although each step in the process is important, the rightness or wrongness of the entire process hinges on and is determined by the objective correctness of the intellectual information about the real world with which the process begins. And this is determined by the intellectual virtue of "science". Clearly, the integrity of the individual scientist's information is critical in the decision making process leading to the integrity of his data (Shamoo and Annau, 1987; Shamoo, 1991, 1992A).

There is one final interesting (and perhaps cryptic) remark which Aristotle made about this process, a remark which concerns the integrity of the "man" [Fig. # 8]. Roughly as we have just seen, only a good thinking man acts good; but, he adds, only a good acting man thinks good (Aristotle, "Ethica Nichomachea", in McKeon, 1941, p. 1035). In other words, the process is actually circular. And the implication is that if a person habitually acts unethically, sooner or later this habit can effect even his or her ability to think objectively and correctly about the physical world itself - which, in turn, will cause his decision making processes to start with incorrect information about the physical world - which, in turn, will corrupt every step in his entire individual decision making process - etc., etc. In fact, the use of incorrect information or data can negatively impact not only scientific and public policy decision making - but even moral decision making as well. And this in turn will negatively impact the integrity of the individual and his or her relationship with society and the environment. The issue now becomes the integrity of the scientist! "A small error in the beginning ......" actually works both ways. And thus this Great-Chain-of-Decision-Making has just become a small Circle.

B. Institutional decision making

But how does this relate to decision making on the organizational or social levels [Fig. # 9]? Briefly, we need to consider the correct understanding of the "common good". Besides being an individual, "man" is, according to Aristotle, also a "social animal" (Aristotle, "Politica", in McKeon, 1941, p. 1129), and therefore requires relationships with "others" in order to flourish. But the mistake should not be made that the "common good" is anything other than the equivalent of what is objectively and commonly good for each individual human being as human. Organizations and societies are not their own raison d'etre. They should exist fundamentally to foster or further on a social level the ability of each individual human being to flourish. In other words, there is really no such thing as a big individual particular substance called a "Committee" or a "Society" which is walking down the street with its own Good. It is not a thing or an individual itself - but only a concept or a term which we use to name or designate a collection of real individual human beings who make it up. And it is in their roles of fostering individuals (Aristotle, "Ethica Nichomachea", in McKeon, 1941, p. 946) that societies or institutions constitute their place in an even larger Circle (as will be indicated below).

In sum, viable ethical theories can not contain principles such as autonomy, beneficence and justice which become "separated" or "split" from each other, or from the real, live, integrated whole human being - or from his or her critical relationship with society and the environment. In fact, an individual and social ethics would be more realistic and objective if based on all of these ingredients. Unfractured and whole human beings who happen to be autonomous (and who are simply therefore ethically responsible and accountable for their decisions and actions) would ultimately make decisions based on what they can know is objectively true or good or beneficent for themselves as human persons, for others who are human persons (whether autonomous or not), and for their commonly shared environment - i.e., according to what Aristotle called "right reason" (i.e., not simply pure, unadulterated, isolated "reason") (Aristotle, "Ethica Nichomachea", in McKeon, 1941, pp. 1035-1036; McInerny, 1982; Fagothey, 1963). And in so doing they act justly and should be fostered by collective

199

decision-making which is also in accord with those legitimate human goals which human beings hold in common as objectively good.

APPLICATION: THE ROLE OF ETHICS IN SCIENCE AND PUBLIC POLICY

If scientists are really serious about "self-regulation" in order to prevent the prevalence of scientific fraud in contemporary science, such "self-regulation" will succeed only to the extent that individual scientists identify for themselves those elements of a viable individual and social ethics - an ethics which ensures the integrity of the scientist who produces the "data", as well as of those social institutions which so deeply impact on the scientific enterprise itself. What, then, is the role that such an ethics could play in science and public policy?

A. The ethical scientist

Individual "ethics" - accurately understood - does not immediately determine the accuracy of scientific data, statistical probability, computer analysis, the peer-review, grant funding, government regulatory or Congressional decisions. But it does immediately affect the integrity of the "man" who is running these machines, and his decisions - i.e., the person behind the starched white lab coat, as Kornberg might have put it! If the "man" or his decisions are factually wrong - or his or her conception of "ethics" is wrong - - - well, "a small error in the beginning ......". It is often easy to loose sight of the fact that first and foremost the "man" is a human being and a moral agent; and then he or she is a scientist, peer-reviewer, granting agent, government official, journalist or Congressman. Indeed, this is precisely why individual ethical responsibility and accountability accrues all along the entire length of the Great-Chain-of-Decision-Making-Circle. Just as important to understand is that when the individual is a part of a "collective" policy decision making process, the impact of the individual's decisions and actions on others - both positive and negative - are greatly multiplied.

Applicable to the individual scientist is the critically important job of starting off the entire chain of decision making with the correct experimental design - which requires the correct information about his or her particular field of science. Thus the first ethical duty as a scientist (because of the expertise possessed) is to be academically competent in the knowledge and information of his or her field. If the scientist is incompetent about the correct empirical facts of the objective physical world which is within his purview, this incompetence becomes disastrous for everyone and everything that follows. Autonomy for everyone who uses this incorrect data is immediately precluded; harm is caused instead of beneficence or justice. Therefore, in terms of the correctness of the experimental design, or the correctness of the interpretations or accuracy of the data, the scientist him or herself takes responsibility for his or her own scientific competence. In this regard, no one has a greater ethical responsibility in the Great Chain than the individual scientist.

But deliberating about the design and analyzing the data can often be seriously affected by outside pressures as well. For example, clinical researchers have expressed their concerns that several pharmaceutical companies - all of which are simultaneously supporting them on grants - put pressures on them simultaneously to design the protocol (or, interpret the data) in such a way as to make their own drugs or devices look better experimentally than they really are. Or - does this scientist or clinician own stock in the drug companies, biogenetic companies, scientific or ethical software, etc., with which they deal - and therefore "fudge" the data for the "company's" benefit, which is thus to their benefit as well? Or, is a favor owed to the colleague in Neurosurgery - who chairs the university grants program, or who also owns stock?

The list of conflicts of interest affecting the scientist's decision making is endless - our point being that even the very design of the protocol - not to mention the production or the interpretation of the data - can be considerably influenced by various pressures which tantalizingly or threateningly weaken the scientist's resistance and lead to not only incorrect, misapplied or even fraudulent data - but to the very breakdown of his or her character, his or her own integrity as a human being, his or her very commitment to objective truth. And this in turn can become habit forming, becoming easier to do each time the occasion arises anew. Aristotle's "reversal" kicks in - the result, bad data. No longer devoted to unravelling the ever-fascinating mysteries of nature, the scientist instead becomes a mere and grovelling pawn in the hands of corrupt "others", being corrupted and used, instead of respected and admired.

Individual scientists themselves need to effectively identify and resist these corrupting outside pressures. Every scientist is a moral human agent himself, and responsible for his or her own decisions and actions. And they should be respected as such by the "others". Better for a scientist to refuse complicity, rather than to allow one's self to be corrupted. A scientist's integrity should come to be recognized by the scientific community and political institutions as more important than racking up the publications, volumes of articles and books; millions of dollars in grants; medals, honors and accolades in boundless quantities - or even Nobel Prizes - especially if all of these are really built on a house of cards that will fall, eventually, dragging him or her down with it, and causing real harm to all of those "others" along the way as well.

"Harm" is often not considered by the bench scientist. But a scientist is not an island unto him or herself; he or she does not work in a vacuum - as some would often like to believe. Particularly today, when a scientist's work is applied in myriads of ways, he or she can no longer glory in the absolute "freedom of inquiry" in which we all were educationally drenched. "Absolute Freedom of Inquiry" is as mythical as "Absolute Autonomy", "Pure Beneficence", or "Perfect Justice" are in bioethics - they are all really myths or fictions - and sometimes actually only rationalizations. There are limits or bounds to what any one can do - and that includes a scientist. If a scientist's work is going to be applied to potentially millions of innocent human beings or to our shared environment, then this cherished "vacuum" of absolute solitude evaporates - and the scientist does bear moral responsibility of harm or injury done to those "others" because of his or her scientific incompetence, or freely choosing to succumb to corrupt institutional pressures. This is particularly true of the clinical researcher, who's incompetence and moral cracks are born by his or her very vulnerable human patients whose good, or so it is espoused, is primarily the goal.

B. Ethical institutions

On the "collective" level, such "institutions" also do not immediately determine the accuracy of the information or data. But as an integral part of the Great Chain-Circle, they do immediately cause such excessive and misdirected influences and pressures that, again, these influences and pressures in turn can seriously compromise the integrity of the individual scientist and the "others" with whom he or she are affiliated, eventually causing similar harm along the entire length of the Great Chain-Circle, calling into question the integrity of the institution and indeed of the entire scientific enterprise itself. "Collectively" this is perhaps even more problematic, given the hundreds and thousands of individuals whom these institutions directly influence and pressure on a daily basis.

Rather than fostering the common good, institutions can in fact abuse as well as use the scientist - in politics, committees, or organizations; or through unrealistic or overburdening regulations; or by the media. These outside pressures also effect the scientist's decision making processes. For example, inappropriate or inordinate pressures might sometimes be placed on the scientist to conform to supposedly "standard" or currently popular, or politically correct, or politically motivated "scientific" frameworks of reference or explanation - even if those basic "frameworks" might be objectively false. The "politization" of science seems to be running at an all time high.

Similarly, unimaginative and stubborn resistance to innovation is one thing; blocking it, because a committee, organization, industry or political party with power and influence does not want the old "status quo" to be demonstrated wrong - is ethically reprehensible. It corrupts the scientist as both human being and scientist by bringing sometimes unbearable pressures on him or her. It also corrupts the other co-committee members who are also pressured into compromising themselves as moral human agents in consort with each other. And it often corrupts the institution itself. Such pressures or influences require nothing less than the rejection or suppression of the true facts about nature and the substitution of incorrect facts in their place - which facts in turn are used as the false starting point of the Great Chain-Circle.

Or again, a scientist can be abused by oppressive and costly governmental over-regulating, which crushes creativity and unnecessarily bogs down the entire scientific enterprise itself. Nor should undo pressures influence the scientist to produce "perfectly auditable" data, which must sometimes be made to artificially conform to a "financial set" theory. How many times in the history of science have major breakthroughs occurred because of creative and innovative approaches or explanations, or because of simple errors which were honestly recorded and admitted - and which turned out to be true, even though they threw the T-test off?

Nor should scientists be abused by pressures from a media which can hype up the public with unrealistic caricatures, supposedly promising new "miracle" cures or treatments; or which misconstrues or misinterprets a scientific "controversy" - again misinforming the public, sometimes even breaking confidentiality and destroying the reputations and careers of scientists - in order to get a "great story" out first.

On a higher "collective" level, research institutions are causing numerous pressures and challenges among themselves which at times are conflicting. For example, there are great pressures on universities to cash in on their discoveries (Sugawara, 1993); yet at the same time there are serious concerns about the presence of a conflict of interest (Shamoo, 1992A, 1993A). There are pressures on the FDA to accelerate drug approvals, e.g., for AIDS patients; yet the FDA must continue to be concerned with the safety and efficacy of these drugs (Stolley and Lasky, 1992). There are pressures from universities on funding agencies to use merit in funding research projects; yet universities themselves exercise the power of pork barrel to achieve an increasing amount of funding, bypassing all peer-review systems (Marshall, 1992).

Finally, consider the effect on the integrity of decision making of the current "fad" of "consensus ethics". Probably due initially to fear of legal liability, many group or institutional decisions are now often based on what the majority agrees upon, or the "consensus" of the group. This is not necessarily an ethical judgment or decision, and is unfortunately sometimes used only as a means by which to dilute the moral (or legal) responsibilities of the members. And given that such institutional policies themselves are often the targets of outside pressures, their construction and promulgation by others often serve to provide merely a psychological cover of semi-anonymity for many of those individuals taking part in such collective decision making processes.

It is worth considering that "majority" or "consensus" decisions - even on the national scale - have at times been simply wrong and unethical. Most of the time it seems to work - but not necessarily always. We need to question constantly whether the "collective" decision of the majority actually compromises the integrity of each of the individuals in the minority - or of the institution itself? Ethically, at least, each and every member of that committee or institution taking part in that "consensus" bears the individual moral responsibility and accountability for his or her own decision.

In addition to "consensus ethics", we are now seeing a move toward "consensus science". But how can we ensure that this "consensus science" is actually scientifically correct? The scientific establishment wants "consensus science" to be the only science accepted in the courtrooms (Marshall, 1993). These same groups complain bitterly about government guidelines to be used for ensuring the integrity of scientific data. Such guidelines, they complain, will stifle new and creative science, and by definition these guidelines are not approved by "consensus". Yet often there is simply no consensus within science itself on important and critical issues.

For example, there is the major ongoing debate about the very definition of "scientific misconduct" itself between the two most important agencies of the federal government which fund science - the NSF and the NIH. NSF would like to retain in the definition of "scientific misconduct" the broad clause: "or other serious deviation from accepted practices in proposing, carrying out, or reporting results". Yet NIH has dropped this section from their definition (Zurer, 1993), thus narrowing the definition as well as tying the hands of future investigative bodies. The claim that scientists are usually objective and unbiased would seem to run contrary to NIH's insistence on such a narrow definition of "scientific misconduct" because they fear potential abuse if the definition is "too broad". Such lack of objectivity within this scientific institution calls to mind Gerald Geison's comments on Pasture's "scientific objectivity". "Pasteur's message for contemporary science" was to puncture the "hopelessly misleading" image of science as "simply objective and unprejudiced," a myth that scientists have perpetuated in order to advance their work and attain a "privilege status" (Russell, 1993). Will the scientists' call for "self-regulation" be ultimately a myth as well?

CONCLUSIONS

One last check on reality, then. There are no easy answers to the questions about government regulations vs. self-regulation. But if overly-burdensome government regulations, required to assure the integrity of scientific data - as well as the public policies which are often based on that data - is so objectionable to scientists, "self-regulation" is in order. Scientists can't have it both ways. Especially in view of the very real harm which scientific fraud can and does cause, it must be dealt with clearly, firmly and unambiguously - one way or the other.

Yet "self-regulation", invoked by the scientific community to assure scientific integrity, must be based on much more than what is "consensual", "efficient", "productive", or statistically valid. It involves more than considerations of protocol designs and accurate data. Cryptically or not, the wisdom of the empirical experience of the centuries is unmistakably clear: real "self-regulation" requires a consideration of the integrity of the individual scientist as a human being and as an individual decision maker and actor. It also involves consideration of the integrity of the many institutions whose decisions and actions heavily influence and supposedly foster the scientist both as an individual and as a member of a "collective". This requires a grounding in a theoretically and practically viable personal and social ethics, itself grounded in a realistic and objectively based philosophy. The only other viable alternative, we would argue, is governmental regulation.

There is more at stake, then, than the integrity of experimental designs, the integrity of information, or the integrity of the data. More fundamentally at stake is the integrity of us as human beings - whether scientist, clinical researcher, quality analyst or controller, peer-reviewer, university, industry or government funder, regulator, journalist or Congressman. The Great Chain does not just "start" with "information" - but with a human being - who produces, insures, reviews, funds, regulates, reports on or governs - or, to complete the Great Circle, who is harmed by or compromised by not only the information or data, but by each other in their various levels of relationships, decisions and actions. Ultimately, it is the scientific enterprise itself, we would suggest, that is at stake.

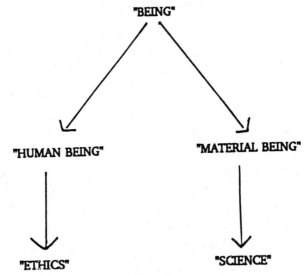

Figure 1.

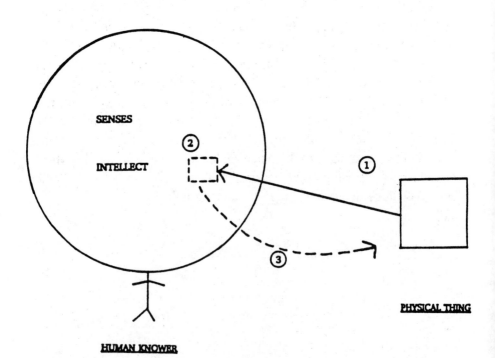

Figure 2.

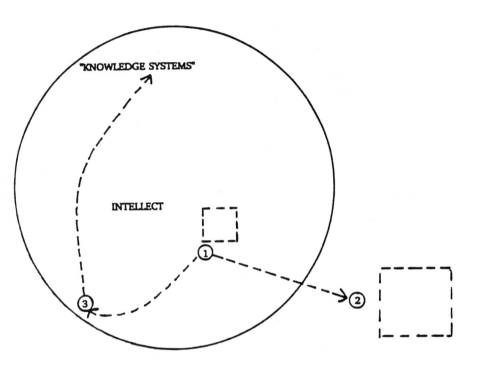

"KNOWLEDGE SYSTEMS"

INTELLECT

① ② ③

PHYSICAL THING

HUMAN KNOWER

Figure 3.

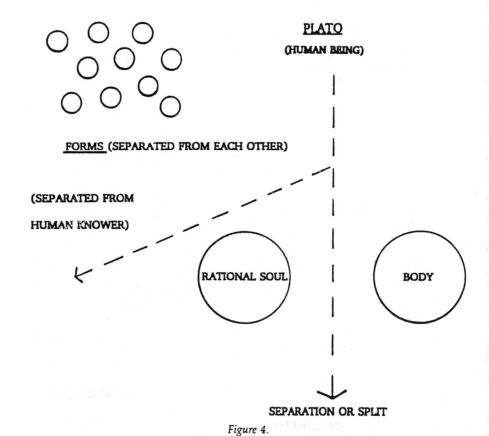

Figure 4.

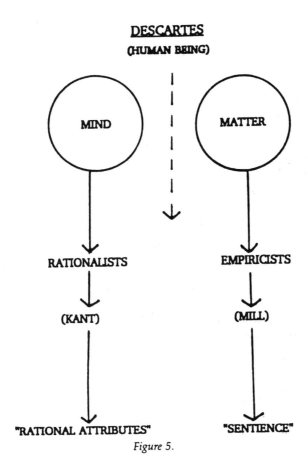

Figure 5.

210

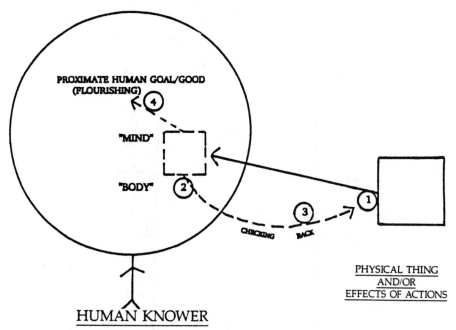

PROXIMATE HUMAN GOAL/GOOD
(FLOURISHING)
④

"MIND"

"BODY" ②

③
CHECKING BACK ①

HUMAN KNOWER

PHYSICAL THING
AND/OR
EFFECTS OF ACTIONS

Figure 6.   Aristotelean "Framework"

GOOD DECISION MAKING

1. "OBJECTIVELY" CORRECT INTELLECTUAL INFORMATION—*SCIENCE

    A. UNBIASED AND INDEPENDENT OBSERVATIONS OF PHENOMENA

    B. UNBIASED AND INDEPENDENT SELECTION OF DATA

2. GOOD DELIBERATION

3. GOOD CHOOSING OR DECIDING

4. GOOD ACTING

5. GOOD REFLECTION ON PREVIOUS DECISIONS AND ACTIONS

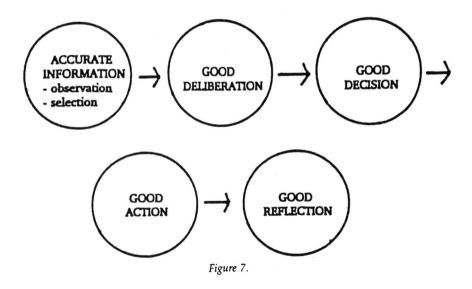

Figure 7.

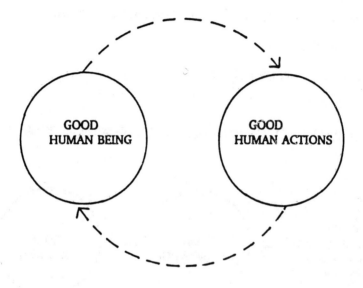

GOOD HUMAN BEING ⇄ GOOD HUMAN ACTIONS

Figure 8.   The Small Chain-of-Decision-Making-Circle

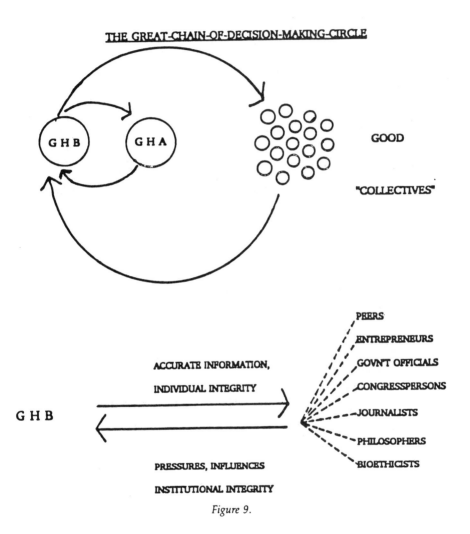

THE GREAT-CHAIN-OF-DECISION-MAKING-CIRCLE

G H B   G H A

GOOD

"COLLECTIVES"

GHB

ACCURATE INFORMATION,

INDIVIDUAL INTEGRITY

PRESSURES, INFLUENCES

INSTITUTIONAL INTEGRITY

PEERS

ENTREPRENEURS

GOVN'T OFFICIALS

CONGRESSPERSONS

JOURNALISTS

PHILOSOPHERS

BIOETHICISTS

Figure 9.

REFERENCES

*** An edited version of this paper was originally presented by Dr. Irving at the Third Conference on Research Policies and Quality Assurance, Baltimore MD, May 2, 1993.

1. McKeon, Richard (1941) The Basic Works of Aristotle. New York: Random House.
2. Beauchamp, Tom L. and Childress, James F. (1979) Principles of Biomedical Ethics. (1st ed.) New York: Oxford University Press, pp. 7-9, 20; ibid. (1989)(3rd ed.), 51.
3. Beauchamp, Tom L. and Walters, LeRoy (1978) Contemporary Issues in Bioethics. (1st ed.) Belmont, CA: Wadsworth Publishing Company, Inc., pp. 3, 51; ibid. (1982) (2nd ed.), pp. 1-2, 23; ibid. (1989) (3rd ed.), pp. 2, 12, 24, 28.
4. Bourke, Vernon J. (1951) Ethics. New York: The Macmillan Company, p. 192.
5. Burns, Stephen J. (1991) Auditing high technology ventures. Internal Auditor 486:56-59.
6. Copleston, Frederick (1962) A History of Philosophy. New York: Image Books, Vols. 1-9.
7. Cottingham, John, Stoothoff, Robert and Murdoch, Dugald (trans.) (1984) The Philosophical Writings of Descartes. (Vol. 2) Meditations on First Philosophy. New York: New York Press Syndicate of the University of Cambridge, (Sixth Meditation) p. 59-60.
8. Crombie, A.C. (1959) Medieval and Early Modern Science. New York: Doubleday Anchor Books.
9. Edwards, Paul (1967) The Encyclopedia of Philosophy. (Vol. 1, reprint edition 1972) New York: Collier Macmillan Publishers, pp. 352-353.
10. Englehardt, H. Tristram (1985) The Foundations of Bioethics. New York: Oxford University Press, p. 111.
11. Fagothey, Austin (1963) Right and Reason. (3rd edition) Saint Louis, MO: The C.V. Mosby Company, pp. 92ff, 101-113, 198.
12. Finnis, John (1982) Natural Law and Natural Rights. Oxford: Clarendon Press, pp. 85-97, 134-156.
13. Gilson, Etienne (1963) Being and Some Philosophers. Toronto: Pontifical Institute of Mediaeval Studies.
14. Hamel, Ron P., DuBose, Edwin R. and O'Connell, Laurence J. (1994) A Matter of Principles? Ferment in U.S. Bioethics. Valley Forge, PA: Trinity Press International.
15. Hare, R.M. (1988) When does potentiality count? A comment on Lockwood. Bioethics 2 3:216, 218, 219.

16. Irving, Dianne N. (1991) Philosophical and Scientific Analysis of the Nature of the Early Human Embryo. (Doctoral dissertation, Georgetown University: Washington D.C.).

17. Irving, Dianne N. (1992) Science, philosophy, theology and altruism: the *chorismos* and the *zygon*. in Hans May, Meinfried Streignitz, Philip Hefner (eds.) Loccomer Protokolle. Rehburg-Loccum: Evangelische Akademie Loccum.

18. Irving, Dianne N. (1993A) Scientific and philosophical expertise: an evaluation of the arguments on personhood. Linacre Quarterly 60, 1:18-46.

19. Irving, Dianne N. (1993B) The impact of scientific 'misinformation' on other fields: philosophy, theology, biomedical ethics, public policy. Accountability in Research 2, 4:243-272.

20. Irving, Dianne N. (1993C) Philosophical and scientific critiques of 'autonomy-based' ethics: toward a reconstruction of the 'whole person' as the proximate ground of ethics and community. (delivered to the Third International Bioethics Institute Conference, San Francisco, CA, April 16, 1993.)

21. Jowett, B. (1937) The Dialogues of Plato. New York: Random House.

22. Kischer, C. Ward (1993) Human development and reconsideration of ensoulment. Linacre Quarterly 60 1:57-63.

23. Klubertanz, George P. (1963) Introduction to the Philosophy of Being. New York: Meredith Publishing Co.

24. Kornberg, Arthur (1992) Science is great, but scientists are still people. Science (Editorial) 257:859-859.

25. Kuhn, Thomas (1970) The Structure of Scientific Revolutions (2nd Edition). Chicago: The University of Chicago Press, p. 7.

26. Kuhse, Helga and Singer, Peter (1986) For sometimes letting - and helping - die. Law, Medicine and Health Care 3:4; also, Kuhse and Singer (1985) Should the Baby Live? The Problem of Handicapped Infants. Oxford University Press, p. 138.

27. Lockwood, Michael (1988) Warnock versus Powell (and Harradine): when does potentiality count?. Bioethics 2:3:187-213.

28. Marshall, Eliot (1992) George Brown cuts into academic pork. Science 258:22-22.

29. Marshall, Eliot (1993) Supreme Court to weigh science. Science 259:588-   590.

30. McCormick, Richard A., S.J. (1974) Proxy consent in the experimentation situation. Perspectives in Biology and Medicine 18:127.

31. McInerny, Ralph (1982) Ethica Thomistica. Washington, D.C.: The Catholic University of America Press, p.63-77.

32. Moore, Keith L. (1982) The Developing Human. Philadelphia: W.B. Saunders Company, p. 1.

33. Pellegrino, Edmund D. (1993) Ethics. Journal of the American Medical Society 270 2:202-203.

34. Robertson, John A. (1986) Extracorporeal embryos and the abortion debate. Journal of Contemporary Health Law and Policy 2:53.

35. Russell, Cristine (1993) Louis Pasteur and questions of fraud. Washington Post Health. February 23, 1993, p. 7.

36. Shamoo, Adil E., and Annau, Z. (1989) Data audit: historical perspectives. in Principles of Research Data Audit. ed. A.E. Shamoo. New York: Gordon and Breach, Science Publishers, Inc., Chapter 1, pp. 1-12.

37. Shamoo, Adil E., and Davis (1990) The need for integration of data audit into research and development operations. Principles of Research Data Audit. A.E. Shamoo (ed.). New York: Gordon and Breach Science Publishers, Inc., (Chapter 3) pp. 22-38; also in Accountability in Research 1:119-128.

38. Shamoo, Adil E. (1991) Policies and quality assurances in the pharmaceutical industry. Accountability in Research 1:273-284.

39. Shamoo, Adil E. (1992A) Role of conflict of interest in scientific objectivity: a case of a Nobel Prize work. Accountability in Research 2:55-75.

40. Shamoo, Adil E. (1992B) Introductory Remarks. Accountability in Research 2:i.

41. Shamoo, Adil E. (1993A) Role of conflict of interest in public advisory councils. in Ethical Issues in Research. D. Cheney (ed.), Frederick, Maryland: University Publishing Group Inc, (Chapter 17) pp. 159-174.

42. Shamoo, Adil E., and Irving, Dianne N. (1993B) The PSDA and the depressed elderly: intermittent competency revisited. Journal of Clinical Ethics 4, 1:74-80.

43. Shamoo, Adil E., and Irving, Dianne N. (1993C) Accountability in research using persons with mental illness. Accountability in Research August (present journal volume).

44. Singer, Peter (1981) Taking life: abortion. in Practical Ethics. London: Cambridge University Press, pp. 122-123.

45. Stolley, Paul D., Lasky, Tamer (1992). "Shortcuts in drug evaluation". Clinical Pharmacology Therapeutics 52:1-3.

46. Sugawara, Sandra (1993). "Cashing in on medical discoveries". The Washington Post/Business. January 4, 1993, p. 1.

47. Tannenbaum, A.S., and Cook, R.A. (1978). Report on the Mentally Infirm: Appendix to Research Involving Those Institutionalized as Mentally Infirm. 1-2.

48. Tooley, Michael (1974) Abortion and infanticide. in Marshall Cohen et al (eds.) The Rights and Wrongs of Abortion. New Jersey: Princeton University Press, pp. 59, 64.

49. U.S. Codes of Federal Regulation (1989) 45 CFR 46.

50. U.S. National Academy of Science (1989) On Being A Scientist. Washington, D.C.: National Academy Press, p. 9.

51. Veatch, Henry B. (1974) <u>Aristotle: A Contemporary Approach</u>. Indiana: Indiana University Press.

52. Vlastos, Gregory (1978) <u>Plato: A Collection of Critical Essays</u>. Indiana: University of Notre Dame Press.

53. Wilhelmson, Frederick (1956) <u>Man's Knowledge of Reality</u>. New Jersey: Prentice-Hall, Inc.

54. Zurer, Pamela S. (1993). Divisive dispute smolders over definition of scientific misconduct", <u>Chemical and Engineering News</u>. April 1993, 5:23-25.

218

SECTION THREE: PUBLIC POLICY

In this section we will consider just some of the consequences of using the erroneous scientific, philosophical and bioethics "theories" discussed in Sections One and Two by focusing on some of their recent applications in public policy formulation.

In 1973, the <u>Roe</u> Court conceded that if the Court were to admit that the human fetus is a "person", the fetus' right to life would then be guaranteed specifically by the Fourteenth Amendment. So they decided that the word "person" does not "include the unborn". They continued with the following empirically absurd statement: "We need not resolve the difficult question of when life begins. When those trained in the respective disciplines of medicine, philosophy and theology are unable to arrive at any consensus, the judiciary, at this point in the development of man's knowledge, is not in a position to speculate as to the answer." They conclude that the human fetus is only "potential human life", or a "potential person".

The real issue at stake is: "when does the life of any human being begin?" For the Court to claim that it would be "speculative" to give an objective answer, and that there was then no consensus as to when the life of a human being begins was as factually and blatantly false and disingenuous in 1973 as it is today. There is absolutely no question, scientifically, when the life of a human being begins. It begins at fertilization. That is a scientific fact and represents a scientific consensus. This remains true no matter what philosophers, bioethics or theologians, throughout all of the ages or from all cultures, try to proclaim. The proof is under the microscope. There is also no such thing, as was assumed and declared by this Court, as a human embryo or a fetus who is a "potential human life," or a "potential human person." There is, to the contrary, an already existing human being with the potential to grow and develop further.

By their action, the Court has established what they want us to believe to be an insoluble and "difficult" question. Consequently, the Court saw fit to impose certain specific philosophical, bioethical and theological opinions about "delayed personhood" on the entire

219

country, in the guise of a "neutral" or "consensus-driven" public policy.

Why is the correct human embryology being rejected in so many different areas? Why are so many new yet obviously aberrant definitions of "personhood" being put forward and perpetuated? In the first article, "A New Wave Dialectic: The Reinvention of Human Embryology and a Futuristic Social Policy for Mankind", the author pursues the odd and scientifically fake but extensively referenced term of "pre-embryo" (or "pre-person"), and its use and extension in grounding a "new" kind of social policy.

The developmental biologist, Clifford Grobstein, appears to have coined the phrase "pre-embryo" in 1979, six years after Roe vs. Wade. Grobstein is not a human embryologist, yet he assigned the term to the human embryo, in effect de-humanizing it. The term is so scientifically false, that he must have had some specific agenda in so persistently promoting it. He in fact has openly promoted that agenda in several of his published writings, including a chapter in a recent book edited by Darwin Cheney, Ethical Issues in Research. It is the only article in that book with absolutely no references, an interesting editorial decision in itself. The application of this social theory would not be limited to just the area of abortion. It would necessarily permeate the entire structure of our society. That article is reviewed and critiqued in our first article.

Developing chronologically along side of such manipulation of science for social and political purposes has been the "creation" of philosophical, and especially bioethical, theories and principles for social and political consumption as well (often by the same people and organizations). As noted in our preceding Section, the "bioethics principles" of autonomy, justice, beneficence and nonmaleficence were forged out of the 1978 Belmont Report of the National Commission, almost instantaneously impacting social and public policy from the very top of our society and government. These public policies are explicitly grounded on "principlism" (or some version of it), and they include (to mention but a few): the President's commission Report (1979-1983); the NIH Fetal Tissue Transplantation Research Conference Report (1988); the Federal OPRR Regulations for the Protection of Human Subjects in Biomedical Research (1979-1989, incorporated into the 1991

Common Rule which applies to fifteen federal departments); extensive numbers of NIH and other federal guidelines in related areas; Hospital Ethics Committee Handbooks and Guidelines used in hospitals, nursing homes and other health care facilities across the country; CIOMS/WHO International Guidelines (1993) for the use of human subjects in biomedical research (especially targeted to Third World countries and epidemiological research); the Final Report of the Advisory Committee of Human Radiation Experiments (1995); the State of Maryland Attorney General's Initial Report of the Attorney General's Research Working Group (1996) (recommending guidelines for the use of mentally incompetent human patients in biomedical research); and will most certainly be used as the basis of the new National Bioethics Commission's rationale for determining the "ethics" of ever-burgeoning bioethics issues – especially for federal public policy in these areas.

One of the most obvious recent examples of the application of a new social policy using the combination of the above manipulated science and made-up bioethics principles is specifically in the area of human embryo research. An advisory panel to the National Institutes of Health was convened recently to determine the "moral and ethical" acceptability of research proposals involving the production and use of living human embryos through in vitro fertilization (IVF) and other methods solely for their use in destructive experimental research. Almost all of the kinds of human embryo research proposed have already been rejected by most other countries, and are presently illegal in most of our states.

The second article in this section, "Individual Testimony Before the NIH Human Embryo Research Panel", was a deliberately strong statement of protest against the proposed human embryo research delivered before the NIH Panel. The author refutes the Panel's use and acceptance of the scientifically false term "pre-embryo", as well as their reduced "moral status" for the early human embryo intended by that term. Basic elements of research ethics, as articulated by several international declarations on research ethics, would also preclude this kind of research. The problematic make-up of the Panel is addressed, including its many conflicts of interest and the undue influence from bioethics "theories" and "theorists" (several of whom were on the Panel). There is a call for Congressional investigations and for a genuine mandate from the American public, most of whom are still unaware of these hearings and recommendations, not to mention "principlism."

In the third article, "The Third Holocaust: The War Against the Human Embryo and Fetus," and the fourth article, "NIH Human Embryo Research Revisited," the authors further examine the NIH Panel itself, as well as these new human embryo research proposals and recommendations.

There were several inherent conflicts of interest with this Panel. Many members had either served on the earlier National Commission, which had constructed the now-famous and now-defunct bioethics "principles"; or on the President's Commission, which had concluded that fetal research was "ethical"; or served on the NIH Fetal Tissue Transplant Research Panel, voting pro-abortion and pro-fetal tissue transplant research; or are presently serving on the National Bioethics Commission scheduled to decide again the "ethics" of human embryo research (among other issues); or had ties with very prominent national and international abortion or eugenics organizations. The most obvious conflict of interest was that since 1987, 10 of the 19 Panelists have received over $21 million in NIH grants for their own research, in areas similar to those now to be regulated by them.

The NIH Human Embryo Research Panel has already issued its recommendations, basing them on their conclusion that the "pre-implantation" human embryo " ... does not have the same moral status as infants and children. This is because of the absence of developmental individuation in the preimplantation embryo, the lack of even the possibility of sentience and most other qualities considered relevant to the moral status of persons, and the very high rate of natural mortality at this stage." It is more than interesting that these very "delayed personhood" bioethics theories are precisely among those by Grobstein and McCormick, Singer, Kuhse, Buckle, Dawson and Hare, addressed in this anthology and almost exclusively referenced in the Panel's recommendations. And, it borders on the incredulous that the only "scientific" reference in these recommendations for its "human embryology" chart and its list of scientific terms, is a recent book, Human Embryo Experimentation, written by Australians: Singer (a philosopher), Buckle (a philosopher), Kuhse (an "ethicist"), Kasimba (a lawyer) and Dawson (a geneticist, but not a human embryologist). Even in that Australian book, the scientific chart and definitions are not scientifically referenced.

NIH's Director, Dr. Harold Varmus, was to consider the Panel's recommendations as to which proposals for human embryo research should "ethically" be funded by the U.S. government. To date he has not done so. It is likely that Varmus will ultimately approve final guidelines for human embryo research. But even if none of the proposed human embryo research is approved now, the acceptance and funding of these research proposals will continue to be brought up again and again. And, by their own admission, this Panel, or a different "panel", or even simply the Director of NIH himself, may make exceptions to any final guidelines, or change human embryo research classified as "unacceptable" to "acceptable" at will, probably on the recommendation of the new National Bioethics Advisory Commission.

A NEW WAVE DIALECTIC:[1]

The Reinvention Of Human Embryology
And A Futuristic Social Policy For Humankind

by C. Ward Kischer

In 1973 Roe v. Wade was adjudicated by the Supreme Court. This landmark decision proved to be the watershed between science and the law.

Statements made within the decision, and since, concerning human development, have been disingenuous, irresponsible or deliberately deceitful.

One would like to believe that Supreme Court Justices, acting as learned and wise servants of our society, exercise great and considerate care in making decisions that not only affect our daily lives, but impact the evolution of our culture in the most moral and responsible way. We also want to believe they seek out all available facts concerning a case before coming to decisions. Alas, such is not the case.

Justice Blackmun: The Roe and Webster Decisions

It is clear that Attorneys Jay Floyd (before the Court of 7) and Robert Flowers (before the Court of 9), arguing for the unborn during Roe v. Wade were unprepared in biological knowledge to answer Justice Blackmun's questions about the beginning of life, and when a fetus becomes a person. Blackmun, himself, was (and still is) woefully ignorant of the concept of "biological life". Unable to come to terms with the ordinary understanding of life as a biological life he confused the issue by including in a question to Flowers, concerning when a fetus becomes a person, "a religious person, a medical person, a philosophical person". If personhood implies, at all, a usefulness, a newborn would be no more a person than the fertilized ovum!

Nevertheless, Blackmun eventually concluded that those in "medicine, philosophy, and theology" could not come to a consensus

224

as to "when life begins". This was intellectual dishonesty at its worst.[2] Justice Blackmun failed to become properly informed by the time he wrote the decision for the Webster case (1989), because he depended upon an *amici curiae* brief in which 167 "distinguished scientists" concluded: "there is no scientific consensus that a human life begins at conception, at a given stage of fetal development, or at birth."[3]

This statement misleads the reader. They use the term "conception" only in a biological sense. What follows from conception, biologically, is a *continuum*, which, realistically, never ceases. Thus, a biological life is defined by its inception *and* destiny, both of which are inseparable and interdependent. It follows, then, that under conditions which we have come to understand as normal, there is no point of arbitration, even after birth and unto death. Therefore, interposing "stages" which purport to have meaning for biological development are wholly arbitrary, specious and disingenuous at best. All of development, therefore, from first contact between sperm and ovum is a *fait accompli*.

The *amici* further state: the beginning of a human life "cannot be answered by reference to scientific principles". They then invoke more than a biological consideration by stating that the answer "will depend on each individual's social, religious, philosophical, ethical and moral beliefs and values."

If these kinds of lifes are assigned to an embyro or fetus, they would be done so arbitrarily. If they are acquired, this would occur as a learned belief or value long after birth!

But, their statement removes the biological imperative; therefore, they compound there own pronouncement and, in effect, pose a problem of "life" for the newborn, infant, juvenile, and, in fact, for any age of an individual. In point of fact, scientific principles can and do define when life begins (for the new individual), simply by recording the results of each pregnant woman, the issue of which we know is derived from a union of sperm and ovum! The question is, and has been, answered, repeatedly, over the time of many thousands of years, ever since hominids first appeared on the earth.

These same *amici* make still another profoundly gratuitious statement: "The question of when a human life truly begins calls for a conclusion as to which characteristics define the *essence* of human life. While science can tell us when certain biological characteristics can be detected, science cannot tell us which biological (sic) attributes

225

erratum: **page 226, line 35, quote from Blackmun - should read:**

"I'd like to think that I've written in other areas of law [sic] some other significant decisions. . . "

establish the existence of a human being."

Here, the *amici* do not equivocate the biological imperative, as they did when asking when a human life begins. They cannot have it both ways.

Wendell M. Stanley, Nobel Prize winner and discoverer of the tobacco mosaic virus, stated it clearly:

"The essence of life is the ability to reproduce. This is accomplished by the utilization of energy to create order out of disorder, to bring together into a specific predetermined pattern from semiorder or even from chaos all the component parts of that pattern with the perpetuation of that pattern with time. This is life."[4]

It is important to know that of the 167 "distinguished scientists", cited in the above mentioned *amici curiae* brief, only 31 had "index-described" terms related to embryology, that is, 'development' or 'developmental' being used in part of the descriptions of their fields. However, only one (l) of those 31 was a self-defined embryologist, and that one not even as a human embryologist![5]

Obviously, there is a major problem. The Roe v. Wade decision was regarded as a decision that legalized abortion within the first two trimesters, by rendering it a private matter between doctor and patient. But, it was much more than that, because it indirectly declared the embryo and fetus up to the time of "viability" (assumed to be, but not declared as such, approximately 24 weeks post-fertilization) a non-person! Justice Blackmun believes the issue is resolved. Interviewed on ABC Nightline, on 2 December, 1993, ANATOMY OF A DECISION: Roe v. Wade, he stated: "the basic issue is decided . . . . the constitutional issue is decided, and not on moral grounds".

It is disturbing that Blackmun would separate "constitutional" from "moral". There is an axiom which used to be taught in law which says: ALL LAW COMES FROM MORAL LAW. Although sophisticated pundits of the law would now argue this, a reading of the history of law would confirm it.

Blackmun later made this statement: "I'd like to think I've *written into law* [sic] other significant decisions, but one gets tagged with one - and, there it is". I have always believed that the Supreme Court is not supposed or empowered to write into law (making law),

226

but to interpret law. Is it not the function of the legislative branch of government to make, or write law?

The Fallout From The Court's Decisions

The Supreme Court has had several chances to reconsider the effects of Roe v. Wade, the latest efforts being the cases of J.M., Individually v. V.C., et al., and Alexander Loce v. The State of New Jersey. The Supreme Court of The United States, in its October Term, 1993, elected not to hear those cases.

Still to be decided by the high court are the crucial questions of (1) when *legal* life begins, (2) when establishment of the individual (personhood) occurs, and (3) will there be an invokation of equal protection under the law (14th amendment) for the embryo and fetus. The Roe Court, and subsequent Courts in the cases of Webster, Akron and Casey have not addressed these questions; but more importantly, the biology - the HUMAN EMBRYOLOGY - referred to in those cases was in error. For the benefit of the Supreme Court, a proper dialogue has never taken place!

Since Roe v. Wade, there has been an inundation of one-sided monologues, appearing in lay and scientific publications, newspapers, interviews, talk shows, virtually all forms of media, calling into question the quality and status of the embryo and early fetus-especially by persons with no experience, training and little knowledge of human embryology. Why do they do this if the Roe decision essentially obviated, forever, as Blackmun believes, claims of personhood prior to "viability", and confirmed the seeming finality of a woman's right for an abortion?

It appears the answer is that most of the proponents of choice know that they successfully prevented the biological truth from entering into the Court hearings and decisions, and, anticipating that eventually this truth would out, have been rewriting human development by skewing, distorting and outright lieing about the known facts, and by constructing an intellectually dishonest social policy concerning human development, most of which has gone unchallenged in the more common media sources.

227

Clifford Grobstein and the Preembryo

One of the most active and prolific contributors to this problem is Clifford Grobstein, who is a developmental biologist, not a human embryologist, and who is a member of The American Fertility Society. In addition, he has authored a book entitled: "Science and The Unborn", subtitled: "Choosing Human Futures" (Basic Books, Inc., New York, 1988).[6] He writes articles for lay publications, is interviewed by others, such as Psychology Today, and promotes his ideas about human development through computer networks, all without challenge. He also may have invented the term *preembryo*[7], a term which has been and is being used to reduce the status of the early embryo to that of a non-person and non-human.

He identifies his most active professional area as "public policy". He has had some success in politicizing human embryology and even in finding some allies among, of all places, the scientific world of Human Embryology, who are willing to inject his "New Wave" definitions into the jargon of human development. Keith Moore, who is an author of several texts on human embryology, poses a question on page 71 of the third edition of: Before We Are Born (W.B Saunders Co., Philadelphia, 1988)[8] asking: "When does the embryo become human?" On the next page he gives two answers, the scientific one and the political one, then asks the student to choose between them! However, it must be said in his latest edition (1994) he still gives the two answers but does not ask the student to choose between them. In addition to that, Moore, in his latest (5th) edition of The Developing Human (W.B. Saunders, Co., Philadelphia, 1993)[9] uses for the first time, albeit in a contradictory way, the term *preembryo*, a politicized reference to the first week of human development. This is the first recorded use of the term in a textbook of human embryology! Interestingly, however, when this author protested use of the term to Moore, he offered to remove it in the next printing, which he did in his third printing of that textbook.

Grobstein obviously agrees with Blackmun, concerning the presumed finality of the Roe decsion, because now Grobstein writes about the futures he has planned for the aborted individuals in evermore confident tones, but, again, without apparent dialogue!

He is, perhaps, the leading spokesman for "choice", but prefers to identify it as *'public policy'*, and a leading sponsor of human embryo

228

"research". Grobstein is the *avant-garde* of those reinventing human development, and those writing a new social policy for the status of the new individual.

Grobstein's *New Wave* Embryology and Future Social Policy

He has written a chapter in a book entitled: "Ethical Issues In Research", edited by Darwin Cheney and published by The University Publishing Group, Inc., Frederick, Maryland (1993).[10] This chapter seems to bring together his previous manipulations of the science of human embryology with his intended uses and disposal of "materials" important to our human futures, under the guise of a *New Wave* social policy. That policy is predicated on reinvented science.

Therefore, a careful critique of what he says is requisite, if for no other reason but to inform an unsuspecting public as to the direction our evolution might take us. Only a well-informed public can apply the necessary pressure to restore the proper reverence for human development.

Our culture is at stake. The evolution of our society and, indeed, the very root of societal endurance, its moral base, is being redefined, virtually by *fiat*. There must be reasonable dialogue, and those properly prepared in science without a political agenda must be heard, lest once more science becomes darkened with demonic doctrines.

Herein, is the critique of Grobstein's New Wave human embryology, and futuristic social policy with appropriate excerpts from his chapter on "The Status and Uses of Early Human Developmental Stages":

• *The funding pattern for human embryo research*

"The focus of this chapter is on the moral and legal status of early human developmental stages, with emphasis on how these stages should be treated in laboratories and in clinical practice. . . . With regard to the topic of **research on early human** development, this

229

chapter will direct attention to the moral considerations that exert external directive pressure on research, its funding, and its outcomes . . . . What is not so immediately obvious is the extremely limited funding (approaching zero) currently available from US federal sources **for studies on early human** developmental stages. Moreover, the dearth of such funds clearly is not accidental; rather it is traceable to deliberate policy of the Federal Department of Health and Human Services (HHS). . . . the existing funding pattern strongly suggests that understanding of early human development is of far less interest and importance than that of other species such as, say, the mouse."

> *Not so. The funding pattern has been, and is, relatively low because of medical, legal and ethical restrictions concerning acquisitions of human embryonic or fetal tissues. In spite of the many abortions performed each year, most are performed in clinics on early stages of embryos by saline treatment or mechanical disruption which destroys the embryo or early fetuses, and often renders the tissue unusable. Procurement of the best and most viable tissues would mean surgical intervention. Most physicians and patients are unwilling to undergo such a radical procedure. However, since President Clinton has lifted the ban on funding of fetal tissue research, and the NIH is currently conducting hearings on ethical and moral considerations of human embryo research, funding is likely to rapidly increase.*

"Moreover, reference to the next millennium is not incidental. I refer to it because in this research area religious teachings exert significant pressure on US funding--even though the issues involved are certainly not solely religious, and teachings of various religions **are hardly** always **concordant** on the matters involved."

> *Left out of this statement are the legal restrictions. These are not going to be removed, easily, or at all. They may be explained by the age-old legal maxim: <u>all law comes from moral law</u>, and moral imperatives have their origin in religion. To remove the moral*

basis for restrictions is to remove virtually all restrictive control for society. What then would be left? - a kind of social anarchy which would declare that the end justifies the means.

Acquisition of early embryos and fetuses from in utero and even in vitro fertilization followed by culturing through early stages has been restricted because of the revered quality traditionally applied to the new individual and because of the self-imposed restrictions by physicians applying the technique solely in cases of fertility problems. However, if a different quality can be applied, it is likely to be followed with a different value.

". . . Defenders of current restrictive policies on funding for research on early human developmental stages argue that because human abortuses constitute a possible source of study materials, increases in the number of authorized and funded early human studies will promote a higher frequency of abortion."

And this is true, not only for "a possible source of study materials", but for many experimental procedures. "60 minutes" ran a piece in 1993 about a clinic in Russia set up to make fetal cell and tissue injections into children afflicted with Down's Syndrome. One part of this clinic was given over to free elective abortions. The fetus was removed alive, dissected and living tissue preserved for experimental injections. The fact that this occurred in Russia does not preclude the likelihood of similar clinics or operations eventually appearing in this country. In fact, at least two diseases are regarded as lending themselves to fetal cell or tissue implants for therapeutic relief, albeit temporary at best: 1) Parkinson's, and 2) Diabetes mellitus. Only living cells can afford any benefit. Therefore the best assurance for that is the living fetus, and the model for the use of those has already been established by the Swedes.[11,12]

"To others, aware of the issue, this argument is tenuous at best; it is little more persuasive than the suggestion that wider research use of adult human tissues will increase the frequency of capital punishment. In both instances, an unjustified conflation of unsubstantiated assertions is claimed to demonstrate causal connections that are then advanced as though they were objective fact."

> *Unsubstantiated assertions converted to objective fact have actually been the rather high-profile domain of Clifford Grobstein and others, e.g. claims to different "stages of individuality",[5,13] inferences that human embryos display "gill slits and tails",[14] and invoking "thought" occurring at 30 weeks of age post-fertilization.[15]*

•*New knowledge through new experiments on human embryos*

"Rather than such loose logic, what seems to be needed at this point is careful evaluation of the potential gains and losses if early human developmental stages were more accessible to scientific study. I will provide an appraisal along these lines, based on a preliminary analysis which, persuasive to me, proves that under appropriate oversight and with suitable safeguards early human developmental stages should be available to gain otherwise unobtainable important new knowledge."

> *It is only fair to ask, at this point, how important the "unobtainable new knowledge" might be. To date, no human embryologist is advocating experimentation with human embryos. Grobstein is a developmental biologist. Experimenting with vertebrate and invertebrate embryos is part of the discipline of developmental biologists. They are tinkerers, fiddlers, and doodlers, the contemporary biological engineers. Now, they propose for human embryos what they previously have done as a career discipline. The problem is they see little, if any, distinction between human embryos and those of other vertebrates.*

"... the zygote is genetically a new formulation capable of producing a lineage of like cells in a multicellular individual."

Read: "the zygote is genetically a new formulation . . ." as: ". . . a new individual . . .". To accept Grobstein's description would, at least, require him to arbitrarily decide how many cells establishes the new multicellular individual.

"However, the significance of these facts as stated are the subject of major controversy and, from my point of view, are substantially misinterpreted by some commentators who insist on regarding the resulting genetic individual as immediately equivalent to the total individuality of an adult."

What kind of significance is Grobstein talking about, and the "facts" are significant to whom? - the new individual or those wanting to intervene in development of this new individual?

"Accordingly, these commentators declare the zygote to be a "person" in the full moral and legal sense. Other commentators however, reject this notion as naive and misguided, pointing out that--like the preformationism of more than a century ago--the interpretation grossly miniaturizes and distorts the significance of the subsequent developmental process."

This is a good technique by Grobstein, tieing a moral and a legal interpretation to a biological one, then comparing it to a discredited false theory of more than 300 years ago. In effect, he characterizes those claiming full "personhood" for the zygote as charlatans.

"The fact, of course, is that during development the established genetic individuality is translated and transformed through step-wise expression into the much more complex reality of the new generation."

*Just as it continues from newborn to adult to old age
to death.*

"The zygote does have important characteristics beyond those of either egg or sperm alone. But the zygote also lacks many key features of a person, which are readily identified in a newborn and even more clearly in an adult."

Which means that the newborn also lacks "many key features" of an adult!

•*Cloning and the new individual*

"To be more specific (and extrapolating from studies on other species) the single-celled zygote is not yet even committed to becoming one individual. As it divides to form a small cluster of cells, each derived cell--if separated from the others--can make a whole new individual."

No properly constructed experiments have, as yet, been performed on human embryos to provide evidence for this assertion. So-called cloning of human embryos was reported in Science[16] (not via a research publication) from the work of Hall and Stillman, but does not provide evidence for several reasons: 1) the embryos chosen were those from 2 to 8 cell stages and they were chromosomally abnormal embryos (multiploidys with an extra set of chromosomes). 2) Separated blastomeres were grown through only the next few divisions, which would have occurred naturally, anyway, and 3) there still is no evidence that the blastomeres are exactly equivalent, which is the definition of a clone.

Commitment towards one individual may well have taken place at fertilization; then, again, it may not have. Grobstein draws a conclusion based on many experiments performed on several <u>other</u> species, most of them from Sea Urchin embryos. What he is describing is known to embryologists as "determinant *or indeterminant cleavage". In the latter case, determination occurs late in cleavage thereby preserving pluripotentiality in the blastomeres of early embryos. In the former case, the opposite would be true, thereby obviating the pluripotentiality early in development. It is postulated that peptides or proteins, acting as determinants are released at the proper time to determine differentiation.*

The truth is no "determinants" have ever been identified in the case of humans. Therefore, it is not known if, in fact, blastomeres of early embryos contain "determinants" which may or may not be inhibited, suppressed or masked, or that they may be added only at a later stage, say at the stage of the primitive streak, about 14 days, post-fertilization (P-F). If a suppressor or inhibitor is suspected, then similarly, one must propose appearance of an agent to remove or override the suppressor or inhibitor. The truth is, there is no evidence to support any of this speculation.

What is definitely known is that 30% of all monozygotic twins are determined early in development, at the first 2 or 3 division stages P-F.[17] This fact conflicts directly with Grobstein's claim that singleness does not occur until the onset of the primitive streak. Furthermore, Grobstein raises the case of monozygotic twins which occurs in only 1 of every 270 live births. He offers no account as to when singleness would occur for the other 269 individuals.

"The result is equivalent to natural twinning, which, of course, occurs with low but regular frequency in human development and produces litters of genetically identical individuals in armadillos. Genetic individuality, therefore, is not the same as developmental individuality; instead, the one precedes the other."

Genetic and developmental individuality are two of six arbitrarily invented "stages" by Grobstein, which support his special theories.

His so-called "developmental individuality" can be

235

identical with "genetic individuality" because it is known that approximately 30% of monozygotic twins are derived from the first two cleavage divisions - the two or four cell stage.

Further, Grobstein is applying a condition for all cases of human development based on what is known to occur in only 1 of about every 385 live births.

Lastly, "developmental individuality" does not have to be the same as "genetic individuality" in order to identify a new individual. After all, any succeeding moment is not the same as any preceding moment. The significance is not that they are different but that one follows the other, because all of development is a continuum, borne from a fait accompli initiated by first contact of sperm with ovum.

"Furthermore, as cell division proceeds, the many cells produced aggregate as a collective that develops a central fluid-filled cavity within an outer cellular peripheral wall. By this stage, the developing entity has normally travelled down the oviduct and arrived in the uterus. There, its outer cells interact with the uterine lining, leading to its implantation or incorporation into the uterine wall. In this process, the peripheral cells of the developing entity do not become part of, or contribute to, the embryo proper--defined as the direct precursor to the new individual-to-be. Rather, the outer cells of this stage contribute to the early placenta--the organ of exchange with the mother--which normally is discarded at birth."

The evidence is not conclusive to substantiate Grobstein's claim that "the outer cells" do not contribute to the embryo proper. Virtually all human embryology texts up to the present time, have stated that the "outer cells", spec. the cytotrophoblast, contributes cells which eventually cover the lining cells of the primitive gut. Carlson's new text,[18] indicates the covering of the cells of the gut come from the gut itself. However, this is true for the monkey, but no study has been done for the human. Larsen's new text states that the origin of the covering cells, the

236

extraembryonic mesoderm, is, as yet, still theory.[19] It really makes no difference. In actuality, those outer cells are acting on behalf of the embryo proper. If they do not, the embryo will die. It is difficult, if not impossible, to see how Grobstein can so easily separate the two functionally, as if one exists without the other.

"Therefore, the cellular aggregate produced by early divisions of the zygote is better referred to as a pre-embryo than as an embryo."

Nonsense. Many of the cells in the early cluster are destined to become part of the embryo proper. We simply don't know which ones they are. One might reasonably theorize that as mitotic divisions continue, an outer layer is distinguished from inner cells. However, it is not known whether or not this positioning is static or if, in fact, some cells change places with others. In fact, in a two-cell stage, no one knows if one or both of these cells will eventually become part of the embryo proper or only the "feeding" layer, as Grobstein puts it. Nevertheless, cells of the "embryo proper" certainly appear long before implantation!

The term pre-embryo is pure invention, arbitrary and probably was introduced by Clifford Grobstein in a 1979 article in Scientific American.[7] Traditionally, all of the early stages derived from the fertilized zygote have been regarded as the embryo, and this is confirmed by contemporary authors such as Carlson, Larsen and O'Rahilly. Ronan O'Rahilly, in fact, has a footnote in his 1992 text in which he states: "The ill-defined and inaccurate term pre-embryo . . . is said to end with . . . the primitive streak . . . the term is not used in this book."[20]

"It is only somewhat later that the actual precursor cells of the embryo--and the eventual human adult-become conspicuously separate from the so-called trophoblast (feeding layer), which contributes to the placenta."

The cells and tissues of the "embryo proper" are not "conspicuously" separated from the so-called trophoblast. There is a contiguity of tissues which joins the embryo with the placenta, most importantly, the blood vessels which grow from the embryo proper to close approximation with maternal blood lakes in the uterus via the placenta.

"(Interestingly, the trophoblast cells sometimes escalate on their own, undergoing malignant transformation, and take the life of either the mother, the offspring, or both.)"

The same may happen from cells of the "embryo proper" in the form of teratomas.

•*Status: preembryos are pre-persons?*

"What should be the status of the developing entity of the pre-embryonic stage? I prefer the following tentative approach to this important and difficult question. By virtue of its earlier developmental activation, the pre-embryo has potential to become a person in the full sense. This means that it has among its alternative futures possible maturation into a person. It is, in this sense, a preperson and this must be taken into account in its treatment and status."

Heros are often artificially made by erecting straw men, then knocking them down in public view. Unfortunately, this is what Grobstein is doing by promoting this false concept of a "pre-embryo", then lamenting: what should be done with it?" As many human embryologists, as Grobstein may have supporters, will claim there is no such stage as the "pre-embryo". The basic reason is that such artificial stages are significant only to the extant political discourse. It is of no value to human development because all of development from fertilization to birth

238

*(and beyond) is a <u>continuum</u>. As such, it is supreme
evidence of the <u>fait accompli</u> begun by initial contact
of the sperm and ovum. Most importantly, under
normal conditions the continuum of development is
not subject to <u>any</u> intrinsic arbitration!*

"What might such a status entail? First, since we should and do
attach very high value to persons (in part because the category includes
each of us as a self) and pre-persons are the only source of persons,
every feasible opportunity and priority should be provided to
pre-persons to continue their development to personhood. However,
this does not require and does not mean that pre-persons are
automatically and immediately persons. Rather, it means that
appropriate formulation of the status and rights of pre-persons is a task
of high priority, taking into account the status and rights of the
mother."

*It would seem that once a straw man is constructed it
can arbitrarily be given a heart, a brain and courage,
at some arbitrary future time. Thus, the straw man is
now a "pre-person".*

"Second, pre-persons, as genetic individuals, are members of
the kinship network of both of their parents. In the absence of the
genetic parents as decision makers at a critical time, an agreed-upon
procedure for surrogate custodianship should exist within each human
community, whether it is applied to a particular subgroup (family) or to
a larger community having a reliably stable consensus within it."

*It is interesting that Grobstein admits to the derivation
and subsequent decision making, of "pre-persons"
through <u>both parents</u>. In fact, an equal consideration
of a genetic father's vested interest in the fate of
embryos and fetuses (Grobstein's pre-person) was
submitted to the Supreme Court for adjudication in
1993. The court refused to hear the case.*

*There is another, ominous aspect to this concept of
Grobstein. Some states do not require consent from
both parents for a pregnant minor to get an abortion.*

239

Who then would constitute the "community" and who would become the "custodian"? Read on!

"Third, if acceptable custodianship based on kinship has not been provided for a given pre-embryo, it should become the responsibility of a designated public authority, which may appoint a trustee to make suitable decisions on behalf of the pre-person, with priority given as indicated in the preceding first principle.

Fourth, if all possibilities for providing continued development to personhood have been exhausted, <u>a pre-person may be made available for other purposes</u> (my emphasis) approved under rules to be formulated and monitored by a publicly responsible oversight body."

This is perhaps the most odious statement made, yet. In pre-World War II Nazi Germany, the mentally defective, Pastors, Priests, Gypsies & others were declared "non persons" and routinely executed. It is the "Second Holocaust", which is rarely written about, and included more than 10,000,000 people.[21] Is there a parallel here with the infamous Nazi medical experiments in the WWII concentration camps? Jews, Russian POWS, Polish inmates and even some Germans were considered "nonpersons" and thereby useful in yielding information presumed beneficial for soldiers in the field or for the good of science.

The fact that we have, on the one hand Nazi authority, and on the other, federally sanctioned guidelines by the Ethics Committee of the American Fertility Society, experimenting on "nonpersons", makes no difference. In both cases the objectives were and are driven by an abject denial of moral imperative.

"Fifth, it is assumed that such pre-persons will be maintained in an optimal frozen state pending disposition--but that they will not be so maintained for periods longer than one year unless accumulating experience indicates otherwise. Careful records should be maintained for all individual pre-embryos so as to allow modification of the one-year preliminary recommendation in response to cumulative experience.

These principles are intended to apply to pre-embryos as pre-persons, the developmental stage most often dealt with in clinical centers providing in-vitro fertilization and related techniques for treating subfertile couples. This set of applications does not, however, exhaust the growing possibilities for beneficial intervention during development *in utero*, whether the benefit be to the mother or the offspring. There is, therefore, growing need for greater scientific understanding of both embryonic and fetal development to support these clinical possibilities.

•*Preembryos are now embryos*

Thus, the first point made earlier with respect to the status of pre-embryos is equally valid for embryos--it is essential both to protect their potential as prepersons and to better understand the nature and properties of such potential. We need therefore to define the status of embryos so that their pre-personhood is appropriately respected, while allowing knowledge about them to be effectively expanded."

> *This seems contradictory. Grobstein says that "it is essential both to protect their potential as pre-persons and to better understand the nature . . . of such potential."*
>
> *Which has priority? The best way to protect the "potential of pre-persons" is to permit no intervention so they can be born!*
>
> *Further, Grobstein equates pre-embryo with pre-person and states "the status of pre-embryos is equally valid for embryos"; that is, "pre-persons are not", according to Grobstein, "automatically and immediately persons"!*
>
> *This is the very concept placed before the NIH advisory panel on Human Embryo research in the spring of 1994. As we read on we shall see how Grobstein claims the entire embryonic period (his definition up to 7 weeks P-F) may be subjected to human embryo research.*

241

"The embryonic period can be defined as beginning with the appearance of the head-to-tail body axis and extending to the onset of bodily movement at six to seven weeks. The main body axis is first recognized by appearance of the so-called primitive streak in the cup-shaped layer of cells which, ten to fourteen days after fertilization represents the nascent embryo. Shortly thereafter, in line with and ahead of the primitive streak, the neural folds appear as the first visibly precursor of the central nervous system and the brain."

Grobstein is reinventing human embryology. All traditional teaching in human embryology has heretofore taught that the embryonic period ends and the fetal period begins on or about the ninth week of development post-fertilization, based on 3 things occurring at that time: 1) more rapid development of the face, 2) completion of the formation of all major organ fields, and 3) the onset of differentiation of the reproductive structures.

•*A new definition for the transition of embryo to fetus*

" . . . By six to seven weeks, neuromuscular connections have been established in the neck region sufficient to support primitive turning movements of the head. This is a reasonable marker for the transition from primary organogenesis of the embryo to fetal growth and maturation, which continues on to birth and beyond."

Simply, not so. Turning of the head is not a reasonable marker for transition from embryo to fetus. First, it is in direct contradiction to what has been previously accepted and taught. Second, there is the vague inference here that turning the head may suggest such psychological traits as query, curiosity or willful response. There is no evidence for such veiled inferences. In fact at 5 to 6 weeks, limbs and/or head may move in response to two stimuli: 1) chemical, effecting a change in tissue balance of O_2 and CO_2, and 2) mechanical, including that produced by a

242

surgeon's probe. A consortium of sarcomeres (contractile units) in differentiating voluntary muscle is probably not necessary for this kind of movement, because many cells contain microfilaments, which represent primitive contractile systems.

Grobstein's not-so-veiled inferences are "The New Wave" of science.

"Movement, particularly when it seems purposeful, has significant impact on observers; accordingly, at the much later time of quickening, this was a traditional clinical sign of advancing pregnancy and fetal well-being. Today, embryonic movement is visible to ultrasonography as early as six to seven weeks of gestation and affords welcome testimony about fetal welfare. Moreover, movements imply a significant level of maturation, including the presence of receptors, neural transmitters, and effectors such as muscles. Thus movement as behavior, even when rudimentary, becomes a potential form of communication and thus an indicator of an internal state that may later include the beginnings of sensation, awareness, and comfort--all assumed to require at least minimal brain function."

There is nothing really incorrect in what is said here. However, Grobstein has probably justified Bernard Nathanson's claims in his production of "The Silent Scream"!

However, it should be said that Grobstein's use of the word "purposeful" is a rather long reach, and has no scientific support. In fact, applying this even to the newborn is suspect.

"With these developments, concern legitimately rises about influences and treatments that may evoke pain or other significant discomfort. Very much more knowledge about these matters is needed to deal intelligently and humanely with the "rights" of quasi-persons during their course to full subjective existence.

•*Added value through added signals*

Recapitulating, although the human developmental course is

243

gradual and cumulative, there are several fundamental horizons that are recognizable as major transitions. These include, in addition to fertilization, embryonic axis formation and onset of behavior as indicated by bodily movement. Each signals a new level of organization and integration, which can justify assignment of added value with regard to realized function and imminent social potential."

> *Each does signal a new level of organization and integration. But it does not follow that "added value" means value to the political or social structure of the society in which the embryo is developing. This is specious and arbitrary, because "added value" may apply to any stage, including newborn (which in the past were subjected to infanticide in some cultures) or adult (decreased value of which is prompting aided death by Kervorkian).*
>
> *Because of the continuum character of development, stages or ever new levels of differentiation are important only in a taxonomic way to human embryologists and obstetricians.*

" . . . even at birth full independence as a person is still some years ahead. Nonetheless, in most contemporary societies full protection as a person is mandated for any newborn. Yet, the fetus, particularly in its early stages, is a far cry from a normal newborn, and no general consensus has been achieved on when in fetal life *in utero* a person definitely exists. There is, however, consensus that any fetus capable of survival after delivery ("viable") is a person from the time of delivery."

> *Grobstein finally admits that not even birth confers full "personhood" upon an individual. Thus, assigning this socio-legal quality at any time is simply arbitrary.*
>
> *The only consensus that viability and personhood are linked is that of a majority of the Supreme Court arrived at in 1973 in Roe v. Wade.*

" . . . What seems clear is that there is no moment or single step when, or by which, a person in the full sense suddenly exists. Rather, a human being in the full sense gradually emerges through a series of

244

steps, with no way of progressing immediately from a pre-person to a person. Nonetheless, each step makes a contribution, and we do not yet fully understand all of the steps or exactly how each contributes. Some steps can be clarified by study of other species, but no other species undergoes the full changes that are so diagnostic of humanity."

He contradicts himself, because this means that not even his arbitrary stage of "developmental individuality" confers personhood, nor does birth, nor does puberty.

" . . . Clearly needed is wider awareness that essentially ideological considerations are pinching off an important area of biomedical research--an area involving critical aspects of reproduction and development.

•*"Family of value issues"*

To summarize the problem in the context of this book, experience has taught us that a number of ethical issues regularly arise in the conduct of scientific research. At the primary level this book presents much about misrepresentation of data, the responsibilities of authorship, and the conflicts of interest that may arise when scientists function in centers of national policy or in corporate board rooms. These indeed are important issues and call for careful attention.

But there is another family of value issues that has plagued the interaction of science with society for centuries, perhaps as long as the two have existed."

I believe it is not by accident that Grobstein uses the phrase "family of value issues". This is a thinly veiled attempt to establish some sense of credibility, not to mention ethical and moral value to his gratuitous tone by offering a contorted syntaxical phraseology of "family values". Traditional family values are the bed rock of societal stability. He knows that; therefore, he makes a rather lame attempt to invoke this concept.

"It has to do with the product of science rather than its methods or even its objectives. To attach value to scientific knowledge often means to detach value from what was previously thought to be reliable knowledge."

Therefore, the end, indeed, would justify the means.

" . . . The firm belief that a complete person begins at conception and that, consequently, both contraception and abortion are moral equivalents to murder rests on supposed knowledge from which value now has to be detached. The much more difficult present reality that a person emerges gradually in complicated ways from a single cell is knowledge to which value now has to be firmly attached. Neither the substance of this relatively new knowledge nor the evidence that supports it is easily communicated throughout the body politic. Nonetheless, it must somehow become part of the scientific and technological literacy, which we are all urged to share more widely with the general community."

Development does not stop at birth. The fundamental processes of embryology are continued even into old age and death. This is so because all of life is a continuum. Therefore, the human, the person, the individual are all identical in the conceptual sense. Hence, the <u>value</u> *of life is established at the initial contact of sperm and ovum and cannot be "detached" because of a self-serving or arbitrary reinvention of human embryology.*

References

1.   *New Wave* is used as opposed to *New Age* because the former connotes: a movement or trend, as in art, literature, or politics, that breaks with traditional concepts; whereas the latter connotes: a social movement embodying American Indian traditions, holism, concern for nature, astrology, vegetarianism, etc.
2.   Syllabus: The Supreme Court of The United States, Roe et al. v. Wade, District Attorney of Dallas County, No. 70-18, decided January 22, 1973.

3. *AMICI CURIAE* Brief of 167 Distinguished Scientists and Physicians, Including 11 Nobel Laureates, In Support of Applellees. In The Supreme Court of The United States, October Term, 1988, Re: William L. Webster, et al. v. Reproductive Health Services, *et al.*

4. Proc. Amer. Philosp. Soc., 101:357-370, 1957.

5. Solomon, Susan., personal communication.

6. Grobstein, Clifford. 1988. Science and The Unborn: Choosing Human Futures. Basic Books, Inc., New York.

7. Grobstein, Clifford. 1979. External Human Fertilization. Scientific American, 240:57-67.

8. Moore, Keith L. 1988. Before We Are Born. p. 71. W.B. Saunders Co., Philadelphia.

9. Moore, Keith L. 1993. The Developing Human. 5th edition. W.B. Saunders Co., Philadelphia.

10. Grobstein, Clifford. 1993. The Status and Uses of Early Human Developmental Stages. *in* Ethical Issues In Research, ed. Darwin Cheney, The University Publishing Group, Inc., Frederick, Maryland.

11. I. Strömberg, M. Bygdeman and P. Almqvist. 1992. J. Comp. Neurol., 315:445.

12. Lindvall, et al., 1992. Annals of Neurolology, 31:155-173.

13. Grobstein, C. 1989. Psychology Today, September Issue, pp. 43-46.

14. Singleton, Rivers, Jr. 1989. Persp. Biol. Med., 32:174-179.

15. Sagan, C. and A. Drugan. 1990. Parade, The Sunday Paper Magazine, April 22, pp. 4-8.

16. Kolberg, R. 1993. Science (Research News), 262:652-653.

17. Moore, K.L. 1988. The Developing Human, 4th ed., p. 125, W.B. Saunders Co., Philadelphia.

18. Carlson, Bruce. 1994. Human Development and Developmental Biology, Mosby Books, New York.

19. Larsen, William J. 1993. Human Embryology, Churchill Livingstone, New York.

20. O'Rahilly, R. and F. Müller, Human Embryology and Teratology, page 55, Wiley-Liss, New York.

21. O'Malley, W.J. 1986. America, June 14, 492-494.

Individual Testimony Before the NIH Human Embryo Research Panel March 14, 1994 Bethesda Marriott Hotel

Dianne N. Irving, M.A., Ph.D.

My name is Dr. Dianne N. Irving, and I would like to thank the Panel for allowing me to testify today as a concerned individual - although five minutes is woefully insufficient time, and although I know that nothing I say will have any impact whatsoever on your deliberations. I am preparing a longer written statement for the record.

I am a former research biochemist, and worked here at NIH/NCI in radiation biology and viral oncology. I subsequently received my Master's and Doctoral degrees in philosophy (with concentrations in both the history of philosophy and bioethics) from Georgetown University. As my publications will demonstrate, I am clearly not anti-research or anti-science - indeed scientific research was my first career. I am against unethical research and scientific research fraud, however, and so, for example, am on the Board of Editors of the journal <u>Accountability in Research</u>. I am also not anti-individuals or anti-families with diseases - indeed, I currently work with the families in NAMI in ethical issues concerning psychiatric research using persons with mental illness.

My remarks are offered simply as "reality checks". In this short time I want to focus on only two of many of my major concerns - basic requirements for ethical scientific research, and the status of bioethics and "expert" bioethicists - and then mention some suggestions.

I. Basic requirements for ethical scientific research

My first major focus is on the ethical (not legal) considerations for scientific research, of which I will only mention three: (1) that the science used to ground and develop the research project is **correct science**; (2) that the **design of the experimental protocol** is ethical, and (3) that the scientific goal - no matter how lofty that goal is or may seem - as well as **the means used** in the experiment in order to reach that goal - are also ethical.

(1) First, concerning the use of **correct science**: For over 15 years much of the human embryology stated in arguments about "human personhood" is simply incorrect human embryology. This should be important to NIH for two reasons. One, the bottom-line ethical requirement for any scientific research is that the science itself is correct - as Dr. Van Blerkom so eloquently pointed out. We certainly do know the correct human embryology - it simply is not being acknowledged or used in these issues. To use incorrect human embryology as your starting point in designing, performing and analyzing your scientific experiments renders them scientifically invalid, meaningless - and unethical.

Recent bioethics arguments for so-called "delayed personhood" - apparently designed to justify theoretically what is in fact unethical - have been grounded specifically on this incorrect human embryology. This in turn has led to equally incorrect conclusions about the moral and legal status of human embryos. The persistent use of this incorrect human embryology, and the legal and ethical impact of the incorrectly derived definition of "personhood", have implications for your own definition of **"human subjects** of research", as well as for how OPRR regulations needs to be reconstructed in order to protect all **human subjects** (discussed below).

My doctoral dissertation was precisely on whether it is ethical to use surplus IVF human embryos in destructive experimental research - research that is not for the direct benefit of that human embryo. I did, actually, originally sense that I would have argued for "delayed personhood" at 14-days, based primarily on the "embryology" that I was reading in the journals and books. I analyzed 23 representative arguments on "delayed personhood" - using three criteria: (1) is the science used correct; (2) is the philosophy - especially the definition of a "human being" or "human person" - historically correct or objectively defensible; (3) do the conclusions follow logically from the major and minor premises? To my own amazement I discovered that in all 23 arguments the science was incorrect (in multiple areas of science), the philosophy was historically incorrect or indefensible, and that none of the conclusions followed logically from their premises.

For our present purposes, this very same incorrect human embryology (which has been disseminated for so many years, especially by long time members of the American Fertility Society Ethics Committee, and paid consultants of NIH) is yet again presently being used in your own materials, debates and invited papers - even published in the <u>Washington Post</u>. The purpose of this incorrect human embryology is to designate a so-called human "pre-embryo" - i.e., a human "pre-person"; and consequently these human "pre-embryos" or "pre-persons" would have different ethical and legal rights and protections than "real" human persons do - precisely so that they can be used in experimental research with few if any regulations or concerns by the American people who pay for this research. The "philosophy" used to support this conclusion, by the way, would also render the mentally ill, Parkinson's patients, Alzheimer's patients, the comatose, drug addicts, alcoholics, etc., also human "pre-persons" - a fact which seems to escape most of those to whom these academically indefensible theories would be applied (including your enthusiastic family member advocates testifying here).

Still you continue to condone and perpetuate the use of incorrect human embryology, which can only lead to scientifically invalid experiments. Furthermore, regardless of your own ideological positions on abortion or fetal research, the conceptual precedents of "delayed personhood" now in place in these debates are easily transferrable to millions of adult human beings, yet it is rarely pointed out that these academically incorrect (both scientific and philosophical) concepts of "personhood" could quite easily be applied to these other categories of human beings.

I submit for the record: (1) a copy of my 400-page dissertation precisely on this topic, as well as other of my peer-reviewed publications on this and related issues; (2) a copy of an arrogant letter sent to me by a journalist of the <u>Washington Post</u> who recently used a chart in his article about this Panel which contained this same incorrect human embryology (which he received from NIH); and, (3) a written statement from Dr. C. Ward Kischer, a professor of <u>human</u> embryology for over 30 years, documenting agreement by him and many experts in human embryology that this Grobstein-McCormick "human embryology" (successively used and elaborated by Ford, Cefalo and many others) is objectively, scientifically wrong, and that the term "pre-embryo" is objectively and scientifically invalid. I would add that even Clifford Grobstein himself - who is not a human embryologist, but an amphibian embryologist - agreed with me, in front of a scientific conference, that the "embryology" he was using was not human embryology (it is actually amphibian embryology), but that he was "just trying to be helpful"! Additionally, Keith Moore, who Grobstein and McCormick directly quote in their argument, also agreed that this "embryology" and the use of the term "pre-embryo" was scientifically incorrect and inappropriate.

Aside from the obvious ethical criteria of using correct science as the starting point in any human embryo research, the larger question is the credibility of NIH and the greater scientific community itself. Why have NIH and the scientific community allowed this incorrect science to go uncorrected in the literature for over 15 years - with no censure -, and continued to use scientists and bioethicists who perpetrate this incorrect science as their paid consultants and grantees? Why is there no **human** embryologist on this NIH **Human Embryo** Research Panel? Additionally, your earlier discussions (in your meeting minutes) on "how to define the human embryo" - that on which you are attempting to regulate research - was, from an objective scientific point of view, mortifying and embarrassing. Does NIH - one of the greatest scientific research institutions in the world - mean to have political scientists, sociologists, feminists and bioethicists define **scientifically** what a human embryo is?

(2). A second ethical requirement of scientific research is that the **design of the protocol** itself be ethical. For our purposes here, if the very design of the protocol used in human embryo research is unethical - i.e., specifically designed to destroy a living developing human being during the process of experimental research - then the entire experiment is fundamentally unethical.

NIH's credibility in funding research in which the very design of protocols is unethical is currently already in question - and I ask that this Panel take seriously the real harm to human beings caused by all such unethically designed protocols. Grants of millions of tax-payers dollars have been given to researchers whose protocols were specifically designed not for the health and benefit of the patients, but solely for the "advancement of scientific knowledge". For example, some recent proposals required sham surgeries - holes bored into the skulls of Parkinson's patients to be use as "controls" in fetal brain tissue research; and other researchers' protocols which required and produced the purposeful inducement of relapses in patients with schizophrenia - without their informed consent - in order to "study the biochemical processes of relapses" in patients with schizophrenia - are protocols approved for many years by NIH's IRB's (so much for IRB's).

(3). A third ethical requirement is that not only the **goal**, but the **means to achieve that goal**, are ethical. And here even the credibility of the existing OPRR regulations themselves are in question. For example, these regulations make "exceptions" for just about everything, if the "information cannot be obtained in any other way" - or "for the sake of scientific knowledge alone". I strongly disagree with such clearly utilitarian "ethics" - an ethics which is certainly not normatively "neutral". No human being - human embryos included - should be used in experimental research for someone else's good or for the greater glory of scientific knowledge itself - without their informed consent. This was precisely the legacy of Nuremberg - a legacy which, frankly, realistically no longer exists.

The advancement of scientific knowledge can take place ethically, albeit more slowly, within the context of therapeutic research - research which is only for the direct benefit of that particular individual human being. Such research is ethically permissible even with vulnerable populations of human research subjects - e.g., human embryos, fetuses, the mentally ill, prisoners, children, etc., - those whose informed consents are compromised (as long as valid proxy consent has been obtained). Given that human embryos **are** human beings/persons - much as that fact escapes so many of you - it is not only unethical, it is, frankly, sick to use vulnerable human embryos as means to the lofty goals of the "common good" - or the "good" of other human beings - or for the greater and speedier glory of scientific knowledge (and scientists) - no matter how lofty and beneficent those goals may seem.

Thus these OPRR regulations themselves need an ethical overhaul. Specifically, they should eliminate all such references to "exceptions" for "knowledge which cannot be obtained in any other way" or "for the advancement of scientific knowledge" when referring to research using any vulnerable human populations. They should also include the mentally ill and human embryos and fetuses as "vulnerable" human research subjects.

Also in question is NIH's real commitment to actually protect all human subjects used in research. For example, a policy presently exists here at NIH which allows cognitively impaired human subjects to give "informed consent" to appoint a "surrogate" who can then decide by proxy to enroll that cognitively impaired patient in both therapeutic and experimental **research** (not health care) - a policy which is both ethically and legally "irregular". There are other irregularities and concerns about this Panel - to cite just one example, the advantageously incorrect summary of what the Massachusetts State statutes actually conclude about the use of living versus dead human embryos, fetuses and neonates which was included in the background papers prepared for the panelists.

II. The status of bioethics and "expert" bioethicists

But I want to move on to just mention briefly the second major area of concern I have about these proposals. That concern pertains to the status of the field of bioethics itself and of "expert" bioethicists, which I think might inappropriately and unduly influence the questions before you. As with the "scientific" concerns, I hope no one takes this personally, but it is about time that someone articulate at least a question about the credibility of the field of bioethics itself, especially when there is now and has been historically an intimate - one might almost say incestuous - connection between the fields of bioethics and medical research public policy. I don't expect several of you to be particularly pleased with my comments.

Quite briefly, as I look back on my participation in bioethics (which goes back to 1979), I am beginning to seriously question the credibility of the field of bioethics itself. Similar to Dr. Van Blerkom's comments relative to the lack of real scientific expertise on the part of many involved in the field of IVF, I see a similar lack of real academically meaningful credentials in the field of bioethics. And this concern, by the way, is not unique to me - there is a growing body of literature, including those who were the inventors of the field of bioethics itself, reflecting this same basic concern about bioethics and bioethics "expertise".

Bioethics "degrees" simply do not reflect the kind of rigorous course work and examinations required of real Ph.D. philosophers. Students come into graduate philosophy programs from sociology, law, medicine, history, literature, administration, etc. - with little or no undergraduate course work in philosophy, especially the history of philosophy which is usually required for undergraduate freshmen and sophomore philosophy majors. Practically no two "bioethicists'" course work is alike. The result is a very watered-down curriculum leading to watered-down credentials (leading to sloppy academically deficient theories and conclusions of "ethics" and what constitutes "ethical" practices). What is worse is that by far the majority of "bioethicists" in the field in this country do not even have this meager background, but simply take a few courses from a bioethics "think tank" or read a few "bioethics" text books - and voila - a professional "bioethicist".

There is a very real credibility crisis emerging concerning the de facto expertise of these seemingly self-appointed "bioethics" gurus who are genuinely convinced that they can proclaim to the American people what is "ethical" and what is "unethical", and who purposefully and successfully impact major public policy decisions. Academically these persons are not real philosophical ethicists, nor can their several ethical "theories" stand up to harsh philisophical criticism and analysis.

The term "bioethicist" should be changed to "moral lobbyists", or "political consensus groups", or whatever more accurately describes their true credentials, "expertise" and role. This is not to negate some of the very good efforts of so many good people involved. Unfortunately, just as the really good ethical scientists will go down with a handful of unethical scientists, so too will these good and ethical people in "bioethics" lose their own credibility in time because of the arrogant and intellectually abusive theories and practices of those who are unethical.

In sum, my concerns about the credibility of this Panel and these research proposals centers on: the lack of the presence on this Panel of several nationally recognized human embryologists; its persistent perpetuation of 15 years of incorrect human embryological (and other) science; its incestuous relationship over as many years with a tightly controlled "bioethics" super-system which silently or overtly determines such a great deal of American public policy; questions about other possible conflicts of interests within this Panel that need to be raised [see paper specifically on this Panel]; and an apparent willingness to disregard even the most basic ethical requirements of any scientific research proposal - most of which deal simply with scientific soundness, accuracy and design. It is all, in my opinion, simply built on a house of cards - and one which is about to crumble.

The consequences are wide-reaching. There really seems to be no real **accountability** of any one to any one. Blatantly unscientific and unethical experiments are about to be condoned - indeed hailed as

254

"progress" and "beneficent" goals. Yet human harm of epic proportions will be caused by such unethical experiments approved by you. Additionally, true informed consent has virtually been precluded - for aborted women, their pre-born children, the donors of sperm and ova, the researchers who unwittingly perform such experiments - indeed the members of this very Panel - since none actually know about or refuse to acknowledge the real and correct human embryology and the implications of that correct human embryology for any meaningful future experiments or regulations. Furthermore, any real "democratic" process concerning these issues - either in these hearings or within the broader American community - is obviously impossible.

Because the research and bioethics "institutions" have for so many years arrogantly refused to acknowledge, deal with or correct their theoretical and practical problems; because so much real harm has been, is and will be caused; because of the sheer arrogance of this Panel in even considering so seriously and enthusiastically these clearly unethical experiments using such helpless vulnerable <u>human embryos who are human beings and human persons</u>; because such little (or no) notice was given to the American people, their real elected representatives, or others professionally involved in these issues; and because no input by other experts who might disagree with the Panel was allowed (indeed the Panel acknowledged in their minutes that only those experts who agreed with the Panel's proposals would become members of the Panel) - this Panel has lost any credibility.

Consequently I would support a call for Congressional hearings, in order that these fundamental discussions and decisions of life, death and harm can be brought back to the American people where they properly belong. I am certain that the American people in general have no concept of what has taken place recently in the areas of medical research, regulations and bioethics, nor any clue that all of these weird theories and such incorrect science could and might be applied to them later through "conceptual transfer" (it has happened once before in recent Nazi history). And all this, using their own tax monies!

Congress should close these hearings down immediately, and hold the appropriations of these research funds until such time as the Congress and the American people can be caught up on these issues, and then have them decided by referendum in their state legislatures.

Congress should also immediately begin investigations into the following related matters:

1. The investigation of presently operating in vitro fertilization clinics and programs: the professional competency of their researchers and staff; and, the documentation of any harmful consequences to patients or to their offspring who have been treated during their participation in this experimental IVF research. They should also consider medical follow-ups and studies of the patients and their offspring, and appropriate compensation given for harms sustained.

2. The appropriate academic credentials of those who would serve on such panels as this, and the mechanism by which such panel members should be selected.

3. Any possible conflict of interests such members might have - financially or politically: e.g., would any Panel members be the recipients of any of these Federal research funds; do Panel members own stock in pharmaceutical or biotech companies who would profit from and be involved in this research; do they have any conflicting interests in past, present or future patents, drugs or devices; have they had or have potentially compromising affiliations with bioethics "think tanks", eugenics-based programs or societies, global economic roundtables, the American Fertility Society, A.C.O.G., NABER, Planned Parenthood, or the major funding foundations, etc. - including resource materials, instruction programs and political contacts which could also seriously compromise the Panel's "objectivity" in considerations of public policy concerning such experimental research. At least Panel members ought to be required to file a financial "conflict of interests" form, as do other high-level government employees, judges, etc.

4. The establishment of real, effective oversight, monitoring and enforcement mechanisms by Congress to prevent scientific fraud, unethical experimentation, and physical/psychological harm to all human research subjects.

5. The determination of legal accountability, fines, etc., when such research is unethically influenced, designed, performed or analyzed, or when conflicts of interests are involved.

6. An immediate educational process for members of Congress and the American people concerning these bioethics and medical

research issues, and the implications these issues have for their basic health and welfare.

In this democracy it is the American people who should be deciding whether or not human beings should be produced or used in unethical destructive experimental research - not a self-aggrandizing, self-appointed NIH Panel which is willing and ready to impose its own ideological brand of utilitarian or consensus "ethics" on the rest of us - and at our expense.

THE THIRD HOLOCAUST:

The War Against The Human Embryo and Fetus

C. Ward Kischer, Ph.D.
and
Joseph R. Stanton, M.D.

One of the emerging truths of the 1990s is the admission that our country is in a profound moral decline. More precisely, as many political analysts have said: "We are in a cultural war"!

We contend that the first and greatest casualty in this war has been and continues to be the human embryo and fetus. This is The Third Holocaust. The status of both embryo and fetus has been arbitrarily reduced to that of a non-person, one of the new "Untermenschen".

The Reinstitution of the Untermenschen

The concept of the "Untermenschen" as less than fully human persons was an essential characteristic of the dehumanization in the Third Reich, more than a half century ago. That dehumanization led scientists, physicians, and others, in the service of the state, to abandon ethical medicine and carry out fatal experiments on piteous non-consenting human beings. These fatal experiments were regarded as useful in yielding information presumed beneficial to the war effort, or simply for the advancement of science. Dehumanization led directly to the concentration (death) camps, the gas ovens and the deaths of millions of innocent human beings in what is known as The Holocaust, and the lesser known Second Holocaust, which included the mentally defective, the crippled, pastors, priests, gypsies, Poles, Russians, Germans and political dissenters.

The nations of the free world acting as one, indicted, tried, convicted and sentenced to imprisonment or death responsible officials and physicians. The charge at Nuremberg was "crimes against humanity". "Never again" was the universal cry as the Nuremberg trials drew to a close.

Some will object that today is not the 1930s, that this is not Nazi Germany and that it is offensive to draw any analogy to those times. But, the record shows that it was in academic medicine in the Third Reich that eager recruits were found and the concept of Lebens Unwertenleben (lives unworthy of life) and its deliberate pursuit began there. Ideas do have consequences, and words do mean things, and are not to be dismissed lightly. Particularly virulent is the concept that human lives are not worthy of protection under the law.

In a nation terminating 1.5 million normal pregnancies each year only those regarded as convenient and the wanted survive. The dehumanization of the human conceptus so evident in the abortion debate and in the denial of personhood and equal protection under the law is now being rendered complete by the imminent approval of experimentation on the human embryo as sanctioned by the Clinton administration through the National Institutes of Health (NIH) and to be paid for by taxpayer's dollars.

This is part of redefining the human being, which has been going on since Roe v. Wade, adjudicated in 1973. This has been eminently demonstrated by public hearings held by a select NIH Advisory Panel On Human Embryo Research. Those hearings began in January, 1994 and were conducted monthly with the last one held in September, 1994. Those meetings were for the purpose of constructing guidelines for research on the human embryo. To establish credibility for such research, they first concluded that the human embryo is not entitled to the same protection as a human being.

The Preembryo

What is society to make of such attempts, under academically impeccable auspices, sponsored by the U.S. government, to declare the early human conceptus, during its first 14 days of life (or beyond), as less than fully human? What is society to think of this attempt to acquire federal funding for exploitation and non-therapeutic experimentation on human life in its early stages?

An ancient aphorism states: "It's money that makes the mare go". This applies with particular emphasis to medical research in The U.S. Indeed, were federal funding to suddenly disappear the medical research establishment would essentially collapse like rising souffle responding to a slamming door. Events currently unfolding at NIH with the prospect of non-therapeutic research on the early human conceptus threaten to create immense problems in conscience for persons sensitive to the rights and inherent dignity of the early human conceptus and our moral responsibility as taxpayers.

Dr. Seuss' charming allegorical children's story "Horton Hears A Who" with its conclusion: "A person's a person no matter how small" does not cut the mustard inside the beltway or with The American Fertility Society (AFS) or The American College of Obstetrics and Gynecology. To prepare for this latest assault on the U.S. Treasury, for research funds, they have invoked a reinvented human embryology, which has been roughly 15 years in the making. In 1979, Clifford Grobstein, Ph.D., a developmental biologist, created a new term, the "preembryo", designed and used to dehumanize and isolate that tiny island of humanity, whose normal residence is in the womb, specifically to cut it off from the moral concern due one human in origin and immortal in destiny.

Grobstein, who is not a human embryologist, and The Reverend Richard McCormick, S.J. have been the principal spokesmen in this dehumanizing process. They and others formed an arbitrary Ethics Committee of the AFS in 1986, reconvened in 1990, and initially designed, then slightly amended and reaffirmed, statements removing a moral status and protection of the conceptus up to 14 days post-fertilization.

If, in fact, the early human embryo remains what it always has been considered, a member of the human species, it is crucial that the American public understand the significance of the struggle now raging. Bogus human embryology tailored for a specific political strategy must not provide a warrant for calculated dehumanization and a sneak attack on the taxpayer's wallet.

The term "preembryo" did not exist in the literature anywhere before 1979. To our knowledge, it has never been proposed for any specie other than the human. Further, to our knowledge, no human embryologist accepts this term. It has been used to 'scientifically' justify early abortion, and, now, to justify experimentation on early individual human life up to 14 days of post-fertilization age. This includes creating human embryos, their exploitation, experimentation and destruction at will. The term is commonly used by the AFS and the

ACOG. The NIH now uses the terms "preembryo" and "Ex Utero Embryo" interchangeably.

Compounding this devilment, Grobstein is now extending his interpretations of human embryology. He currently proposes that the definition of "preembryo" should apply to at least 7 weeks post fertilization.

During the Reagan-Bush years, 1980-1992, no non-therapeutic research using IVF-bred human embryos and no IVF research was governmentally subsidized. This is because an Ethics Advisory Board was required by law to approve any such grant, and no such permission was forthcoming. The Ethics Advisory Board was allowed to go out of existence and no new appointees were named. The issue became essentially moot. Additionally, in existence have been 25 states with laws regulating fetal research and 15 of these have laws controlling human embryo research. Further, there is wide-spread public opposition to exploitation of the human embryo and fetus.

The Revitalization Act of 1993 And Its Fallout

To rescue the AFS and the ACOG and their research plans, Senator Edward Kennedy, Massachusetts, and Representative Henry Waxman, California, pushed and helped enact the NIH Revitalization Act of 1993. An obscure section overturned the existing Ethics Advisory Board approval requirement and allowed the NIH to appoint a Human Embryo Research Panel "to provide advice as to those areas acceptable for Federal Funding". The appointed Panel included members of the AFS and the ACOG, and first met in January, 1994. Among the members were 3 cellular or subcellular biologists, 1 primate anatomist, 5 physicians, 2 lawyers, 2 University Presidents, 1 sociologist, 2 educationists, and 3 philosophers. While appearing to be academically impeccable it had no human embryologist or a known opponent of human fetal or embryo research among its members! In fact, we do not know of a single human embryologist who advocates human embryo research. Why are the developmental biologists, the molecular biologists, compulsively lobbying for human embryo research? They are the contemporary biological engineers, and perhaps 75% of all that ever lived in the world are alive and working today. They are the tinkerers, the fiddlers, the doodlers. What they have done with invertebrate and vertebrate embryos they now propose to do with human embryos without compunction or moral restraint.

It is doubtful that a significant number of members of Congress realized that the Ethics Advisory Board requirement was being eliminated when they voted for the NIH Revitalization Act of 1993. Nor were they aware that they were ceding to the NIH the power to appoint a stacked committee in an area of such great moral concern to many Americans.

It is of special significance that the Fact Sheet instructed the Panel to "address the profound moral and ethical issues raised by the use of human embryos in research, and develop guidelines to govern the review and conduct of federally-funded research".

Although not included in the wording of the "Panel Charge" it was clear as to the considerations demanded by the NIH. In fact, the overwhelming testimonies presented to the Panel (a maximum of 5 minutes each) were opposed to recreational experimentation on the human embryo. That is, opposition was heavily against non-therapeutic research from In-vitro fertilization procedures. For example, at the June 21st public session all 12 testimonies opposed the panel's agenda. Yet, the Panel overtly rejected most of this testimony, often to the point of overt contestation. They also virtually ignored thousands of written criticisms, while proceeding toward their recommendations.

At the May 4th, 1994 meeting of Panel members Professor Brigid Hogan did suggest that a licensing authority should be set up for embryo research in the U.S. Panel appointee Professor Patricia King rejected this concept pointing out that it might end embryo research "for the next 20 years because such a licensing authority requires an act of Congress and *if we start getting into that bailiwick everything gets totally messed up*". (emphasis added) So much for Congress!

Human Embryo Research Proposals

Discussions by this Panel, as indicated by the official transcripts, included the following non-therapeutic human embryo experiments:
1. the creation or manufacture of human embryos as research objects with no intent of implantation.

2. removal of ovaries from brain-dead women and aborted fetuses so eggs (ova) can be recovered for laboratory fertilization and manipulation.

3. testing a panoply of drugs on the developing human embryo.

4. human parthenogenesis, until now an oxymoron, an attempt without fertilization by a sperm and by manipulation to force the ovum to form an embryo.

5. use of human embryos to create specific cell lines.

6. separating cells from human embryos to duplicate individuals, or to freeze and save as potential "spares".

7. tests on human embryos for developing new lines of contraception.

8. fusion of animal specie cells or DNA fragments with those of the human embryo with the expectation of further development.

At the June 21st-22nd meeting, the panel took preliminary votes and approved of the following research: 1) use of donated eggs and sperm for creation of "research" embryos, 2) experimentation on embryos up to 14 days post-fertilization age, 3) parthenogenesis studies, 4) genetic testing of isolated embryonic cells, 5) experiments beyond 14 days of age involving the neural tube, 6) use of human embryos to produce cell lines for culture, and 7) cloning, the introduction of a healthy nucleus of a cell into an egg whose impaired nucleus has been removed, with further culture.

These votes were sustained and recommended in the final report of the panel to the Director of NIH. The Director presumably submitted the report and recommendations to another advisory group, after which he was to decide on the guidelines, presumably due sometime in December, 1994, or shortly thereafter. To date, January 1977, he has not done so.

The Continuum of Life

Justifying all of the "recreational" experimentation is the application of the terms "preembryo" or "human embryo exutero", as used by the Panel, to the first 14 days after fertilization. The assumption is that up to a certain stage the individual is not there and while it may be treated with profound respect it is not owed the *full* respect due to an 'authentic' human being. The implication is that we are to accept manipulation and exploitation of the "preembryo", and this can be done with impunity and, of course, subsidized with tax dollars.

Obviating all of the bogus and esoteric embryology including the assumed recognition of the term "preembryo" is the undeniable truth that all of human development (indeed, all of life) from initial contact of egg and sperm to birth (and beyond to death) is a continuum and is not subject to any arbitrations under what the scientific world recognizes and accepts as normal circumstances. Therefore, the human being, the individual, and the person, are one and inseparable, and are present at the moment of contact between sperm and egg. So-called stages overlap and are useful only to human embryologists and Obstetricians in the taxonomic sense as markers.

Thus, the creation of any stage during development, such as "preembryo", or one which identifies the appearance of the "individual" is purely specious and arbitrary, as even some of the NIH Advisory Panel members admit. The reason for inventing these stages is to justify the experimentation proposed for the human embryo. Even though non-therapeutic procedures may kill the human embryo, advocates may claim such experiments would be redeeming if they render useful results. In other words, the end would justify the means!

Dr. Henry K. Beecher in Experiments in Man (1950, JAMA 169:486) pointed out that, "if an experiment is moral it is moral from the outset. "It does not become moral because it produces valuable data or results." Already a number of other nations have considered and rejected the path down which our NIH is proceeding.

"For Whom The Bell Tolls"

The hour is late in our nation. The public must become concerned. It would be well to reflect on a statement found in philosopher Hans Jonas' "Philosophical Reflections On Experimenting With Human Subjects, (1969, Daedelus, 98:244) "Progress is an optimal goal not an unconditional commitment. Let us remember that slower progress in the conquest of disease would not threaten society, grievous as it is for those who have a disease which has not yet been conquered. But, society would indeed be threatened by the erosion of those moral values whose loss possibly caused by too ruthless a pursuit

264

of scientific progress would make its most dazzling triumph not worth having."

This government and the taxpayer should not tolerate the invoking of bogus embryology by any agency of this government to create a free fire zone for exploitation of the human conceptus. Not for 1 day, not for 14 days, not for 270 days should that stage of human life, which each of us living passed through, be dehumanized as born "Untermenschen" were more than 50 years ago.

One of the more odious concepts concerning the status of the human embryo has come from Judge Michael J. Noonan, presiding over Municipal Court at Morris County, New Jersey in April of 1991. This was the trial of Alexander Loce, and friends, for attempting to block the entrance of a woman, pregnant with an embryo Loce had fathered, to an abortion clinic. In finding the accused guilty of criminal trespass, Noonan also had this to say: "I find that the eight week fetus (sic) in this case was a living human being that was *legally executed* pursuant to the United States Supreme Court decision in Roe V. Wade."

Certainly, if an 8 week embryo, supremely innocent, can be executed there is no hope for any previous age, which the NIH Advisory Panel is now amplifying!

This bizarre concept, surprisingly, has ancillary support from the medical profession through the fact that many graduating medical students are now swearing, not to the Hippocratic Oath, and its restrictions of doing harm or taking part in an abortion, but to a different oath, The Oath of Lasagna, which includes the statement: "It may also be within my power to take a life; this awesome responsibility must be faced with great humbleness and awareness of my own fraility".

Truly, demonic doctrines, once more, threaten to darken the earth with The Third Holocaust.

After Nuremberg the medical declaration of Geneva, which became the "Gold Standard" held: "I will maintain the utmost respect for human life from conception"! And the U.N. Declaration On The Child, November 20th, 1959, to which the U.S.A. was a signatory held: "The child by reason of his physical and mental immaturity needs special safeguards and care, including appropriate legal protection before as well as after birth". Verily!

ADDENDUM

Following the final report issued by the NIH Human Embryo Research Advisory Panel, there has been an effusion of editorial comments in the press. The Washington Post blasted the recommendations by the Panel, as did articles in the Washington Times and the Wall Street Journal. The New York Times published an editorial debate on November 25th, 1994, in which Philip Boffey, speaking on the pro side in defense of the recommendations by the Panel, uses the standard descriptions of the early human embryo previously used over several years, and lately, by the Panel: "The clump"; "no sense of self"; "no feeling"; "no bigger than a period". Of course, such descriptions of ourselves in our earliest moments of development would not be originated by any human embryologist, and some of them could easily refer to you and me at any age!

But, the real down side of the "debate", briefly discussed by Mary Cantwell, on the supposedly con side, was when she agreed with the Panel that "young embryos do not have the same moral status as infants and children"! Unfortunately, she does not understand the concept of *the continuum*. The wrong persons are answering to the wrong concepts, as has been the case in many instances over the past 20 years. Therefore, the dilemma does not get resolved for the public in the mainstream media.

At about the same time, President Clinton announced that no federal funds would be used to fund the creation of research embryos, because of the great moral implications. But, he said nothing about leftover embryos from IVF procedures - "spare" embryos. They are equivalent. Therefore, if a "reduced moral status" is applicable to one, it would be applicable to the other, also. And so said the NIH Panel. In reality, a "reduced moral status" is the corruption of a magnificent story. Remember, science did not assign a "reduced moral status" to the early human embryo. This assignment is purely arbitrary and political.

The battle still rages and the war continues.

NIH and Human Embryo Research Revisited:
What is Wrong With This Picture?[*]

by   Dianne N. Irving, M.A., Ph.D.

I. Introduction

The rapid advance of medical technology has left a plethora of profound ethical, social and political issues unresolved. No longer restricted to the archaic deliberations within the halls of academia, Americans in general are finding themselves increasingly affected by these technical medical issues and the corresponding academic "theories" and public policy recommendations constructed by academia - especially within bioethics. Without the technical and academic expertise they perceive necessary to respond cogently to these issues, most people remain in a state of persistent ethical ambiguity, confused by the increasing number of ethical decisions they are being required to make on a daily basis, and motivated more by emotion than by sound reasoning.

Questions abound. Are there really troubling medical experiments with human beings taking place? Are there no realistically effective controls on all of this "new reproductive technology"? Will my children or grandchildren end up in some scientist's petri dish? Will I or my children be able to get insurance if we carry a "bad" gene? Do we have a social duty to forego our own individual ethical decisions about these medical technologies in deference to some larger social gain for the betterment of our society in general? Could we ever countenance a national policy, such as in China and other Third World

---

[*] This paper is based on a similar paper delivered to the De Sales School of Theology Washington Breakfast Meeting, in the law offices of Gardener, Careton and Douglas, Washington, D.C., December 7, 1994.

countries, where families with more than one child must be aborted, or children with the wrong sex or with disabling genes must be eliminated?[1]

Recently, a couple (who are dwarfs) told their genetic counselor that if their fetus was "normal", they would want to have it aborted, because they preferred a child more like them.[2] And consider a recent poll in which close to 30% of the respondents replied that they would abort their child if they knew in advance it would be obese.[3] Now that we supposedly have identified the gene for obesity, would that mean that we could or should abort these affected human embryos?

Despite these and other questions and confusions, perhaps some minimal clarity and objectivity can and should be brought to at least one issue which is fundamental to all of the above concerns, e.g., the on-going and still unresolved debate on human embryo research. The question to be considered is the following. Should any living human embryos be allowed to be used in purely destructive experimental research, including those which are left over from *in vitro* fertilization (IVF) "treatments" ("surplus" human embryos), those created specifically only for research purposes, those produced by parthenogenesis, etc.?

II. The recent response of the NIH Human Embryo Research Panel

Consider the recent NIH Human Embryo Research Panel's recommendations[4] on the use of living human embryos for experimental research. Great benefits can be attained, they claim, e.g., the curing of diseases, the treatment of infertility, and the pure advancement of scientific knowledge. As the advocates of human embryo research complain, who would be so insensitive as to reject human embryo research, when so much good can be realized? They vigorously tout the claim that when so many people agree with the "carefully considered and scientifically grounded" recommendations of the NIH Panel, only ignorant, uneducated, unsophisticated people who linger among the shadows of the irrational and misinformed "far right" could possibly find them objectionable.

However, contrary to these obviously biased and clever complaints, those who do object to this research are not radical, irrational, right-wing, ignorant and uneducated bigots. Nor is this issue one of "balancing one group's belief system against another group's belief system". Nor is this simplistically about religion or pro-life zealots or anti-scientific research mentalities. To the contrary, it can be demonstrated that these NIH recommendations are simply not grounded in or based on sound science, guided by sound moral reasoning, or constitutive of sound public policy.

III. What is wrong with this picture?

The fundamental issue here concerns basic human rights - especially the right to life, on which all the other human rights depend. And those who have taken a stand against this human embryo research come from all religious, non-religious, grass roots, cultural, academic, professional, and political persuasions. There have been over 53,000 letters of protest against the NIH Recommendations (including many from overseas), compared with only 1,300 letters of support. Most of this research has already been rejected by every other country, and violates many of our own state laws. The United States would be the first and only country in the world to sanction most of this research.

Furthermore, these NIH recommendations are in fact the product of a small but clever and powerful group of academic and political elites - particularly in the fields of bioethics, the hard sciences and the social sciences. After over 30 years of unchallenged educational efforts and publications, they have crafted and fabricated a working set of "ethical principles" and bogus theories of "human nature" on which to ground their "ethical" positions - positions which have heavily influenced the formulation of public policy for many years now. Unfortunately, in the present case (as in several others) they have also exploited the current epidemic of infertility and childlessness, as well as the difficult problems associated with genetic imperfections, using these affected patients and their family members to lobby in favor of human embryo research in order to advance their own research agendas.[5] (Over 75% of infertility is caused by scar tissues formed from abortions, the use of contraceptives and sexually transmitted diseases; some is caused by the *in vitro* infertility "treatment" itself). What is wrong with this picture?

Many have probably registered a bit of uneasiness in response to some of the discussions and reports concerning the NIH's recommendations - quite aside from their individual political affiliations or positions on abortion. This same uneasiness and caution describes my own reaction in a slightly different but related situation only a few years ago upon finishing the first part of my analysis for my dissertation on the philosophical and scientific arguments on the nature of the early human embryo and the ethics of human embryo research.[6]

I had originally intended to argue that "personhood" (or the moral status of the early human embryo) began about 14-days - given the 25 years of scientific and philosophical arguments so popular in the academic bioethics literature at the time. I had retrieved the mountains-high stacks of articles and books on the subject, and had selected just 23 "representative" arguments on "delayed personhood" - arranging them in chronological order along the continuum of the biological growth and development of the human being - from fertilization through birth and early childhood. But my focus was on the supposedly gray area between fertilization and 14 days.

I analyzed these arguments according to three criteria (no religion or theology): scientific accuracy; historical philosophical accuracy and defensibility; and logic. After literally years of verifying these criteria, I reluctantly concluded that in virtually all 23 arguments, the science used was incorrect; the philosophy used was historically inaccurate or embarrassingly indefensible; and that none of the conclusions followed logically from their major and minor premises. The statistical chances of this happening are, frankly, zero. Half-way through the dissertation, then, I sat back and asked myself - "What is wrong with this picture?"

IV. Political evolution of the issue

In order to begin to unravel the present "picture", consider how the recent situation concerning human embryo research came about. For over 20 years a ban, or moratorium,[7] had been placed on the use of federal funds for fetal tissue transplant research and IVF research. One common misconception is that all fetal research had been banned. However, the moratorium banned only fetal tissue transplant research, and not all other types of fetal research, which have been going on for years in both private and federally funded labs (including NIH, which has a central retrieval and distribution center in Seattle, Washington, which has supplied live human embryos and human fetuses to

researchers for over 30 years.)[8] Under the moratorium, IVF research
was conditioned on approval by an Ethics Advisory Board. Because
this Board was never appointed, the moratorium also precluded
federally funded IVF research (which would have required the use of
early human embryos) as well. However, human embryo research was
not even articulated as part of the original restriction on IVF research -
another common misconception.[9]

President Clinton, upon his election, lifted the moratorium on
fetal tissue transplant research by signing into law the NIH
Revitalization Act of 1993.[10] It was through this Act, by a very clever
move, that IVF research was - by default - Congressionally sanctioned.
As proponent Joseph Palca, writing in the Hastings Center Report, so
effusively and unabashedly stated: "With lobbying support from the
American Fertility Society, and the willing cooperation of Senator
Kennedy and Representative Waxman, they hit on the strategy of
simply eliminating the requirement that the EAB approve IVF research
projects. Language doing that was "slipped into the NIH Revitalization
Act of 1993....attracting very little attention".[11]

V. The recent NIH Recommendations

Immediately NIH set up their Human Embryo Research Panel
to address the "profound moral and ethical issues" connected with the
use of living human embryos in destructive experimental research.
After almost 9 months of "public" hearings, the Panel concluded as
ethically acceptable much of the proposed research. Human embryos
could be acquired by: producing them specifically for research
purposes by IVF; using those left over from IVF treatment (so-called
"surplus" human embryos) with the informed consent of the donor;
embryo flushing; parthenogenesis; and production with sperm from
anonymous male donors. Ova could be obtained from: the donation of
ovaries from female cadavers if they had given previous consent, or if
their next of kin agreed (without transfer); women undergoing IVF
treatment; and, women undergoing regularly scheduled pelvic
surgery.[12]

Several categories of research were found to be acceptable,
including ("but not limited to") studies on: IVF pregnancy rates;
contraceptives; parthenogenesis (without transfer); embryonic stem

cell cultures (only with "surplus" IVF embryos, without transfer); nuclear transplantation (without transfer); the verification of important scientific data; and, those concerning preimplantation genetic diagnosis (with and without transfer).[13]

Needing further review ("for now") included: studies using human embryos after 15 days until the closure of the neural tube (about 18 days); cloning (without transfer); the use of oocytes from aborted female fetuses, which are matured, and then fertilized and used (without transfer); nuclear transplantation (without transfer); and, the development of stem cells using embryos fertilized specifically for this purpose. Unacceptable ("for now") included: cloning (with transfer); preimplantation genetic diagnosis for sex selection (except for sex-linked diseases); fertilization of fetal oocytes (with transfer); nuclear cloning (with transfer); the use of human embryos after the closing of the neural tube (after 18 days); the formation of human/human and human/non-human chimeras (with or without transfer); cross-species fertilization, except those which have already been used for some time, e.g., those involving chimeras formed with hamster sperm and human ova to test for sperm fertility [no mention of those already used to produce "transgenic mice" or other human/non-human chimeras, e.g., those used in AIDS research]; the transfer of human embryos for extrauterine or abdominal pregnancies [not mentioned, e.g., male pregnancies; or transfer into gorillas, chimpanzees, etc.]; and, the transfer of human embryos into non-human animals for gestation [no mention of the transfer of non-human embryos into humans for gestation].[14]

VI. Analysis of the NIH Recommendations

But, as enticing and exciting as all of this sounds to the proponents of human embryo research, what are some of the serious problems involved with this agenda, problems about which the vast majority of the American people and their elected representatives seem to be unaware, and problems which the proponents of this research continue to successfully ignore? Let me point out just a few considerations.[15]

1. It is important to understand that research now considered unacceptable or needing further review can be immediately sanctioned by Dr. Varmus anyway at his own discretion, including those studies in

the unacceptable and needing further review categories, and including that single and limited category which President Clinton just recently wanted banned because of the "profound moral and ethical problems" connected with them (i.e., human embryos produced solely for research using federal funds). Clinton's statement was deceptive, as it would not include human embryos produced solely for research using private funds, or "surplus" human embryos from IVF, parthenogenesis, etc. Furthermore, Dr. Varmus can override any objection, even the President's and Congress', at will.[16]

2. As the Panel itself frankly admits, the 14-day marker research limit is purely arbitrary. Indeed, several of the panelists insisted that in order to scientifically validate many of these presently proposed studies, eventually the marker will have to be gradually erased all together so that the researcher can determine the actual success or failure of his or her earlier interventions.[17]

3. The legal status of this Panel is in question. It is alleged that the Panel violates several provisions of the Federal Advisory Committee Act.[18]

4. The composition of the Panel's membership has met with strong objections. In their minutes the Panel admits itself that it was purposefully stacked only with members who would approve of this research.

Many of the members have participated in similar commissions before, aggressively taking partisan positions[19] and even defining *per se* the "ethical principles" which were used *a priori* in the earlier commissions' considerations as well as the present NIH Panel's recommendations.[20]

For example, several members served on the National Commission which, as recently admitted by one of its members, basically made up the "bioethics principles" of autonomy, beneficence and justice, later used as the very basis of the conclusions and recommendations of the President's Commission, the NIH Fetal Tissue Transplant Conference, the OPRR regulations for the use of human subjects in research, the recent CIOMS/WHO International Guidelines on the Use of Human Subjects in Research (especially addressing epidemiology research and research in Third World countries) - indeed this present NIH Panel's Recommendations.

Many of the members have also been involved publicly for years in national and international abortion, euthanasia, and eugenics organizations and industries.[21]

Other possible conflicts of interests involve 10 of the 19 members of this Panel who have themselves already received over $21 million from NIH from 1989 to the present to conduct research similar to that human embryo research presently under their review.[22]

And amazingly, there is not even one <u>human</u> embryologist on this NIH <u>Human</u> Embryo Research Panel, raising questions about the kind of "human embryology" they used (in fact they were using amphibian embryology rather than human embryology) which obviously could have skewed their discussions and conclusions.

5. This incorrect "human embryology" was in fact the basis for the Panel's so-called "balanced" claim that the moral status of the early human embryo is less than that of born children and adults. If NIH cannot empirically sustain and defend that grounding "human embryology", then they cannot sustain and defend their subsequent philosophical claim about the "reduced moral status" of the early human embryo which is derived from that incorrect "human embryology". If they cannot sustain their claim about the "reduced moral status" of the early human embryo - which is their self-proclaimed basis for their many recommendations on human embryo research - then it would seem that all of their recommendations are *per se* groundless, arbitrary and invalid.

6. There are in fact several major objections to NIH's "balanced" claim that the moral status of the early human embryo is less than that of born children and adults:

a) The opinions they are really balancing are not those of the popular citizenry, but of those academics whose "theories" on human nature and delayed personhood have been bandied about unchallenged in bioethics for years.[23] To imply that these bioethicists' "theories" are representative of the pluralistic opinions of the American public is disingenuous in the least. They are not even representative of the majority of bioethicists working in the field.

b) Even the claim that moral and ethical rightness or wrongness is determined by consensus, by "balancing" opinions, or by balancing the risks/benefits is not a neutral ethical claim at all. In fact, there is no such thing as a "neutral ethics". Their position is clearly based on a normative utilitarian ethical theory, which is riddled with

274

theoretical and practical problems - and only one ethical theory among many other ethical theories.[24] Why should utilitarianism be afforded such exalted status over and above any other ethical theory - especially in a "pluralistic" society?

c) Why were bioethics principles fabricated? And if they don't work, as admitted now even by their creators and by so many practitioners in the field,[25] then why are they still being invoked as the basis of ethical evaluations - especially in the formulation of public policy - such as in this NIH Panel's recommendations?

d) Ideas have consequences, especially when applied to millions of people. Why is there no discussion concerning any harm that is and will be caused by the application of these inaccurate, indefensible and impractical theories and ideas? And who is going to be legally accountable for the concrete harm that is and will be caused? It is simply not true that one idea or theory is just as good as another idea or theory. Some match reality, and some do not. Some can be defended, and some cannot. Some cause harm, and some do not.[26]

e) The NIH's claim about the "moral status" of the early human embryo, as I have indicated, is really based on journal articles and books produced in the last 25 years primarily in the field of bioethics. Many of the papers which I analyzed in my dissertation are actually referenced by the present NIH Panel to support their claim about the moral status of the embryo in their Recommendations (one of the most influential being that of Clifford Grobstein and Richard McCormick, S.J.). None of these arguments can be sustained scientifically, philosophically or even logically.

f) On a further rather amusing note, the "human embryology" chart and the list of "scientific terms" which the NIH Panel uses in the Appendix of their recommendations[27] are not referenced by a single scientific text book, but rather by an Australian bioethics book,[28] written by authors who all have argued for infanticide in the bioethics literature for many years, and who have used the very same incorrect science, philosophy and logic in their own publications. These authors are Peter Singer, a philosopher; Helga Kuhse, an "ethicist"; Steven Buckle, a philosopher; Pascal Kasimba, a lawyer; and Karen Dawson, who is a geneticist, but who is not a human embryologist or even a developmental biologist, and who sometimes even argues against several of the scientific statements of her co-authors. Even this Australian bioethics book does not give any scientific references for its own "human embryology" chart or for its own list of "scientific terms"[29] - all of which NIH uses in the Appendix of its own human embryo research recommendations.

Why would NIH, supposedly one of the greatest scientific research institutions in the world, with immediate access to almost infinite scientific resources and experts, decide to use only an Australian bioethics book, which itself has no scientific references, to reference its own "human embryology" chart, its own "scientific definitions", and several of its other major recommendations? What Is Wrong With This Picture?

7. Why have many academic scholars, who have tried for years to correct the scientific and philosophical inaccuracies and misconceptions in the popular and academic press been precluded from publishing those corrections?[30]

VII. Protections of the basic human rights of research subjects

Regardless of the great benefits obtainable by creating and then destroying some human beings in order to help other human beings, or to advance scientific knowledge, national and international declarations and precedents have unambiguously stated that the means used to those laudatory ends may not include the harm or death of human subjects. For example, the Nuremberg Code[31] states that regardless of goods yielded to society, research using human subjects must conform to certain ethical and legal concepts, primary among which are the use of qualified scientists and correct scientific information, the human subject's informed consent, and a minimal level of personal risk to the subject. The Declaration of Helsinki states: "In research on man, the interests of science and society should never take precedence over considerations related to the well-being of the subject."[32] Even the NIH's OPRR regulations ensure that unborn children, whose parents intend to abort them, are as equally protected from research harm if they survive the abortion as are those children intended for live birth.[33] And where in our Constitution or Bill of Rights is there a guarantee of the rights of some human beings, or even the government, to purposefully create other human beings to be destroyed or donated for "the greater good of society or of science"?

Despite the catastrophe of the Nazi medical experiments with "sub-humans" (who were going to die anyway and so they might as

276

well get some good out of them), shadows of that rationale keep emerging, even in our own society, from time to time. Consider the Willowbrook experiments, in which mentally retarded children were purposefully infected with infectious diseases in order to study the diseases to prevent later populations from infections. Or the Tuskeegee experiments, in which black males suffering with syphilis were not administered penicillin, in order to observe the progression of the disease. Elderly male nursing home patients were injected with cancer viruses to see if they would form antibodies.[34] Mentally retarded children in state institutions were fed feces to study hepatitis.[35] And most recently, consider the radiation experiments sponsored by the United States Government from 1945-1973 performed on thousands of unsuspecting patients, service personnel and urban populations. All of these experiments were performed without the informed consent of the human subjects experimented on.

It is interesting that many of such breeches of research ethics took place in experiments involving vulnerable populations of human beings, whose "personhood", perhaps, was considered to be less than adequate. It is also interesting that much of it was federally funded, and justified "for the greater good of society", for the advancement of scientific knowledge or for national security reasons.

VIII. Conclusions

Considering the above facts and analysis, even from a scientific or ethical perspective these human embryo experiments are unacceptable. The basic science that is used to determine the "moral status" of these early human embryos is grossly incorrect. There is absolutely no question whatsoever, scientifically, objectively, that the life of every human being begins at fertilization. There is no question philosophically that any attempt to split a human being from a human person is both theoretically and practically indefensible. Personhood begins when the human being begins - at fertilization.

Therefore, any experiment which would require the intentional destruction of innocent human beings - even if for the greater good of society, or for the advancement of scientific knowledge, or for the national security - is automatically unethical. Great benefits do not justify unethical means.

And finally, given the questionable status of the famous "bioethics principles", as well as the questionable makeup of this NIH Panel and its inherent conflict of interests - and given the Panel's indefensible theory of the moral status of the early human embryo, a theory which is selectively utilitarian and grounded on unscientific bioethics books and literature - none of their Recommendations can be defended, and so are invalid.

But that does not mean that these experiments have not or will not take place. They already have taken place,[36] and they will continue, unless our collective basic common sense is restored and the inherent value and dignity of every human being is acknowledged and protected - regardless of its quality of life - and until everyone becomes informatively and actively involved in this critical human rights dialogue.

References

1. John Rennie, "Trends in genetics: Grading the gene tests", Scientific American (June 1994), 270:6:88-97.

2. Science News (1994), Vol. 146, p. 299.

3. See article on obesity, by Rick Weiss, "Born to be fat; Will an obesity gene tilt the scales toward social acceptance?", Washington Post (Dec. 6, 1994), p. 10-14.

4. National Institutes of Health: Report of the Human Embryo Research Panel, September 27, 1994; available free of charge from Ms Peggy Schnoor, Division of Science Policy Analysis and Development, National Institutes of Health, Bldg. 1, Room 218, 9000 Rockville Pike, Bethesda, MD 20892; phone 301-496-1454.

5. C. Ward Kischer, "A new wave dialectic: The reinvention of human embryology", Linacre Quarterly (1994), 61:4:66-81; Kischer, "Human development and reconsideration of ensoulment", Linacre Quarterly (1993), 60:1:57-63; Kischer, "Quid sit veritas?", Science For Life (July 1994), 4:1:1-10; Dianne N. Irving, "Testimony before the NIH Human Embryo Research Panel", Linacre Quarterly (1994), 61:4:82-89; Irving, "Academic fraud and

conceptual transfer in bioethics: Abortion, human embryo research and psychiatric research", in Proceedings of the Conference: Life and Learning IV (New York: Fordham University Press, Fall 1994), in press; Irving, "'New age' embryology text books: Implications for fetal research", Linacre Quarterly (1994), 61:2:42-62.

6. Dianne N. Irving, Philosophical and Scientific Analysis of the Nature of the Early Human Embryo (Dissertation submitted to the Graduate School, Georgetown University, Washington, D.C., April 9, 1991). For shorter summaries, see Irving, "Science, philosophy and expertise: An evaluation of the arguments on 'personhood'", Linacre Quarterly (1993), 60:1:18-46; Irving, amicus curiae brief (for University Faculty For Life, Members of Congress, organizations and individuals) in support of petition of certiorari, Alexander Loce vs The State of New Jersey, cert. denied __ U.S. __ (1994) (No. 93-1149).

7. 45 C.F.R. Part 46 (1993).

8. Central Laboratory for Human Embryology, University of Washington, Seattle, Washington; Director, Dr. Fantell (I am indebted to Suzanne Rini for this information. For details, contact NIH; or Suzanne Rini, Bioethics Consultant, American Life League, Stafford, VA; phone 703-659-2586).

9. Suzanne Rini, Critique of Letter From Dr. Harold Varmus to Congressmen, Regarding IVF and Human Embryo Research (Stafford, VA: American Life League, 1994; phone 703-659-2586).

10. NIH Revitalization Act (1993), P.L. No. 103-43, codified at U.S.C. sec 289a et seq.

11. Joseph Palca, "A word to the wise", Hastings Center Report (Mar.-April 1994), p. 5.

12. National Institutes of Health: Report of the Human Embryo Research Panel (see note 4), p. 5-7.

13. Ibid., p. 10.

14. Ibid., p. 11-12.

15. See Rini, note 9; also see series of articles on this issue since January 1994 by: Mary Meehan, in National Catholic Register, Richard Doerflinger, in National Right to Life News and The Catholic Standard; Mark Zimmerman, in The Catholic Standard; and American Life League (Stafford, VA, phone 703-659-2586). Also see articles by: Rev. John Richard Neuhaus, "Don't cross this

threshold", <u>Wall Street Journal</u> (Oct. 27, 1994), and the Ramsey Colloquium's statement, "The inhuman use of human beings: A statement on embryo research by the Ramsey Colloquium" to be published in <u>First Things</u> (Jan. 1995); Peter Riga, "Letter to the Editor", <u>Wall Street Journal</u> (Nov. 14, 1994); David Walsh (CU), "Benefits don't make it ethical", <u>The Washington Post</u> (Oct. 27, 1994), A23; "Editorial", <u>The Washington Post</u> (Oct. 2, 1994); George Weigel, "A Brave New World is hatched", <u>Los Angeles Times</u> (Nov. 27, 1994); series of letters to Dr. Varmus from Rep. Robert K. Dornan and Congressional members of the Pro-Life Caucus, U.S. House of Representatives (phone 202-225-2965); statement to Dr. Varmus by Archbishop James Cardinal Hickey, Nov. 12, 1994 (all of the statements pro and con this research which were sent to NIH are open for public reading). Also see Dianne N. Irving, "Embryo research: A call for closer scrutiny", <u>National Catholic Register</u> (July 17, 1994). Also see Irving, interviewed by: Diane Gianelli, "Embryo research decision set to spark controversy", <u>American Medical News</u> (June 1994), p. 7; Pete Sheehan, "Moral experts concerned about reported cloning", <u>The Long Island Catholic</u> (Nov. 3, 1993), p. 9; Mary Meehan, "Halt these proceedings", <u>National Catholic Register</u> (June 1994); ibid, "Dialogue: Dianne Nutwell Irving on embryology and bioethics" (Oct. 16, 1994), p. A1; Richard Szczepanowski, "NIH decision on embryo research said to be based on faulty science", <u>Catholic Standard</u> (Nov. 3, 1994), p. 4; Edward C. Freiling, "The attempted justification of embryo research", <u>The Wanderer</u> (Dec. 8, 1994), p. 12; and by Cheryl Wetzstein, "Activists oppose embryo research", <u>The Washington Times</u> (Dec. 8, 1994) p. 12.

16. NIH Revitalization Act 1993 (see note 10 above), 42 U.S.C. sect. 289 a-1(b)(1).

17. <u>National Institutes of Health Human Embryo Research Panel: Transcripts of the Meetings</u> (Feb. 2-3, Mar. 14, Apr. 11-12, May 3-4, June 21-22, and Sept. 27), available free of charge from Ms Peggy Schnoor, Division of Science Policy Analysis and Development, National Institutes of Health, Bldg. 1, Room 218, 9000 Rockville Pike, Bethesda, MD 20892; phone 301-496-1454. Also free of charge are copies of all of the "invited papers" from the "experts" which NIH commissioned for this Human Embryo Research Panel.

18. Federal Advisory Committee Act, 5 U.S.C. App. sect 5(b)(2); see petition for injunction, <u>Mary Doe</u> vs <u>Donna Shalala, et al</u>, U.S. Dist. St. MD, No. PJM-94-1703, filed Aug. 1994, denied.

19. See articles by Mary Meehan and Richard Doerflinger (note 15).

20. Dianne N. Irving, "Testimony before the NIH Human Embryo Research Panel", <u>Linacre Quarterly</u> (1994), 61:4:82-89; Irving, "Academic fraud and

conceptual transfer in bioethics: Abortion, human embryo research and psychiatric research" (see note 5).

21. Rini (note 9); Meehan, and Doerflinger (note 15).

22. Rini (note 9).

23. D. Irving (note 5); see also, Francis J. Beckwith, "Book review: 'A Matter of Principles: Ferment in U.S. Bioethics', in Ethics and Medicine (Fall 1994).

24. Dianne N. Irving, "Which ethics for science and public policy?", Accountability in Research (1993), 3:2-3:77-99; Irving, "The impact of scientific 'misinformation' on other fields: Philosophy, theology, biomedical ethics and public policy", Accountability in Research (April 1993), 2:4:243-272; Irving, "Quality assurance auditors: Between a rock and a hard place", Quality Assurance: Good Practice, Regulation, and Law (March 1994), 3:1:33-52. See also, DuBose, Edwin, Hamel, O'Connell (eds.), A Matter of Principles? Ferment in U.S. Bioethics (Valley Forge, PA: Trinity Press International, 1994); Raanan Gillon (ed.), Principles of Health Care Ethics (New York: Wiley, 1994); (many other cites found on BIOETHICSLINE under "analytics/bioethics").

25. Albert Jonsen, "Preface", in DuBose et al; and Gillon (note 24); Daniel Callahan, "Bioethics: Private choice and common good", Hastings Center Report (May-June 1994), 28-31.

26. D. Irving, "Academic fraud..." (note 5); ibid, "Impact of scientific 'misinformation...'" (note 24); ibid, "Psychiatric research: Reality check", The Journal of the California Alliance for the Mentally Ill (Spring 1994), 5:1:42-44; ibid, "Can either scientific facts or 'personhood' be mediated?", Pontis (The Center for Medical Ethics and Mediation, San Diego, CA)(March 1994), 2:1:3-5; ibid, "Politization of science and philosophy: The 'delayed personhood' debates and conceptual transfer", Life Science And The Concept of 'Person', Centre d'Etudes sur la Reconnaissance de la Personne Humaine (CERPH, CHU La Miletrie, B.P. 577, 86021 Poitier, France), forthcoming; ibid., "Neurobiological research using human subjects: Ethical choices for decision makers", Accountability in Research (Feb. 1995), forthcoming.

27. National Institutes of Health: Report of the Human Embryo Research Panel (see note 4), p.110-111.

28. Peter Singer, Helga Kuhse, Stephen Buckle, Karen Dawson, Pascal Kasimba, Embryo Experimentation (New York: Cambridge University Press, 1990).

29. Singer et al, Embryo Experimentation, p. xiv.

30. Kischer, "Quid sit veritas?", Science for Life (July 1994), 4:1:1-10; also, "A new wave dialectic: The reinvention of human embryology", Linacre Quarterly (1994), 61:4:66-81; Irving, "Academic fraud..." (see note 5).

31. Nuremberg Code, in Jay Katz, Experimentation With Human Beings (New York: Russell Sage Foundation, 1972), p. 305-306.

32. Declaration of Helsinki, in Robert J. Levine, Ethics and Regulation of Clinical Research (New Haven: Yale University Press, 1986), p. 429.

33. United States Code of Federal Regulations: Protection of Human Subjects 45 CFR 46 (available from NIH, Office For The Protection of Research Risks).

34. Paul S. Appelbaum, Charles W. Lidz and Alan Meisel, Informed Consent: Legal Theory and Clinical Practice (New York: Oxford University Press, 1987), p. 217-218; Robert J. Levine, Ethics and Regulation of Clinical Research (New Haven: Yale University Press, 1986), pp. 69-72.

35. Dr. Bernadine Healy, former Director of NIH (under President Bush), debating Ron Green (NIH Panelist and "ethicist") on MacNeil-Lehrer News Hour (Dec. 6, 1994) (Transcripts available from "Strictly Business", P.O. Box 12803, Overland Park, Kansas 66212, phone 913-649-6381).

36. As confirmed publicly by Ron Green, NIH Panelist, on MacNeil-Lehrer News Hour (note 35).

284

286

291

293

The following articles were originally published in The Linacre Quarterly:

In Defense of Human Development. 59:68-75, 1992.

Scientific and Philosophical Expertise: An Evaluation of the Argument of "Personhood". 60:18-47, 1993.

Human Development and Reconsideration of Ensoulment. 60-57-63, 1993.

"New Age" Embryology Text Books: Implications for Fetal Research. 61:42-62, 1994.

A New Wave Dialectic: The Reinvention of Human Embryology. 61: 66-81, 1994.

Testimony Before the NIH Human Embryo Research Panel. 61:82-89, 1994.

The Beginning of Life and the Establishment of the Continuum. (as: A Commentary on The Beginning of Life: A View From Human Embryology). 63:78-78, 1996.

The Big Lie In Human Embryology: The Case of the Preembryo. (In Press).

The Media and Human Embryology. (In Press).

NIH and Human Embryo Research Revisited: What is Wrong With This Picture? (In Press).

The following article is republished with permission of Accountability in Research.

Which Ethics for Science and Public Policy. 3:77-100, 1993.